f 2/14-
ul-15

Solvent Extraction in Analytical Chemistry

GEORGE H. MORRISON, Ph.D.

Head, Analytical Chemistry
Research Laboratories
Sylvania Electric Products, Inc.
Flushing, New York

HENRY FREISER, Ph.D.

Associate Professor of Chemistry
University of Pittsburgh
Pittsburgh, Pennsylvania

Solvent

Extraction

in

Analytical

Chemistry

NEW YORK · JOHN WILEY & SONS, INC.

London · Chapman & Hall, Ltd.

To

EDITH

and

ANNIE

Preface

Although solvent extraction as a method of separation has long been familiar to the analytical chemist, only in recent years has it begun to achieve recognition as one of the more powerful separation techniques. Confronted with increasing demands for analyses that are faster, that are applicable to trace concentrations, and that can be used for highly complex mixtures, chemists have turned to solvent extraction methods for satisfactory achievement of these objectives.

There exists a wealth of literature on solvent extraction procedures and a few brief reviews, but there has been no comprehensive treatment of the field. This book represents an attempt to fulfill this need. In the first part, devoted to the principles of solvent extraction, a systematic classification of extractions is presented and a generalized theory developed. The second section is concerned with the practical aspects of the subject, including apparatus and general techniques. This is followed by a survey of extraction systems and a selection of procedures for the extraction of elements.

We wish to thank Mr. James F. Cosgrove for his invaluable assistance in the preparation of the manuscript.

G. H. MORRISON

H. FREISER

Flushing, New York
Pittsburgh, Pennsylvania
June 1957

Contents

PART 1. PRINCIPLES OF SOLVENT EXTRACTION

Chapter   **Page**
1. Introduction **3**

    1. Classification of Metal Extraction Systems

2. Principles of Solvent Extraction **7**

    1. Phase Rule
    2. Distribution Law
    3. Thermodynamic Derivation of Distribution Law
    4. Distribution Ratio
    5. Percentage Extraction
    6. Process of Extraction

3. Formation of Metal Complexes **16**

    1. Coordination Complexes
    2. Chelate Complexes
    3. Ion Association Complexes

4. Distribution of the Extractable Species . . .   **35**

    1. Solubility and Distribution
    2. Factors Affecting Solubility
    3. Solubility Characteristics of Chelates
    4. Solubility Characteristics of Ion Association
        Compounds

ix

Chapter   **Page**

5. Chemical Interactions in the Organic Phase . . **48**

6. Quantitative Treatment of Extraction Equilibria . **50**

    1. Chelate Extraction Systems
    2. Ion Association Extraction Systems

7. Kinetic Factors in Extraction **72**

    1. Rate of Transfer
    2. Rate of Complex Formation

PART 2. APPARATUS AND GENERAL TECHNIQUES

8. Methods of Extraction **79**

    1. Batch Extraction
    2. Continuous Extraction
    3. Extraction of Solids
    4. Countercurrent Distribution

9. Techniques in Extraction **106**

    1. Choice of Solvent
    2. Stripping
    3. Backwashing
    4. Treatment of Emulsions
    5. Variation of Oxidation State
    6. Use of Masking (Sequestering) Agents
    7. Use of Salting-Out Agents

10. Completion of Analysis **115**

    1. Radioisotopes and Solvent Extraction
    2. Colorimetry and Solvent Extraction

PART 3. EXTRACTION SYSTEMS

11. Ion Association Systems **125**

    1. Fluoride System
    2. Chloride System
    3. Bromide System
    4. Iodide System
    5. Thiocyanate System
    6. Nitrate System

Chapter   **Page**

   7. Perchlorate System
   8. Heteropoly Acid System
   9. Carboxylic Acids
  10. Alkylphosphoric Acids
  11. Trialkylphosphine Oxides
  12. High Molecular Weight Amines
  13. Tetraphenylarsonium and Tetraphenylphosphonium
      Chlorides
  14. Rhodamine B and Other Dyes
  15. Heterocyclic Polyamines
  16. Miscellaneous Extractions

12. Chelate Systems **157**

   1. Acetylacetone
   2. Thenoyltrifluoroacetone (TTA)
   3. Quinalizarin
   4. Morin
   5. 8-Quinolinol (Oxine)
   6. Dimethylglyoxime
   7. Salicylaldoxime
   8. 1-Nitroso-2-naphthol and Related Compounds
   9. Ammonium Salt N-Nitrosophenylhydroxylamine
      (Cupferron)
  10. Cupferron Analogs
  11. 1-(2-Pyridylazo)-2-naphthol
  12. Diphenylthiocarbazone (Dithizone)
  13. Toluene-3,4-dithiol
  14. Sodium Diethyldithiocarbamate
  15. Potassium Xanthate
  16. Miscellaneous Reagents

PART 4.   SEPARATIONS

13. Selected Procedures for the Extraction of the Elements   **189**

Appendix **249**

Index of Extraction of Elements **255**

Subject Index **263**

Part 1

*Principles
of
Solvent
Extraction*

Chapter 1

Introduction

Recent advances in analytical chemistry are characterized by great progress toward more powerful methods of separation, equaling in significance the great forward strides made in instrumental methods of determination. Problems of chemical analysis almost always involve two steps: separation of the desired constituent and measurement of the amount or concentration of this constituent. Much worthy research has been dedicated to the development of more discriminatory methods of estimation, such as spectrographic, spectrophotometric, and polarographic methods, which minimize the need for separation steps preceding the measurement step. However, with the rapid growth of chemical technology, the analytical chemist is called upon to deal with mixtures of increasing complexity. In recent years, many elements previously considered laboratory curiosities have assumed industrial significance. The use of titanium, tantalum, niobium, and zirconium, for example, either as pure metals or as important high-temperature alloy constituents, of germanium in the rapidly expanding transistor field, of uranium, thorium, the lanthanides, and actinides in the nuclear energy program has forced the analytical chemist to take cognizance of these and other elements in his analytical schemes. Despite the availability of the modern, more discriminating methods of measurement, successful solutions to many analytical problems depend heavily on separation processes. It can be further observed that many separation processes of vital interest to the analytical chemist have been successfully translated to plant-scale operations.

Solvent extraction enjoys a favored position among the separation techniques because of its ease, simplicity, speed, and wide scope.[1,2,3] Utilizing apparatus no more complicated than a separatory funnel, requiring several minutes at the most to perform, applicable both to trace and macro levels of metals, extraction procedures offer much to the analytical chemist. A further advantage of the extraction method over the widely used precipitation method lies in the cleaner separations that can be achieved by the former. With the latter, contamination of precipitates by coprecipitation phenomena is a decided limitation which is minimized only with difficulty, whereas the analog of coprecipitation, i.e., coextraction, is almost unknown in solvent extraction.

1. CLASSIFICATION OF METAL EXTRACTION SYSTEMS

Since, in the analysis of metals, we are primarily concerned with samples in aqueous solutions, it should be understood that liquid-liquid extraction as discussed here implies the use of an aqueous-organic solvent pair.

Solubility in organic solvents is not a characteristic usually attributed to simple metal salts. As can be expected from their highly ionic nature, most metal salts are strong electrolytes whose relatively large solubility in aqueous media reflects the beneficial effect of the high dielectric constant of water on reducing the work required to separate the oppositely charged ions. An equally important factor is the tendency of water to solvate the ions. In essentially all metal extraction systems some of or all the water molecules coordinated to the metal ions must be removed before it is possible to obtain a species that can be extracted into an organic solvent.

The formation of an uncharged species is a probable prerequisite for extraction into organic solvents, which generally have low dielectric constants. Such a species may be formed by metal-containing ions through coordination, involving chemical rather than "physical" bonds. The formation of the compound germanium tetrachloride, which is extractable in carbon tetrachloride, might be cited as an illustration. In this category also are the large number of uncharged chelate complexes which have proved so useful in extraction. On the other hand, an uncharged species may be achieved through the neutralization of charge attending the association of ions on the basis of their purely electrostatic attraction. The association of tetraphenyl arsonium ion with perrhenate anion to give $[(C_6H_5)_4As^+, ReO_4^-]$ which is extractable into chloroform is an example of this.

It might be well to point out that there is a smooth transition between true coordination compounds and ion association compounds. For example, there is reason to believe that in the extraction of uranyl nitrate into ether a true coordination compound, $(UO_2)(NO_3)_2(solvent)_4$, is involved whereas for the extraction of the same compound into an alcohol such as isobutanol an association of the $(UO_2)(solvent)_6{}^{2+}$ ion with two nitrate ions forms the extractable species (see page 42).

It is convenient to classify extraction systems on the basis of the nature of the extractable species. Because most extractable species which involve only coordination are chelates, this is the only type so described. The few others will be classed with the ion association types.

In **chelate extraction systems,** compounds such as 8-quinolinol, dithizone, and cupferron easily replace coordinated water from many metals to form neutral, essentially covalent, chelate compounds, many of which are soluble in such organic solvents as hydrocarbons and chlorinated hydrocarbons.

A second category might be termed **ion association extraction systems,** since in these cases the extractable species are formed by the association of ions. In this general category it is possible to distinguish three types. The metal may be incorporated into a very large ion containing bulky organic groups, or it may associate with another ion which is of great size. For example, copper(I) reacts with 2,9-dimethylphenanthroline (neocuproine) to form a large univalent cation which associates with a nitrate or perchlorate anion to form a compound extractable into chloroform. Again, zinc as $ZnCl_4{}^{2-}$ associates with two tribenzylammonium ions $[(C_6H_5CH_2)_3NH^+]$ to give an uncharged species soluble in xylene.

A second type of ion association system is characterized by the important role played by the organic solvent. The formation of an extractable species depends on the combined action of anions such as halides, thiocyanate, or nitrate, and of oxygen-containing organic compounds such as alcohols, ethers, ketones, and esters to displace the coordinated water from the metal. For example, the iron(III) complex extracted out of hydrochloric acid by ethyl ether probably has the formula $\{(C_2H_5)_2O:H^+, FeCl_4[(C_2H_5)_2O]_2{}^-\}$. Inasmuch as the oxygen atom of the solvent molecule coordinates with the metal ion in this type of system, the term **oxonium** extraction system is applied. In view of the direct participation of the solvent in the formation of an extractable species, it is easy to understand why the requirements for a suitable solvent are more stringent in this type of extraction system.

A third type of ion association extraction system may be recognized; in this system the metal ions are incorporated into salts of high molecular weight which "dissolve" in organic solvents in much the same fashion as does a soap in water, that is, by forming colloidal aggregates, or micelles, in which the organophilic portions of the salt molecules are turned out to the organic solvent whereas the ionic portions are shielded from the organic solvent at the center of the micellar structure. This seems to be the case in the extraction of uranium, molybdenum, and other metals by high molecular weight amines dissolved in kerosene, and it might also be involved in extractions such as that of copper(II) caprate into chloroform.

REFERENCES

1. G. H. Morrison, *Anal. Chem.*, **22**, 1388 (1950).
2. H. Irving, *Quart. Rev. (London)*, **5**, 200 (1951).
3. V. I. Kuznetsov, *Uspekhi Khim.*, **23**, 654 (1954).

Chapter 2

Principles of
Solvent Extraction

Recently developed separation techniques, such as chromatography and ion exchange, homogeneous precipitation, as well as solvent extraction, brilliantly highlight the usefulness of phase distribution as a separation principle; in each of these methods movement of matter across phase boundaries is involved.

1. PHASE RULE

For all phase distributions, the classical phase rule of Gibbs,

$$P + V = C + 2 \tag{2.1}$$

where P is the number of phases, V the variance or degrees of freedom, and C the number of components, is most helpful. In the particular case of solvent extraction we are dealing basically with two essentially immiscible solvents and one solute distributed between them, so that $P = 2$ and $C = 3$. At constant temperature and pressure, the rule predicts a variance of unity. This means that if we choose the concentration of the solute in one phase, the solute concentration in the other phase is fixed. Hence, we see that there will be a definite relation between the solute concentrations in each of the solvent phases. This relation is quantitatively described in the distribution law.

2. DISTRIBUTION LAW

Although the phase rule predicts that a system composed of two immiscible solvents and one distributing solute has one degree of

7

freedom, the distribution law reveals greater restraint. The ratio of solute concentrations is shown to be invariant, i.e., independent of total concentration. First stated in 1872 by Berthelot and Jungfleish [1] and elaborated by Nernst [2] in 1891, the distribution law states that a solute will distribute between two essentially immiscible solvents in such a manner that, at equilibrium, the ratio of the concentrations of the solute in the two phases at a particular temperature will be a constant, provided the solute has the same molecular weight in each phase. For a solute X distributing between solvents 1 and 2, we have then

$$X_1 \rightleftharpoons X_2$$

$$K_D = [X]_2/[X]_1 \tag{2.2}$$

where K_D is the distribution coefficient, a constant independent of total solute concentration, and the brackets denote concentrations.

Although this expression of the distribution law is a useful approximation, careful experimental tests reveal serious shortcomings of two types. The first arises because the law as stated is not thermodynamically rigorous. The second shortcoming is encountered when the distributing species is involved in chemical reactions such as dissociation or association in either phase. As will be discussed later, the occurrence of such chemical reactions can be properly accounted for by calculating their effects upon the phase concentrations of the distributing species. Although they add complexity to the distribution expressions, deviations arising from this cause do not represent any essential inadequacy of the distribution law itself.

3. THERMODYNAMIC DERIVATION OF DISTRIBUTION LAW

A thermodynamic explanation of the conditions existing in each of the phases at equilibrium will be useful in understanding the nature of the approximations involved in the distribution law. Equilibrium is attained at constant temperature and pressure when the chemical potentials, Φ (partial molal free energies), of the solute in each phase are equal. Thus

$$\Phi_1 = \Phi_2 \tag{2.3}$$

where the subscripts 1 and 2 refer to the respective solvent phases. Substituting suitable expressions for Φ, we next have

$$\Phi_1{}^0 + RT \ln m_1 + RT \ln \gamma_1 = \Phi_2{}^0 + RT \ln m_2 + RT \ln \gamma_2 \tag{2.4}$$

where Φ^0 represents the chemical potential of solute in a hypothetical ideal 1 molal solution, m, the solute concentration in molality, and γ, the molal activity coefficient. From this we may obtain an expression for the molal distribution coefficient, K_D

$$K_D \equiv \frac{m_2}{m_1} = \frac{\gamma_1}{\gamma_2} e^{-(\Phi_2{}^0 - \Phi_1{}^0)/RT} \tag{2.5}$$

In this equation, the Φ^0's represent constants provided the presence of the solute does not significantly affect the mutual solubilities of the two solvents. Although this condition is generally satisfied in inorganic extractions, it is not universally true. For example, the addition of sufficient acetic acid to water and chloroform increases the mutual solubilities of the two liquid phases to the point of complete miscibility. Again, a high concentration of hydrochloric acid markedly increases the mutual solubility of ether and water. For most of the systems of concern to us, however, the solute is not present in quantities large enough to alter significantly the mutual solubilities of the pair, so we may write eq. 2.5 as

$$K_D \equiv \frac{m_2}{m_1} = \frac{\gamma_1}{\gamma_2} K' \tag{2.6}$$

where K' is a constant for the system at constant temperature. Variation in the distribution coefficient K_D can be seen to result from variations in the activity coefficients in each of the phases. When solute concentration is very low, as the activity coefficients approach unity the value of K_D becomes constant. Thus Grahame and Seaborg,[3] using radiochemical techniques, found the distribution coefficient of gallium chloride between ethyl ether and $6\,M$ hydrochloric acid to remain essentially constant (within 5%) over a concentration range from 10^{-12} to $2 \times 10^{-3}\,M$ gallium chloride. They observed a similar constancy for the distribution coefficient of $(NH_4)_2Co(CNS)_4$ between amyl alcohol and water over the range 10^{-12} to $10^{-5}\,M$.

At higher concentration ranges, constancy in the distribution coefficient might be anticipated over ranges in which the ratio of the activity coefficients remains constant. However, it is not too likely for parallel variation of the activity coefficients to occur over extensive concentration ranges in two solvents so different from one another that they are essentially immiscible.

These considerations notwithstanding, variations in K_D values due to activity coefficient variations over practical concentration ranges are likely to be under one order of magnitude for most systems of interest to us here.

4. DISTRIBUTION RATIO

Of much greater significance because of their effect on the distribution are the chemical interactions of the distributing species with the other components in each phase, since these interactions can profoundly affect the concentration of the distributing species. Since as analysts we are more concerned in the overall or stoichiometric distribution of the component of interest between the phases, it becomes necessary to introduce a more practical quantity to describe the extraction, called D, the distribution ratio. This is a stoichiometric ratio including all species of the same component in the respective phases.

$$D = \frac{\text{Total concentration in organic phase}}{\text{Total concentration in aqueous phase}}$$

If we are aware of all the significant interactions of the distributing species, it is usually possible to properly evaluate them, so that we may arrive at an expression for D as a function of the experimental parameters. To be sure, were conditions ideal, i.e., were the species involved in no reactions in either phase, D would reduce to K_D.

Let us consider as an example the distribution of 8-quinolinol between chloroform and water. Here the situation is complicated by the ionization of 8-quinolinol in the aqueous phase, so that although the distribution coefficient, K_D, of the 8-quinolinol remains essentially constant, the stoichiometry of the extraction varies very dramatically with experimental conditions as shown in Table 2.1.

Table 2.1. Variation of Distribution Ratio of 8-Quinolinol with pH [4]

pH	Per Cent Extracted	D Observed	D Calculated
0	0.59	0.006	0.006
1	5.57	0.059	0.058
2	37.1	0.59	0.58
3	83.7	5.9	5.8
4	97.8	59	58
7	100	720	720
9	100	720	720
10	99.8	500	300
11	98	50	48
12	88	5.0	5.0
13	33.3	0.50	0.50
14	5.0	0.053	0.05

To pursue the example of 8-quinolinol distribution a little further, the reactions may be described in terms of the following equations.

Ionization Equilibria:

$$H_2Ox^+ \overset{K_1}{\rightleftharpoons} HOx + H^+ \qquad K_1 = \frac{[HOx] \cdot [H^+]}{[H_2Ox^+]} = 8 \times 10^{-6} \qquad (2.7)$$

$$HOx \overset{K_2}{\rightleftharpoons} Ox^- + H^+ \qquad K_2 = \frac{[Ox^-] \cdot [H^+]}{[HOx]} = 1.4 \times 10^{-10} \quad (2.7')$$

Distribution:

$$(HOx)_w \rightleftharpoons (HOx)_o \qquad K_D = \frac{[HOx]_o}{[HOx]_w} = 720 \qquad (2.7)$$

where K_1 and K_2 are the ionization constants for the respective equilibria, K_D is the distribution coefficient, Ox^- is the 8-quinolinate anion, and the subscripts w and o represent the aqueous and organic phases, respectively.

From the above equations, D, the distribution ratio, may be seen to be

$$D \equiv \frac{|HOx|_o}{|HOx|_w} = \frac{[HOx]_o}{[H_2Ox^+]_w + [HOx]_w + [Ox^-]_w} \qquad (2.8)$$

which, by suitable substitution, becomes

$$D = \frac{K_D}{\dfrac{[H^+]}{K_1} + 1 + \dfrac{K_2}{[H^+]}} \qquad (2.9)$$

Values of D calculated from eq. 2.9 are in substantial agreement with those experimentally determined as shown in Table 2.1. By means of eq. 2.9 we are now in a position to predict on a sound basis that the course of the extraction of 8-quinolinol at constant temperature and ionic strength depends solely on the pH and is independent of the 8-quinolinol concentration.

In a more complicated case, the distributing solute may be involved in reactions in each of the two phases; e.g., benzoic acid dimerizes in benzene and ionizes in water. An interesting illustration of this situation arises in the distribution of osmium tetroxide between carbon tetrachloride and water.[5,6] The situation may be described in terms of the following equations.

Aqueous Phase:

$$OsO_4 + H_2O \rightleftharpoons H_2OsO_5$$

$$H_2OsO_5 \rightleftharpoons H^+ + HOsO_5^- \tag{2.10}$$

$$HOsO_5^- \rightleftharpoons H^+ + OsO_5^{2-}$$

Distribution:

$$(OsO_4)_w \rightleftharpoons (OsO_4)_o \tag{2.11}$$

Polymerization in Organic Phase:

$$4OsO_4 \rightleftharpoons (OsO_4)_4 \tag{2.12}$$

The distribution ratio would then appear as

$$D = \frac{[OsO_4]_o + 4[(OsO_4)_4]_o}{[OsO_4]_w + [H_2OsO_5]_w + [HOsO_5^-]_w + [OsO_5^{2-}]_w} \tag{2.13}$$

and could be evaluated at all values of pH and total osmium concentration if the values for equilibrium constants for reactions listed in eqs. 2.10, 2.11, and 2.12 were given.

5. PERCENTAGE EXTRACTION

Of ultimate practical interest in describing extractions is the use of the term per cent extracted, $\% E$. This quantity is related to the distribution ratio, D, by the following equation:

$$\% E = \frac{100D}{D + (V_w/V_o)} \tag{2.14}$$

where V_o and V_w represent the volumes of the organic and aqueous phases, respectively. When the volumes are equal, the denominator simplifies to $D + 1$. Figure 2.1 graphically portrays the interconversion of D and $\% E$ at a unit volume ratio. It can be seen that the per cent extraction method of reporting analytical data provides a more useful picture of extraction. When the extraction efficiency approaches 100%, the distribution ratio approaches infinity as a limit. Thus, for differences in extraction in the range 99 to 100%, the distribution ratio will vary from 99 to infinity. Initial observation of such widely differing distribution ratios might erroneously suggest a serious discrepancy, when in reality the extraction would be nearly complete in both instances.

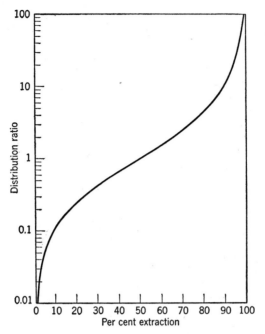

Figure 2.1. Relation of distribution ratio to per cent extraction.

6. PROCESS OF EXTRACTION

Although details of the specific nature of the interactions obviously must differ from one metal extraction system to another, a helpful organizational pattern may be adopted, based on three essential aspects common to every metal extraction process. The three aspects follow.

a. Formation of an Uncharged Complex

This step involves reactions of the metal in the aqueous phase leading to the formation of an extractable species. Complex formation may be accomplished by coordination, including chelation as well as simple coordination, or by ion association.

The case of coordination may be described by

$$M^{n+} + nR^- \rightleftharpoons MR_n \tag{2.15}$$

where M^{n+} is an n-valent metal ion and R^- is an anion of a suitable chelating or coordinating agent. Germanium tetrachloride and copper acetylacetonate are examples of the type of extractable species involving coordination.

In ion association the metal may be incorporated by coordination in either the cation (eqs. 2.16 and 2.17) or the anion (eqs. 2.18 and 2.19) of the extractable ion-pair.

$$M^{n+} + bB \rightleftharpoons MB_b^{n+} \tag{2.16}$$

$$MB_b^{n+} + nX^- \rightleftharpoons (MB_b^{n+}, nX^-) \tag{2.17}$$

$$M^{n+} + (n + a)X^- \rightleftharpoons MX_{n+a}^{a-} \tag{2.18}$$

$$MX_{n+a}^{a-} + aY^+ \rightleftharpoons (aY^+, MX_{n+a}^{a-}) \tag{2.19}$$

where B is a neutral mono- or polydentate ligand, X^- is an anion appropriate either for pairing with the cation as called for in eq. 2.17 or for coordination with the metal as shown in eq. 2.18, and Y^+ is a suitable cation required to form the ion-pair.

An illustration in which the metal ion is part of the cation is found in the extraction of copper as [Cu(2,9-dimethylphenanthroline)$_2^+$, ClO$_4^-$], whereas the extraction of iron as (H$^+$, FeCl$_4^-$) is an example of the incorporation of the metal in the anion portion of the ion pair.

b. Distribution of the Extractable Complex

This is by far the simplest of the three stages from the mathematical standpoint. The distribution of the extractable species between the two liquid phases follows the distribution law. However, factors affecting extractability are quite complex.

c. Interactions of the Complex in the Organic Phase

Reactions involving the extractable complex in the organic phase, e.g., polymerization or dissociation of the complex, interaction with other components, such as the reagent, in the organic phase, are included in this stage.

It might be pointed out that the organizational pattern for the extraction process just described applies with equal facility to solvent extraction of organic compounds. A simplifying modification results from the fact that many organic compounds are themselves extractable and do not require complex-forming reagents to make them so. The three steps in extraction are then expressed as (1) interactions of the compound in the aqueous phase, e.g., ionization; (2) distribution of the compound; and (3) interactions in the organic phase. This rationale may be further generalized to incorporate extractions that do not involve an aqueous solvent phase, such as those employing acetonitrile–

isoamyl ether as the immiscible solvent pair. (This solvent pair has found recent application in metals (Zr-Hf) separation.[7])

Although it is beyond the scope of this text to explore in detail the application of solvent extraction to the problem of analytical separations of organic compounds in general, it might be useful to point out the large body of data giving the distribution ratios of a considerable number of organic compounds in a variety of solvent pairs.[8-12] Much of the discussion which follows will prove helpful in organic extractions as well. The material dealing with basicity (Chapter 3) and with solubility (Chapter 4) is of particular interest for organic extraction problems.

To get a better understanding of the general process of extraction, in the following three chapters we shall examine in greater detail the three basic extraction steps described in this chapter.

REFERENCES

1. M. Berthelot and J. Jungfleisch, *Ann. chim. et phys.*, **26**, 396 (1872).
2. W. Nernst, *Z. physik. Chem.*, **8**, 110 (1891).
3. D. C. Grahame and G. T. Seaborg, *J. Am. Chem. Soc.*, **60**, 2524 (1938).
4. S. Lacroix, *Anal. Chim. Acta*, **1**, 260 (1947).
5. L. H. Anderson and D. M. Yost, *J. Am. Chem. Soc.*, **60**, 1823 (1938).
6. R. D. Sauerbrunn and E. B. Sandell, *J. Am. Chem. Soc.*, **75**, 4170 (1953).
7. E. M. Larsen and L. E. Trevorrow, *J. Inorg. Nuclear Chem.*, **2**, 254 (1956).
8. R. Collander, *Acta Chem. Scand.*, **3**, 717 (1949); **4**, 1085 (1950); **5**, 774 (1951).
9. L. C. Craig, *Anal. Chem.*, **26**, 110 (1954).
10. E. V. Hecker, *Verteilungsverfahren im Laboratorium*, Verlag Chemie, Weinheim/Bergstr., 1955.
11. F. A. V. Metzsch, *Angew. Chem.*, **65**, 586 (1953).
12. D. E. Pearson and M. Levine, *J. Org. Chem.*, **17**, 135 (1952).

Chapter 3

Formation of
Metal Complexes

Since the formation of an extractable complex is a vital step in the extraction process, the nature of metal complexes and the factors governing their formation will now be explored. These will be discussed according to the classification outlined in Chapter 2.

1. COORDINATION COMPLEXES

Our understanding of the metal complexes that may be termed coordination compounds stems largely from Werner's coordination theory. Werner's concept of the coordination of ions or groups in a definite geometric arrangement about a central ion was translated in terms of the G. N. Lewis electronic theory by Sidgwick[1] and Lowry.[2]

a. Acid-Base Character of Coordination Complexes

The application of G. N. Lewis' electronic theory of acids and bases to the consideration of coordination compounds is very useful. According to the Lewis theory, acid-base reactions involve the formation of a coordinate-covalent bond between an acid, defined as an electron-pair acceptor, and a base, or electron-pair donor. A metallic cation, being electron-pair deficient, may be considered as a polybasic acid capable of reacting with several basic entities, the number of which is related to the coordination number of the metal. The coordination number, which refers to the number of groups that can arrange themselves about the central metal ion, is a characteristic of the particular metal ion. The coordination number of a metal ion depends on its ability

16

to accommodate electron pairs in terms of the number and spatial arrangement of the metal's available bonding orbitals. Very often the coordination number will coincide with the number of electron pairs, which gives the metal ion the electronic configuration of the next heavier inert gas. Indeed, the formation of complexes by a metal ion may be interpreted in terms of its tendency to fill up unoccupied orbitals and thereby achieve the stable electronic configuration of an inert gas. The coordination number also depends on the size of the metal ion, for its size reflects its ability to accommodate groups around it.

The basic entities, characterized by possessing at least one unshared pair of electrons, are usually either neutral, as in the case of water or ammonia, or negatively charged, as with cyanide or halide ions.

The nature of the bonds between the acidic metal cation and the basic coordinated groups, called ligands, ranges from almost completely covalent, as is the case with $Fe(CN)_6^{4-}$, to the other extreme of essentially electrostatic, as is the case with $Ca(H_2O)_6^{2+}$, with a large number of coordination complexes having bonds of intermediate character. The transition between electrovalent and covalent bonding may be considered in terms of the polarizabilities of the ions or groups involved.[3] When a metal cation and a ligand approach each other, the attraction of the electron atmosphere of the latter by the metal cation induces a deformation or polarization in the ligand. The cation is also polarized, but because of its relatively small size this is less pronounced. The effect of the polarization is an increase in the extent of sharing of electrons, or of covalent character. Ion deformation is favored by highly charged metal cations, by large ligands, and by metal ions with a non-inert-gas atom electronic configuration.

Regardless of the bond type involved in the complex, it will, of course, carry a charge which is the algebraic sum of the electrical charges of the metal ion and the ligands. Although only uncharged complexes are extractable as such, our interest extends to the charged complexes as well since by further combination, e.g., ion association, a neutral extractable species can result.

b. Factors Influencing Coordination

According to the Lewis theory, we can anticipate that the stability of a metal coordination complex will depend on (1) factors related to the "acidity" of the metal ion, (2) those related to the "basicity" of the coordinating ligand, and (3) special factors related to the configuration of the resultant complex.

Although the transition metals are generally considered to possess the most pronounced tendency to form coordination complexes, most of the metals in the periodic table can form such complexes. What structural parameters are pertinent in the description of the acid strengths of metal ions? From the electrostatic nature of the attraction of the positively charged cation for the electron-rich ligand, we can predict that the higher and more concentrated the cationic charge, the greater its acidity. In this connection, the oxidation state of a particular metal would have an influential affect on its "acidity," i.e., its ability to form complexes. For example, iron(III) forms more stable complexes with chloride ion than does iron(II), and, on this account, is much more readily extracted out of hydrochloric acid into suitable solvents.

The charge concentration of an ion can be described in terms of the ionic potential, defined as the ratio of the charge to the ionic radius. Possibly of more fundamental significance is the ratio of the square of the charge to the ionic radius as a measure of the "acidity," where essentially electrostatic bonding is involved. This factor which arises from the Born equation [4] for the energy of solvation of gaseous spherical ions has been applied to the evaluation of a number of metal complexes (see page 28). The Born equation is

$$\Delta F = -\frac{Z^2}{2r}\left(1 - \frac{1}{\epsilon}\right) \tag{3.1}$$

where ϵ is the dielectric constant, r the ionic radius, and Z the ionic charge.

In general, the stability of metal complexes increases with the ionic potential or the Z^2/r value of the metal involved, but there are enough exceptions to this rough correspondence to emphasize the significance of other factors. For example, the metal ion must have available bonding orbitals for the electron pair(s) it accepts. The nature of the available orbital is intimately related to the strength of the bond formed. The deeper the orbitals involved, the stronger the bonds formed. Hence the transition metals, possessing unoccupied low-lying d orbitals, form bonds much more readily than do the non-transition metals. The orbitals involved in bond formation affect not only bond strength but also the stereochemical arrangement of the complex.[5]

Orbitals Used	Coordination Number	Relative Bond Strength	Configuration
sp^3	4	2.00	Tetrahedral
dsp^2	4	2.69	Planar
d^2sp^3	6	2.92	Octohedral

The role of the oxidation state of the metals assumes a different, but no less significant, role in complexes involving low-lying orbitals. The degree of utilization of these low-lying orbitals by ligands will tend to stabilize certain oxidation states. For example, whereas $Co(H_2O)_6^{2+}$ and $CoCl_4^{2-}$ are far more stable than the corresponding cobalt(III) ions, the positions are reversed for the ammine and other complexes.

A further factor of importance to the acidic nature of the metal ion is its electronegativity, which is measured as the energy necessary to remove electrons from the metal atom and hence reflects the electron-attracting ability of the metal ion. Although other factors are involved, the position of a metal in the electromotive series is some indication of its electronegativity. Complexes of the more electronegative metals tend to be more stable.

Turning next our attention to the ligand partner in complex formation, the base or electron-pair donor, we may profitably consider the question of the similarity of a Brönsted base, defined as a species with an affinity for a proton, and a Lewis base, a species attracted to an electron-pair-deficient ion or molecule. Are substances that are the strongest Brönsted bases the best metal complex formers? It would be difficult to imagine any generally applicable relationship, particularly since metal ions are so much larger than the proton. Hence, steric considerations are much more critical in complex formation than in neutralization. However, in a series of closely related ligands it would seem reasonable to expect a certain correlation between the proton affinity of the ligand and the strength of the complexes it forms. In Table 3.1 are given the complexing tendencies of some simple ligands.

Table 3.1.   Complex-Forming Tendencies of Some Simple Ligands [a]

$NH_3 > RNH_2 > R_2NH > R_3N$
$H_2O > ROH > R_2O > RCOR > RCHO$
$R_3As > R_3P > R_2S$
$CN^- > SCN^- > F^- > OH^- > Cl^- > Br^- > I^-$

[a] R = alkyl or aryl group.

These indicate general trends that are by no means absolute.

For example, among the halides, small electropositive metal ions like Al^{3+} and Fe^{3+} show the strongest complex formation with the F^- ion, and Hg^{2+} and other strongly electronegative cations have the highest affinity for the easily polarized iodide ion. Among the amines, the presence of an increasing number of R groups results in an increasing difficulty of complex formation. This may be attributed to the steric hindrance by the R group to the approach of the metal ion to the nitrogen.[6] Although pyridine is a tertiary amine, the ring structure of the molecule results in a minimization of such steric hindrance so that pyridine forms relatively stable complexes, more like those of primary amines. In a given class of amines, an increase in proton affinity is accompanied by a corresponding increase in complex-forming ability. Coordination complexes with organic oxygen-containing compounds are of particular interest in that such complexes play an important role in oxonium extraction systems.

A further discussion of bases, as well as a consideration of the role of structural aspects of the metal complex, will appear later in the sections dealing with chelates (page 21) and with solvents (page 41).

c. Types of Coordination Complexes

Among the many metal complexes of interest in extraction, several types may be distinguished. First, there are *simple coordination complexes* in which metal ions combine with monofunctional ligands in a number equal to their coordination number; e.g., $Fe(CN)_6^{4-}$, $GeCl_4$, and $CoCl_4^{2-}(ROH)_2$. Some of these complexes are extractable or, if charged, can associate with other ions to form extractable species, although others serve to prevent extraction. A second category derives from the interaction of metal ions with polyfunctional ligands that can each occupy more than one position in the coordination sphere of the metal. These complexes, called *chelates*, will be treated in detail in section 2.

A third category, of which *heteropoly acids* are an illustration, is distinguished by the presence of a central complex ion rather than a central monatomic ion. Heteropoly acids, many of which are extractable into organic solvents, form a large group of oxygen-containing acids possessing an atom of an element such as boron, silicon, phosphorus, or arsenic in combination with a number of atoms of another element such as molybdenum or tungsten. For example, a molybdophosphoric acid might be formulated as $H_wP_xMo_yO_z \cdot mH_2O$, where compounds corresponding to $y/x = 6$ or 12, or some intermediate value, are known. There are 6-acids known where the heteroatom is I, Te, Fe, Cr, Al, Co, Ni, Rh, Cu, and Mn; 12-acids are known where the heteroatom is B, Si, P, As, Ti, Ge, Sn, Zr, Hf, Th, and Ce. Although the theory of the structure of heteropoly acids is far from being in a settled state, there is strong evidence for the 12-acid existing in the form of a central XO_4 tetrahedron (X being the heteroatom) surrounded by twelve MoO_6 (or WO_6) octahedra, each corner of the tetrahedron being shared with three octahedra, each of which in turn shares one oxygen atom with each of its neighbors. This gives rise to four Mo_3O_{13} groups which share corners linking to give the group $(XMo_{12}O_{40})^{8-n}$.[7] The structure is "open" and can accommodate the numerous water or other solvent molecules characteristic of these compounds.

2. CHELATE COMPLEXES

a. General Considerations

Chelating reagents play an important role in extraction of metals because they comprise an impressive body of useful extraction agents and masking agents as well. Metal chelates represent a type of co-ordination compound in which a metal ion combines with a polyfunctional base capable of occupying two or more positions of the coordination sphere of the metal ion to form a cyclic compound. The functional groups of the base must be so situated in the molecule that they permit the formation of a stable ring, generally five- or six-membered. Thus, in the idealized chelating agent $B_1 - (X)_y - B_2$, where B represents an atom having basic character (N, S, or O, for example) and X is usually, but not necessarily, carbon, reaction with a metal ion M, having an assumed coordination number of four, may be represented as

$$M + 2 \quad \overset{B_1}{\underset{B_2}{\diagdown}}(X)_y \rightleftharpoons \overset{B_1}{\underset{B_2}{(X)_y}} M \overset{B_2}{\underset{B_1}{(X)_y}} \qquad (3.2)$$

where $y = 2$ or 3. The physical and chemical properties of a metal chelate will of course depend on factors related to the basic nature of the chelating agent and the acidic nature of the metal, as well as on factors inherent in the metal chelate itself.

A casual perusal of typical chelating agents such as 8-quinolinol or ethylenediaminetetraacetic acid (EDTA) reveals the presence of both acid and basic groups in these molecules. Yet the reagent that coordinates with a metal must have a basic character. There is, of course, no contradiction here. Chelating agents possessing "acidic" groups function as bases by loss of a proton; i.e., the phenolate, carboxylate, etc., anionic form of the molecule is the species actually reacting. A number of typical basic groups are tabulated in Table 3.2, together with an evaluation of their basic strengths, or more accurately, proton affinities, as given by the approximate pK_a (negative logarithm of the

Table 3.2. Representative Basic Groups

Uncharged	pK_a	Anionic	pK_a
Aliphatic amines		*Carboxylates*	
$C_2H_5NH_2$	10.8	Acetate	4.7
$(C_2H_5)_2NH$	10.9	Salicylate	3.0
$(C_2H_5)_3N$	10.8	Oxalate	1.5
H_2N—CH_2—CH_2—NH_2	10.2		
		Phenolates	
Aromatic amines		Phenolate	9.9
Aniline	4.3		
p-Nitroaniline	2.0	*Enolate*	
p-Toluidine	5.3	Acetylacetonate	9.7
Heterocyclic amines		*Mercaptide*	
Pyridine	5.5	Thiophenolate	7.9
Quinoline	5.0		
Piperidine	11.3	*Oximate*	
o-Phenanthroline	5.0	Dimethylglyoximate	11
Miscellaneous			
Carbonyl group	−6		
Ether oxygen	∼0		
Hydroxyl group	∼0		
Nitroso group	∼0		

acid dissociation constant) values of the corresponding conjugate acids in water. It should be noted that basic strength rises with increasing pK_a value.

Chelating agents may be conveniently classified according to the charge type of the basic groups present. If both basic groups of the reagent are uncharged, positively charged metal chelates are formed. If the reagent has one anionic group, neutral chelates usually result. Finally, the presence of a multiple negative charge on the chelating agent may result in negatively charged chelates. Some of the more important types of chelating agents are tabulated in Table 3.3.

Table 3.3. Classification of Types of Chelating Agents

I. Bidentate reagents
    A. Two anionic basic groups
        a. Hydroxycarboxylic acids, e.g., tartaric and citric acids

Copper tartrate

Table 3.3. Classification of Types of Chelating Agents (Continued)

    b. Dimercapto compounds, e.g., toluenedithiol and 1,2-dimercaptoethane
(BAL)

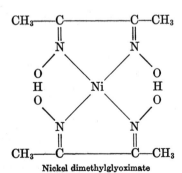

Molybdenum-toluenedithiol complex

B. One anionic and one uncharged basic group
    1. Four-membered ring formers
       a. Dithiocarboxylic acids, e.g., xanthates and dithiocarbamates

Lead diethyldithiocarbamate

    2. Five-membered ring formers
       a. Compounds having reactive grouping **N—C—C—O⁻**, e.g., α-amino
acids, 8-quinolinol, α-benzoinoxime

Gallium 8-quinolinate

       b. Compounds having reactive grouping **—N=C—C=N⁻**, e.g., di-
methylglyoxime

Nickel dimethylglyoximate

Table 3.3. Classification of Types of Chelating Agents (Continued)

c. Compounds having reactive grouping $O{=}N{-}N{-}O^-$, e.g., cupferron

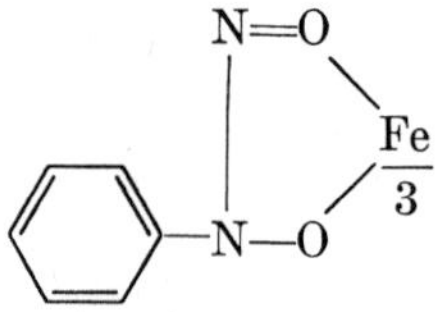

$$\underset{\text{Iron(III) cupferrate}}{\begin{array}{c}
\end{array}}$$

Iron(III) cupferrate

d. Compounds having reactive grouping $N{-}N{=}C{-}S^-$, e.g., dithizone, dithiooxamide

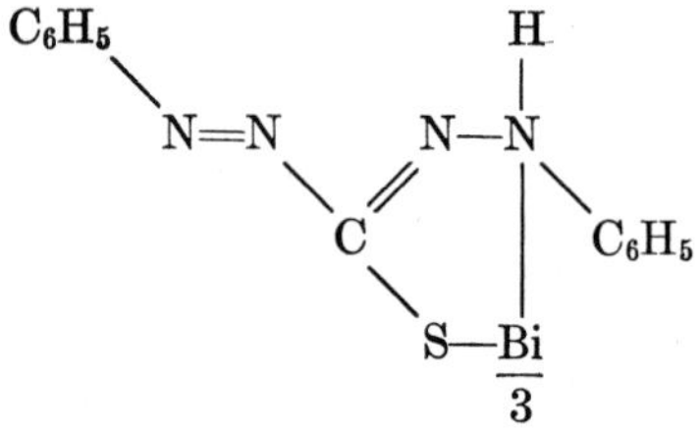

Bismuth dithizonate

3. Six-membered ring formers
   a. Compounds having the reactive grouping $O{=}C{-}C{=}C{-}O^-$, e.g., β-diketones, salicylaldehyde, hydroxyanthraquinone

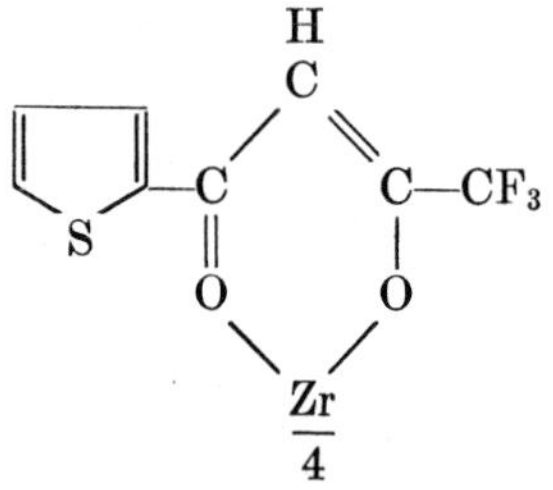

Zirconium thenoyltrifluoroacetonate

b. Compounds having the reactive grouping $N{=}C{-}C{=}C{-}O^-$, e.g., salicylaldoxime

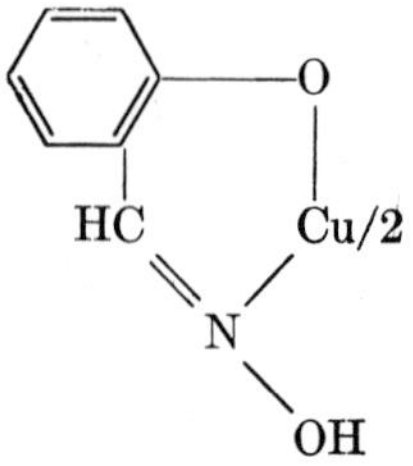

Copper salicylaldoximate

Table 3.3.   Classification of Types of Chelating Agents (Continued)

    c. Compounds having the reactive grouping $O{=}N{-}C{=}C{-}O^-$, e.g., 1-nitroso-2-naphthol

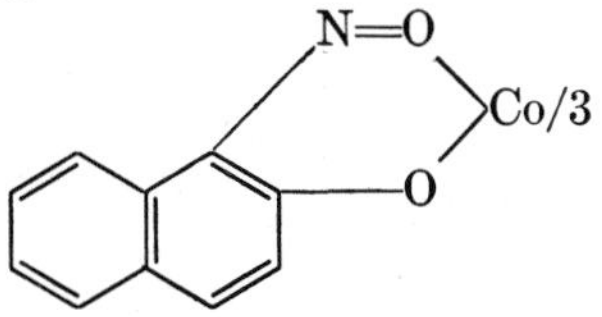

Cobalt(III) complex

C. Two uncharged basic groups

    a. Compounds having the reactive grouping **N—C—C—N**, e.g., ethylenediamine, dipyridyl, phenanthroline

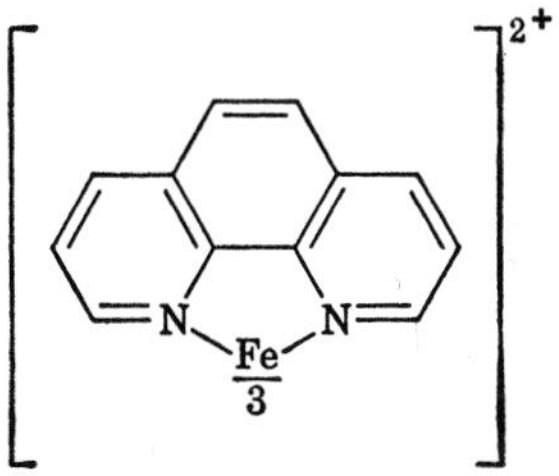

Tris-(phenanthroline)–iron(II)

II. Polydentate reagents

    A. Tridentate, e.g., terpyridyl

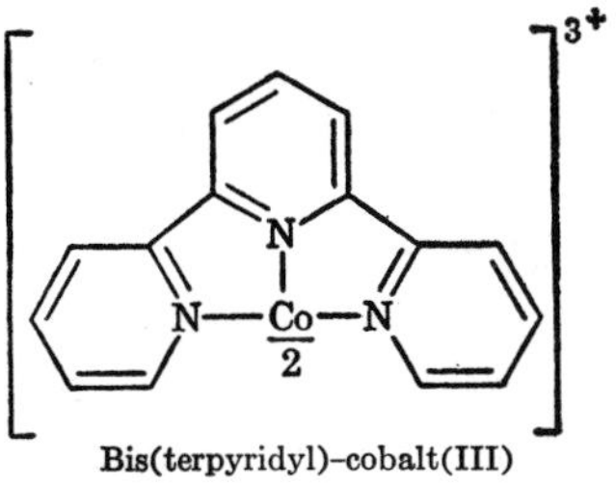

Bis(terpyridyl)–cobalt(III)

    B. Tetradentate, e.g., **thiosalicylideneethylenediimine**

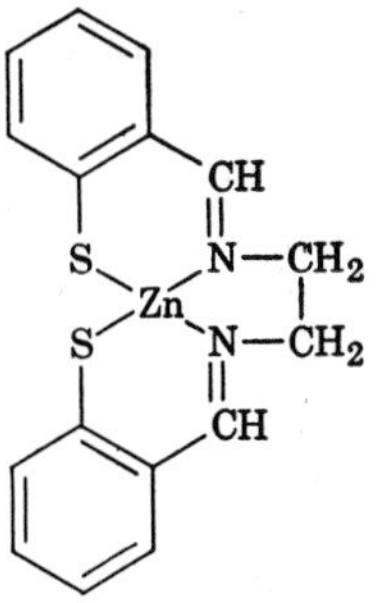

Thiosalicylideneethylenediimine–zinc

Table 3.3. Classification of Types of Chelating Agents (Continued)

C. Hexadentate, ethylenediaminetetraacetic acid (EDTA)

Calcium-EDTA complex

All types of chelating agents find useful application in metal extraction procedures. As a class, the neutral chelates are those most easily extracted into organic solvents such as chloroform, benzene, and the like. Some cationic chelates, e.g., bis(2,9-dimethylphenanthroline)-copper(I), by pairing with certain anions, form uncharged species which can then be extracted into organic solvents. The great usefulness of reagents forming anionic chelates resides in their "masking" action in preventing the extraction of metals with which they react strongly. The use of an extraction agent and a masking agent in combination, as with 8-quinolinol and EDTA, results in a marked increase in the selectivity of the extraction system.

b. Factors Influencing Chelation

Structural factors of reagents determining their effectiveness as chelating agents include the basic strengths of the functional groups, the electronegativity of the bonding atoms, as well as the size and number of the chelate rings formed.

There is a strong direct relation between the basicity of a chelating agent, as measured by pK_a values, and the stability of the chelates it forms. The similarity between the attraction of a donor group for protons as well as for other cationic acids was pointed out by Calvin and Wilson [8] in their study of copper chelates of a series of substituted β-diketones and salicylaldehydes. Although this finding has been since confirmed by others for a number of series of chelating agents, Merritt [9] has found that metal chelates of substituted 8-quinolinols precipitate at lower pH values as the basic strength of the reagent decreases. This serves as a reminder that the extent of chelate formation depends not only on the value of the equilibrium constant of the reaction but on the concentration of the reagent anion as well. Acetyl-acetone ($pK_a = 9.7$), for example, forms more stable chelates than does thenoyltrifluoroacetone ($pK_a = 6.2$), since it is more basic. For the same reason, at any given pH value, the acetylacetonate anion concentration will be lower than that of the thenoyltrifluoroacetonate anion. Of the two conflicting factors, stability and reagent anion concentration, the latter seems to carry somewhat more weight. Under comparable conditions, the thenoyltrifluoroacetone chelates form to a somewhat greater extent than do those of the parent compound.

The electronegativity of the donor atoms of the basic groups in the reagent plays an important role in chelate formation. For the transition metals and others tending to form covalent bonds, the atoms of lower electronegativity tend to form stronger bonds. For example, nitrogen and sulfur are better than oxygen. Thus, diphenylthiocarbazone (dithizone) probably forms more stable chelates than does its oxygen analog, diphenylcarbazone.

Another factor of vital importance to chelate stability is the size of the ring formed. This was implied in the generalized chelation equation (3.2) by indicating the number of atoms between the two donor atoms to be two or three. In order to form a stable ring, i.e., one with a minimum of strain, the bond angles of the participating atoms should be as close as possible to the normal covalent bond angles. The Bayer strain theory, which has proved so successful in classical organic chemistry, may be applied equally well to chelate rings to show that five- and six-membered rings will be most favored in chelate compounds. All other factors being equal, a five-membered ring chelate will be somewhat more stable than its six-membered ring analog.

Chelate stability will rise with the number of rings that are formed. This is not due to any intrinsic advantage of ring formation, but rather to the increasing number of water molecules that are displaced from the metal coordination sphere by one molecule of the polyfunctional reagent. For example, we may compare the increasing stability of zinc complexes with methylamine(I), ethylenediamine(II), and tris-(2-aminoethyl)-amine(III) with the increasing number of waters released per reagent molecule.[10]

Reagents	Rings Formed per Reagent	Waters Released per Reagent	Stability of Complex
I	0	1	$Zn(I)_4{}^{2+}$ $\log k_1 k_2 k_3 k_4 = 9$
II	1	2	$Zn(II)_2{}^{2+}$ $\log k_1 k_2 = 11.1$
III	2	4	$Zn(III)^{2+} \log k = 14.6$

Under comparable conditions, the reaction yielding the greatest increase in the number of molecules or ions will be the most favorable energetically. This has been referred to as the "entropy effect" in chelation. A reaction derives driving force from an increase of entropy, a quantity which can be said to measure the degree of disorder in a system. The entropy increases with an increase in the number of molecules or ions in a reaction. An outstanding example of a chelating agent that forms a number of rings, a polydentate reagent, is the EDTA anion which can occupy six coordination positions (see Table 3.3). Another polydentate chelating agent, one which shows promise as an extraction agent, is thiosalicylideneethylenediimine (see Table 3.3).[11]

Factors affecting the acidic nature of the metal ion, as have been discussed earlier (page 18), reflect the variation in the nature of the bonds formed. Cations of the more electropositive metals such as the alkaline earths and lanthanides may interact in essentially electrostatic fashion with donor bases. In cases of this type, the acidity of the metal may be gaged in terms of ionic forces related to both the charge and size of the metal ion. Thus, Martell and Calvin[12] take the Born equation (page 18) for the energy of solvation of gaseous spherical ions as a basis for using the quantity Z^2/r for measuring metal "acidity." They correlate the stability constants of a number of alkaline earth chelates with the Z^2/r value of the metal ion (see Table 3.4).

Table 3.4. Stability Constants of Certain Alkali and Alkaline Earth Metal Chelates [12]

Log Formation Constant

Ion	Z^2/r	I	II	III	IV	V	VI	VII
Be^{2+}	9.3							0.26
Mg^{2+}	4.9	7.0	3.4	2.8	3.2		3.32	0.19
Ca^{2+}	3.4	5.4	3.0	2.5	3.2	1.2	3.48	0.30
Sr^{2+}	3.0		2.5		2.8	1.1		
Ba^{2+}	2.6		2.3	1.7	2.1	1.0	3.85	
Ra^{2+}					2.0			
Li^{1+}	1.7							
Na^{1+}	1.0						1.17	

I	Eriochrome black-T	V	Succinic acid
II	Oxalic acid	VI	Trimetaphosphoric acid
III	Malonic acid	VII	Nitroacetic acid
IV	Citric acid		

With the transition and heavy metals, interaction with chelating agents may involve bonds of more covalent character where different and more complex parameters of the metal determine acidity. In complexes of this type, the stability of the complex may be related to the electronegativity of the metal atom, although influences related to the possibility of multiple-bond formation and resonance effects may complicate matters. Despite the lack of a complete listing of the cations into a stability sequence, the order of stability of complexes of a limited number of divalent metal ions has been shown by a number of investigators to be fairly independent of the nature of the chelating agent involved. Mellor and Maley [13] list the order thus:

$$Pd > Cu > Ni > Pb > Co > Zn > Cd > Fe > Mn > Mg$$

Two factors of importance to the stability of chelates that are related to the structure of the chelate itself are the so-called resonance effect and stereochemical effects.

The resonance effect, first introduced by Calvin and Wilson [8] to explain why the copper chelates of β-diketones have greater stability than those of salicylaldehydes, refers to the stability increase that results from the contribution of resonance structures of the chelate ring to the structure of the chelate. Thus, in copper acetylacetonate,

resonance structures may be written in which double-bond character is attributed to the Cu—O linkage, resulting in a completely conjugated six-membered ring analogous to benzene.

Another example of interest in this connection is found in the iron(II) chelates of ethylenediamine, dipyridyl, and phenanthroline, which increase in stability in the order named, paralleling the increase in the number of possible resonance structures.

$\log K_f = 9.5$ [14] $\log K_f = 17.6$ [15] $\log K_f = 21.3$ [16]

Stereochemical factors peculiar to the metal chelate itself also influence chelate stability. Of particular interest is the effect of substituents in the chelating agent in certain sensitive positions. Thus, derivatives of 8-quinolinol substituted in the two-position

give less stable chelates than does 8-quinolinol itself because of the steric hindrance to chelate formation caused by the substituent group.[17] With aluminum, no chelation at all is obtained because the presence of the blocking group makes it impossible for the small Al^{3+} ion to fit three such molecules around itself.[18,19]

Similarly, dipyridyls and phenanthrolines having substituents on the carbon atoms adjacent to the nitrogen atoms lose their ability to form the chelates with iron(II) characteristic of the parent compound. Such compounds still retain their reactivity toward copper(I), for the tetrahedral arrangement of the two reagent molecules involved in this chelate minimizes the steric hindrance so that they can be used as the basis for a highly specific copper reaction.[20,21]

3. ION ASSOCIATION COMPLEXES

In addition to coordination compounds, there are a large number of uncharged compounds formed by the association of oppositely charged ions in pairs or clusters of higher order. A major fraction of the extractable species other than those that are chelates exist in the organic solvent as ion association aggregates. Although, in ion-pair formation the forces of attraction are "physical" as contrasted to the "chemical" forces involved in the formation of coordination complexes, both types behave in accord with the law of mass action. Hence, for two ions A^+ and B^- which associate to form (A^+, B^-) according to the equation

$$A^+ + B^- \rightleftharpoons (A^+, B^-) \tag{3.3}$$

the equilibrium expression is

$$K = \frac{[(A^+, B^-)]}{[A^+][B^-]} \tag{3.4}$$

The existence and behavior of such complexes was predicted by N. Bjerrum.[22] Confirmation and amplification of the theory have come largely from the work of Fuoss and Kraus.[23]

Bjerrum's theory relates the value of the ion-pair formation constant K to the dielectric constant of the solvent ϵ, to the temperature, and to the size of the ions involved. Thus,

$$K = \frac{4\pi N}{1000} \frac{e^2}{\epsilon kT} Q(b)$$

$$b = \frac{e^2}{a\epsilon kT}$$

(3.5)

where N is Avogadro's number, e is the unit of charge, k is the Boltzmann constant, T is the absolute temperature, $Q(b)$ is a calculable function, and a is an empirical parameter which has been interpreted as representing the distance between charge centers of the paired ions when in contact. From this equation, using ion-pairs in which a varies from 5 to 7 Å, K is found to range between 10^{15} and 10^{11} at a low dielectric constant value ($\epsilon = 3$) and between 10^4 and 2.5×10^{11} at a dielectric constant value of 10; K becomes negatively infinite at dielectric constant values of 40, 47, and 56 for $a = 7$, 6, and 5 Å, respectively.[24] Since the organic solvents used in extraction have dielectric constants below 40, ion association will be extensive in these solvents. Furthermore, in many ion association extraction systems, the dielectric constant of the aqueous phase is decreased by the presence of salts and the dissolved organic solvent to the point where extensive ion association is possible in this phase also.[24] See Fig. 3.1.

The effect of temperature on the value of K will depend on the temperature variation of the dielectric constant. In solvents of higher dielectric constants, ϵ decreases markedly with temperature so that ϵT values fall with increasing T. In such solvents, ion association increases with increasing temperature. In solvents of very low dielectric constant, ϵT increases with temperature as the value of ϵ does not change much, with the result that ion association falls off with rising temperatures in solvents of this type.

From the Bjerrum equation, it is evident that ion association depends on the value of a, decreasing with increasing a values. If the value of a does not change appreciably with change in solvent, then the value of K, the ion-pair formation constant, can be predicted in any solvent from its known value in one solvent. This follows from

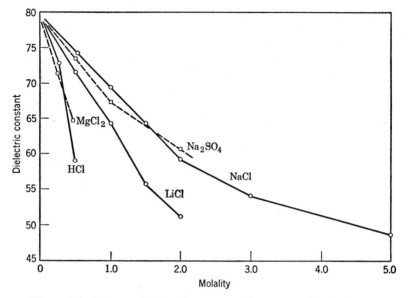

Figure 3.1.   Change of dielectric constant of aqueous salt solutions.[24]

the fact that K depends only on dielectric constant if a and the temperature remain constant.

The extent of ion association is found to vary regularly with ionic size in a series of related salts. As might be expected from the dependence of K on a, a decrease in ion association is found with increasing anion size in the series (Na^+, NH_2^-), $(Na^+, NHC_6H_5^-)$, $[Na^+, N(C_6H_5)_2^-]$. In a series of picrates, K increased from $(C_4H_9)_4N < (C_4H_9)_4P < (C_4H_9)_4As < (C_4H_9)_3S < (C_4H_9)_2I$, indicating that the size of the central atom does not determine the effective size of the ion.[25] A similar order has been observed by Tribalat[26] for the distribution of $[(C_6H_5)_4As^+, Cl^-]$ $(D = 200)$ and $[(C_6H_5)_4P^+, Cl^-]$ $(D = 25)$ between chloroform and water. The distribution ratios of the corresponding perrhenates were also in the same order.

Structural influences other than size also play a role in determining the extent of association. For example, association decreases from $(Na^+, OC_6H_5^-)$ to $(Na^+, NHC_6H_5^-)$ to $(Na^+, SC_6H_5^-)$ to an extent not predictable on the basis of the relative size of the oxygen and sulfur atoms. Substitution of negative groups in anions decreases association, e.g., acetates > chloroacetates. However, negative groups introduced into one of the alkyl groups of a quaternary ammonium cation considerably enhance association.[25]

The occurrence of interactions in addition to those of purely coulombic attraction serves to stabilize the ion-pair. The K value of a tertiary amine picrate (10^{21}), significantly higher than that of a quaternary amine picrate (10^{19}), undoubtedly reflects the influence of hydrogen bonding in the former compound. Obviously, should the ions be capable of interacting by coordination, greatly increased stability would result.

Although the degree of association increases with increasing concentration up to 0.1 molal, a maximum is reached somewhere between 0.1 and 0.3 molal. This seems to be true for all cases of ion association.

Kraus and Fuoss [26] found that ion association in benzene solution proceeds to clusters of larger size, even at low concentrations (greater than $5 \times 10^{-6} M$). Depending on the dipole moment of the ion-pairs and the size of the ions, the dipoles, i.e., ion-pairs, interact to form quadrupoles in varying degree. If both the dipole moment and the size of the ions are large, association to quadrupoles is pronounced. With large ions and small dipole moment, association to quadrupoles is small. If the dipole moment is large and one ion is small, association is very great and soon proceeds far beyond the quadrupole stage. Kraus [25] concludes that all salts having one large and one small ion are highly associated. Particularly large aggregates occur in micellar or colloidal electrolytes.

Ions with long hydrocarbon chains such as the soaps form aggregates, called micellar ions, in aqueous solutions. With conditions favorable to association as discussed earlier, these micellar ions interact with oppositely charged ions, called counter ions, in ion-pairs to give species soluble in organic solvents. With organic solution of such aggregates in contact with an aqueous phase, solvent extraction proceeds in a manner formally analogous to ion exchange, in that the counter ions can be exchanged for others present in the aqueous phase.

REFERENCES

1. N. V. Sidgwick, *J. Chem. Soc.*, **123**, 725 (1933).
2. T. M. Lowry, *J. Soc. Chem. Ind.*, **42**, 316 (1933).
3. K. Fajans, *Naturwissenschaften*, **11**, 165 (1923).
4. M. Born, *Z. Physik.*, **1**, 45 (1920).
5. L. Pauling, *Nature of the Chemical Bond*, Cornell University Press, Ithaca, N. Y., 1940.
6. G. A. Carlson, J. P. McReynolds, and F. H. Verhoek, *J. Am. Chem. Soc.*, **67**, 1334 (1945).
7. J. F. Keggin, *Proc. Roy. Soc.* (London), **144A**, 75 (1934).
8. M. Calvin and K. W. Wilson, *J. Am. Chem. Soc.*, **67**, 2003 (1945).

9. L. Merritt, *Record Chem. Progr.* (*Kresge-Hooker Sci. Lib.*), **10,** 59 (1949).
10. G. Schwarzenbach, *Chimia* (*Buenos Aires*), **3,** 1 (1949).
11. G. Beck, *Mikrochemie ver. Mikrochim. Acta,* **33,** 188 (1947).
12. A. E. Martell and M. Calvin, *Chemistry of the Metal Chelate Compounds,* Prentice-Hall, Inc., New York, 1952, p. 194.
13. D. P. Mellor and L. E. Maley, *Nature,* **159,** 370 (1947); **161,** 436 (1948).
14. J. Bjerrum, *Metal Ammine Formation in Aqueous Solution,* P. Haase and Son, Copenhagen, 1941.
15. J. H. Baxendale and P. George, *Nature,* **162,** 777 (1948).
16. T. S. Lee, I. M. Kolthoff, and D. L. Leussing, *J. Am. Chem. Soc.,* **70,** 2348 (1948)
17. W. D. Johnston and H. Freiser, *Anal. Chim. Acta,* **11,** 201 (1954).
18. L. L. Merritt and J. K. Walker, *Ind. Eng. Chem., Anal. Ed.,* **16,** 387 (1944).
19. H. Irving, E. J. Butler, and M. F. Ring, *J. Chem. Soc.,* **1949,** 1489.
20. J. G. Breckenridge, R. W. Lewis, and L. A. Quick, *Can. J. Research,* **B17,** 258 (1939).
21. G. F. Smith and W. H. McCurdy, *Anal. Chem.,* **24,** 371 (1952).
22. N. Bjerrum, *Kgl. Danske Selskab.,* **7,** No. 9 (1926).
23. R. M. Fuoss and C. A. Kraus, *J. Am. Chem. Soc.,* **55,** 1019 (1933).
24. J. B. Hasted, D. M. Ritson, C. H. Collie, *J. Chem. Phys.,* **16,** 1 (1948).
25. C. A. Kraus, *J. Phys. Chem.,* **60,** 129 (1956).
26. S. Tribalat, *Anal. Chim. Acta,* **4,** 228 (1950).
27. C. A. Kraus and R. M. Fuoss, *J. Am. Chem. Soc.,* **55,** 21 (1933).

Chapter 4

Distribution of
the Extractable Species

Although the distribution of a particular species between two essentially immiscible liquids can be described in relatively simple mathematical terms, the larger question, that of the mechanism of the distribution or extraction, remains a puzzling challenge. Why would certain metal-containing compounds be more soluble in organic solvents than in aqueous media? Indeed, what factors affect the solubility of metal-containing compounds in any solvent?

1. SOLUBILITY AND DISTRIBUTION

Before discussing the questions raised about solubility, it must be pointed out that to uncritically equate the ratio of solubilities of a solute in each of two solvents to the distribution coefficient of the solute distributing between the same two solvents could lead to serious errors. Despite the fact that the underlying mechanisms in both cases are quite similar, it would almost always be incorrect to expect a quantitative agreement of the solubility ratio and the distribution coefficient. Two major factors are responsible for the disparity.

The first of these arises out of the changes that occur in the activity coefficients of the solute in each phase as the total solute concentration changes (see eq. 2.6). Of course, when the solute concentration has reached the saturation level in each solvent, the point has been reached at which the solubility ratio and distribution coefficient may be equated with confidence.

A far more important but seldom recognized cause for discrepancies between distribution coefficients and solubility ratios is the effect of the presence of the second solvent on the solubility of the solute in the first solvent. Since the solvent pair is essentially immiscible, it is a reasonable assumption that the low mutual solubility does not appreciably alter the activity of either solvent. However, the solute may react with the second solvent to form a new species (e.g., a solvate) which may have solubility characteristics completely different from those of the original solute. In such an event, the distribution would bear little or no relation to the ratio of the solubilities determined with the pure solvents. For example, although the solubility of silver perchlorate in water at 25°C is approximately 85 weight % and in toluene 50 weight %, the salt is found entirely in the aqueous phase after distribution.[1] The explanation of this phenomenon probably lies in the formation of a hydrated silver perchlorate which has a low solubility in toluene. If solvation is properly taken into account, the relation of solubility and extractability is brought into proper perspective. In any event, these factors responsible for quantitative differences between distribution and relative solubility must not be allowed to stand in the way of the recognition of the intimate qualitative relationship between the two phenomena. A discussion of the factors affecting solubility will most certainly be of help in understanding extractability.

2. FACTORS AFFECTING SOLUBILITY

Since solute molecules must force themselves between those of the solvent, and vice versa, in the formation of a solution, the solution process involves a complex array of intermolecular forces. The nature of these interactions may be classified along the following lines.[2]

a. Electrostatic Bonds

These bonds involve electrostatic forces, such as those between two ions, two dipoles, or an ion and a dipole.

The solubility of electrolytes in a highly polar medium such as water is aided by electrostatic forces. A comparison of the solubilities of electrolytes having the same or similar free energies of formation indicates the primary role of electrostatic forces. In such a comparison, lattice energies are useful in seeking factors that govern solubility. In the alkali halide series, as the ratio of the radius of the cation to that of the anion decreases below unity while the radius sum is held constant, the lattice energy remains about the same at first and then decreases quite sharply. Since the sum of the magnitudes of the solvation energies of the gaseous ions rises steadily (see Born equation, page 18), a salt will tend to be more soluble as its radius ratio becomes smaller than 1.

b. Hydrogen Bonds

Although these bonds are essentially electrostatic, they are exceptional enough to warrant separate consideration. Much of the solvent action of water is attributable to its hydrogen-bonding capacity. Conversely, solubility of a substance in water or the alcohols is governed more by the ability of the substance to form hydrogen bonds than by its "polarity" as measured by dipole moment.

c. Chemical Bonds

These, of course, depend on the specific system and in general are temperature dependent. In this category acid-base interactions will be of particular interest to us. The solvent action of water as well as of alcohols and ethers on many salts reflects the basic character of these solvents in the Lewis sense. Similarly, the solubility of iodine and other Lewis acids in aromatic liquids follows an order that reflects electron density or basicity in the aromatic nucleus. Thus, as a solvent for iodine, mesitylene is better than xylene which, in turn, is better than benzene, an order which parallels the electron densities in the nucleus of these aromatic compounds.

Solubility of metal salts in water reflects the operation of several of the forces mentioned earlier. Water, a highly polar liquid (high dielectric constant), will permit the charge separation of cations and anions without excessive energy expenditure. Even more significantly, the basic character of water results in the solvation of cations by coordination, e.g., $Ca(H_2O)_6^{2+}$ and $Cu(H_2O)_4^{2+}$, which not only gives a favorable energy change for solution but changes the ions by giving them a solvent sheath so that they experience less electrostatic attraction and are more solvent-like.

Most metal salts, being strong electrolytes, are not appreciably soluble in organic solvents. The primary function of the complex-forming reagents used in solvent extraction of metals is to form with the metal a compound of the sort that is more soluble in organic solvents than in water. In accord with the classification of the extraction systems, the factors affecting solubility of the extractable species will be discussed separately for those that are chelates and those that are ion association complexes.

3. SOLUBILITY CHARACTERISTICS OF CHELATES

Most chelating agents used as extraction agents belong to the type that contain one uncharged and one anionic basic functionality so that both the electrovalency and maximum coordination of the metal ion is satisfied in the chelate formed. The resulting metal chelates, being essentially covalent compounds, are far less soluble in water than they are in organic solvents, which they resemble structurally.

The intermolecular forces affecting the solubility of many of the organic-like metal chelates in organic solvents may be characterized as being relatively weak, and as being physical rather than chemical in nature. For such solutions, in which specific chemical forces are absent, the classical dictum of "like dissolves like" and its modern counterpart, Hildebrand's theory of regular solutions, may be of much help in predicting solubility.

In Hildebrand's theory of regular solutions,[3] a quantity, δ, called the solubility parameter, is introduced. The solubility parameters of solvent and solute, defined as the square root of the heat of vaporization of the liquid per milliliter, which are measures of cohesive energy density or "internal pressure," are compared. The solubility increases with increasing similarity of the solubility parameter values since the heat of mixing of the solute and solvent depends on the difference of their δ values. For the solubility of a solid solute, the same considerations will lead to the choice of the best solvent, for the heat of melting of the solid will affect the extent of solution equally in all solvents. A list of solubility parameter values for a number of solvents is included in Table 1, in the Appendix. Unfortunately, as no investigation of the utility of this approach to the problems of chelate solubilities has been made as yet, no illustrative examples can be cited. It is felt that study directed toward evaluation of δ values for chelates will prove fruitful not only in choosing proper extraction solvents but in extending the range of extraction methods as well.

On the basis of the principle that "like dissolves like," Feigl's useful generalization that solubility in chloroform is a characteristic of metal chelates which have no free acidic or basic groups can be understood.[4] Thus, although these chelates are only slightly soluble or insoluble in chloroform

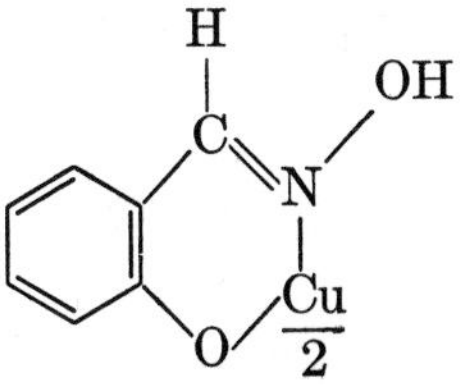

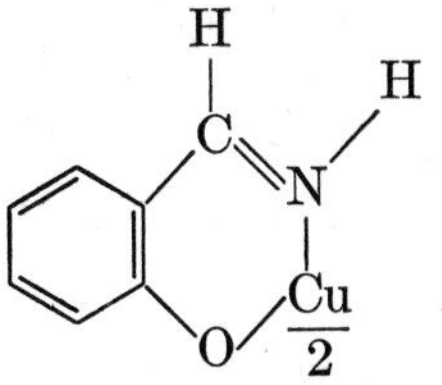

Copper
complexes
of:

Salicylaldoxime

Salicylaldimine

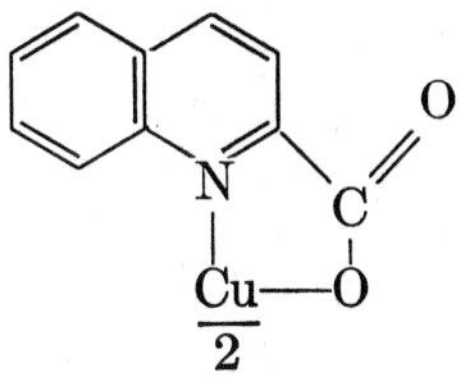

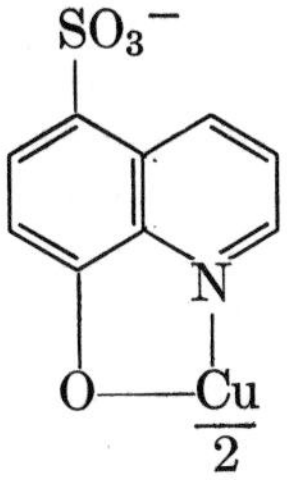

Quinoline-2-carboxylic
acid

8-Quinolinol-5-
sulfonic acid

these shown below are quite soluble in that solvent.

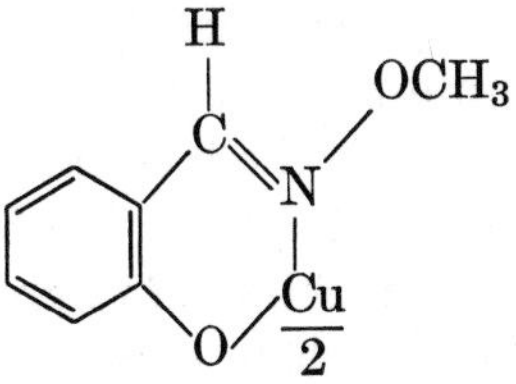

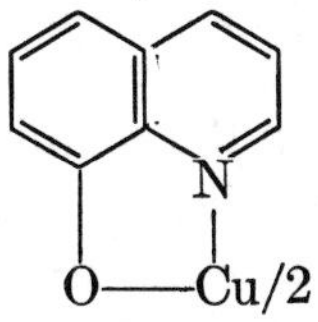

Copper
complexes
of:

N-Methoxysalicylaldoxime

8-Quinolinol

In this connection, also, an increase in solubility of a chelate in organic solvents can be expected to result from a substitution of a hydrocarbon group in the chelate structure, since this substituted chelate would now more closely resemble the organic solvent. Thus, although the neodymium chelate of cupferron is not soluble in or-

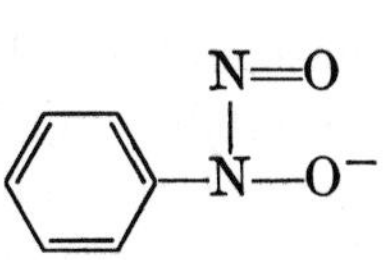

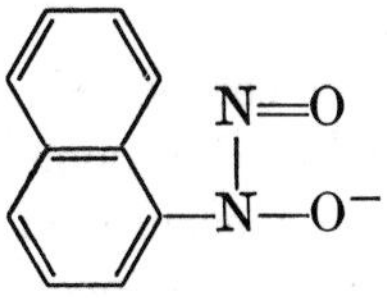

ganic solvents, the corresponding chelate with neocupferron is.[5] Similarly, the nickel chelate of cycloheptanedionedioxime (heptoxime) is more soluble than that of dimethylglyoxime.[6]

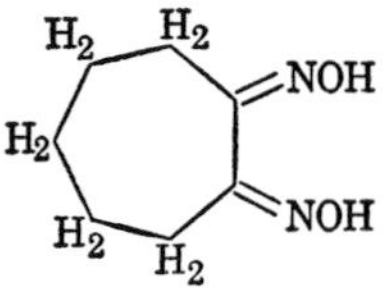

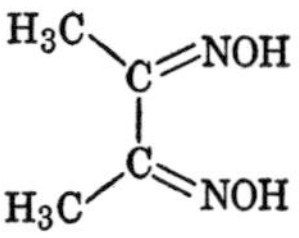

Chelates of divalent metals having a coordination number of six can be singled out for special attention, since water often occupies two coordination positions with the result that the solubility of the chelate in organic solvents is extremely low. To this reason may be attributed the failure of nickel(II) and cobalt(II) acetylacetonates to extract into organic solvents.[7] This effect is especially marked in the chelates of the more electropositive alkaline earth metals. For example, the 8-quinolinates of the alkaline earths are not extracted at any pH by a solution containing 1 g of 8-quinolinol per 100 ml of chloroform. In a recently developed modification of the usual procedure, a higher reagent concentration ($\sim 3\%$) and the addition of a quantity of monobutyl ether of ethylene glycol (butyl cellosolve) are employed for the successful extraction of magnesium [8] and calcium.[9] In an even more revealing study, strontium was found to be extracted by more concentrated 8-quinolinol solutions in chloroform in a form identified as $Sr(C_9H_6NO)_2 \cdot 2C_9H_6NOH$.[10] The success in these extractions can be attributed to the displacement of water molecules by 8-quinolinol molecules in the coordination sphere of the metal ion to give a species that more closely resembles the solvent than does the hydrated chelate molecule. It is possible that, in the extractions carried out in the presence of butyl cellosolve, this oxygen-containing compound itself replaced the coordinated water. As will be seen below, in the oxonium type of ion association extraction system a major role is played by oxygen-containing solvent molecules in the production of an extractable species.

4. SOLUBILITY CHARACTERISTICS OF ION ASSOCIATION COMPOUNDS

Ion association compounds can be considered as polar molecules, i.e., those having dipole moments, whose solubility in organic solvents depends in large measure on their structural resemblance to those solvents. Thus, if the ions involved contain large organic groups, then solubility in organic solvents is a reasonable expectation. For example, the ion-pair $[Cu(I)(2,9\text{-dimethylphenanthroline})_2{}^+, ClO_4{}^-]$ is soluble in chloroform as is the ion-pair $[(C_6H_5)_4As^+, MnO_4{}^-]$.

Oxonium systems occupy a special place among ion association systems because of the participation of the solvent molecules in the formation of the extractable complex. Oxygen-containing organic liquids will serve effectively as solvents for a number of metal salts because the basic character of the oxygen atom enables the incorporation of the solvent molecule in the coordination sphere of the metal ion, giving rise to an ion association compound that bears a structural resemblance to the solvent. Thus, $Co(ClO_4)_2$ will extract into octanol [11] probably as

$$[Co(ROH)_6^{2+} , 2(ClO_4^-)]$$

Even salts of electropositive metals such as $Ca(ClO_4)_2$ are extractable to some extent.[11]

The ability of oxonium solvents to successfully compete with water for the acidic metal ion depends on the basicity of the oxygen in the molecule. The basicity, in turn, will reflect the steric availability of the electrons at the oxygen atom as well as the electron density. Steric considerations are of particular importance in coordination with metal ions, which are, of course, much larger than protons. At the same time, the competitive strength of water may be reduced by the use of high concentrations of salts and acids. High electrolyte concentration helps extraction in three ways: (1) by the mass action effect—if the electrolyte possesses suitable coordinating anions, the high anion concentration makes the replacement of water by the anion easier; (2) by greatly reducing the water activity; and (3) by lowering the dielectric constant, thus favoring ion-pair formation. Consideration of the effect of basicity of the oxonium solvent and of the effect of the use of electrolytes on the course of oxonium extractions will be undertaken serially.

a. Solvent Basicity

Using proton affinity as revealed by infrared spectroscopic measurements [12] to evaluate relative basicity, the observed decrease in base strength of a series of oxonium solvents follows the order: alcohols, ethers, and ketones. With regard to effectiveness for coordination to metals, however, the position of ethers and ketones is sometimes reversed because the carbonyl oxygen, being more remote from the hydrocarbon side chains than the ether oxygen, is less subject to steric interference to coordination. This is illustrated in the effectiveness of replacement of water coordinated to the uranyl cation by various oxonium solvents which is found to decrease in the order iso- and tert-butanols, methyl isobutyl ketone, ethyl and hexyl ethers, and acetone.[13]

Within a given solvent class, electron density and steric availability of electrons will also be discerned as influencing solvation. For example, ethyl ether is more effective for extracting molybdenum out of hydrochloric acid solutions than is either β,β'-dichloroethyl ether, in which there is a decrease of electron density at the oxygen atom, or isopropyl ether, whose oxygen is adjacent to bulkier hydrocarbon groups.[14]

Comparison of the heats of solution of a metal salt in a series of oxonium solvents should reflect their metal-coordinating ability and thus their effectiveness as solvents. The results of a study of the heats of solution of uranyl nitrate dihydrate are shown in Table 4.1.[15]

Table 4.1.   Heats of Solution of Uranyl Nitrate Dihydrate [15]

Solvent	$\Delta H_{solution}$	Solvent	$\Delta H_{solution}$
Ethyl ether	-10.6 kcal	Tetrahydrofuran	-10.7 kcal
Isobutanol	-2.6	Methyl isobutyl ketone	-6.5
Tri-n-butyl phosphate	-10.5	Acetone	-6.7
Monoethyl cellosolve	-9.0	Methyl ethyl ketone	-6.0
Tetrahydrofurfuryl alcohol	-8.5	Ethyl propionate	-6.0
		Ethyl malonate	-4.6
Diethyl cellosolve	-10.9	Ethyl oxalate	-3.1
		Water	-5.4

The observation of greatly different heats of solution for some solvents that are known to be quite effective is one that bears examination. Although ethyl ether is close to the top of the series, isobutanol is at the bottom, with water having a surprisingly low value. This may be accounted for by the formation of a hexasolvated uranyl ion by the isobutanol instead of the tetrasolvated species probably formed with the less basic solvents. To form such a hexasolvate would involve working against the electrostatic attraction of cation and anion in order to displace nitrate anions from the uranyl ion with isobutanol molecules.

$$UO_2(C_4H_9OH)_4(NO_3^-)_2 + 2C_4H_9OH \rightleftharpoons [UO_2(C_4H_9OH)_6^{2+}, 2NO_3^-]$$

The charge separation involved in this reaction would result in an absorption of energy which would otherwise appear in the heat of solution. This suggests that if the butanol activity were lowered so that only a tetrasolvate forms, an increase in the heat of solution would be observed. In confirmation, a value of -10.3 kcal was observed for the heat of solution in an equal volume mixture of butanol and acetone, a weaker base.[15] By contrast, the heat of solution measured for a mixture of butyl phosphate and acetone gave a value intermediate to those observed in the pure solvents.

An investigation of the heats of solution of cobalt and thorium nitrate hydrates in various oxygenated solvents also showed a parallelism between the order of heats of solution and solvent effectiveness.[16] As with uranyl nitrate, with isobutanol a small heat of solution of $Co(NO_3)_2 \cdot 2H_2O$ was observed. Admixture with acetone results in an increase in the heat of solution, as was true with the uranyl nitrate, indicating that hexasolvate formation is involved here, too. Water also gives a higher heat of solution when mixed with acetone. The region of maximum heat evolution (10–20 volume % H_2O) corresponds to the transition region between tetra- and hexahydrated solute as determined spectrophotometrically.[17]

The effect of using a diluent solvent in oxonium extraction systems is to reduce the extractability of the metal in proportion to the decrease in the concentration of the oxygenated solvent. This would be expected on the basis of the hypothesis that solubility of metal salts in oxygen-containing solvents depends primarily on a specific interaction of the solvent oxygen and the solute. Thus, the solubility of $Zn(NO_3)_2 \cdot 6H_2O$ in mixtures of n-hexanol and benzene was found to be almost directly proportional to the alcohol content.[18] Again, the distribution ratio of Pa^{231} from $6\,N$ HCl with diisopropyl ketone–benzene mixtures was shown to vary with the third power of molarity of the ketone.[19] The extent to which dilution of the oxygenated solvent may be carried out without preventing good extraction will naturally depend on the strength of the bonding of the metal ion and the solvent oxygen and on the resemblance of the ion association complex to the diluent solvent. In the case of the extraction of uranium by means of trialkylphosphine oxides in kerosene, an extreme has been reached in that the oxonium ion formed by the interaction of UO_2^{2+} and R_3PO is so stable and the resulting complex so compatible with as non-polar a solvent as kerosene that the phosphine oxide can no longer be considered a solvent. Sufficiently high uranium extractions result from the use of a $0.1\,M$ tridecylphosphine oxide solution in kerosene.[20]

b. Salting-Out Agents

The term salting-out agents is here applied to those electrolytes whose addition greatly enhances the extractability of complexes, particularly those encountered in oxonium extractions where salting-out agents play a most important role. The use of such salts added to the aqueous phase to improve the extraction has meant the difference between success and failure in many oxonium extraction systems. For example, complete removal of uranium from a uranyl nitrate solution by ether extraction is not possible since the distribution ratio gradually decreases from 0.5 in a saturated solution to less than 0.001 in a 0.04 M solution. Mundy[21] and Hecht and Grünwald[22] independently discovered that the addition of ammonium nitrate to the aqueous phase greatly enhanced the uranium extraction. Furman et al.,[21] in a thorough study of a variety of nitrate salting-out agents, have been able to achieve distribution ratio values exceeding 100 at all concentrations of uranyl nitrate. These workers found that although all nitrates could be used, the multivalent metal nitrates with pronounced hydration tendencies proved to be the most effective. See Fig. 4.1.

The function of the salting-out agent would, at first, seem to be

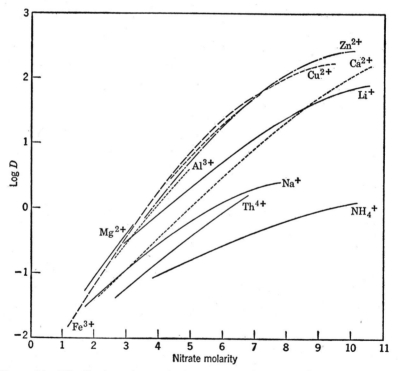

Figure 4.1. Distribution of uranyl nitrate to ethyl ether using various salting-out agents.[21]

primarily one of providing a higher concentration of complexing anion which, by mass action, would increase the concentration of the complex and thus improve the extraction. This is not the only factor, however, for the distribution ratios for uranium were found to vary with the nature of the nitrate used as well as with total nitrate concentration.[21] Differences in salting agents will also depend on their influence on the activity coefficients of the ions participating in the formation of the complex. Then, too, one of the important factors in salting-out is the binding of water by the ions of the salting agent. Water is probably bound as a shell of oriented water dipoles around the ion and thus becomes unavailable as "free solvent." Finally, it is noteworthy that the dielectric constant of the aqueous phase decreases with increasing salt concentration,[23] which will favor the formation of the ion association complex.

The enhancement of extraction of quite a number of other elements has been shown by a number of investigators using salting-out agents. Thorium nitrate extraction, for instance, can be influenced by various nitrates in a manner similar to the way they affect uranyl nitrate extraction. The almost specific effect of certain salting-out agents on the extractability of thorium nitrate is shown in Table 4.2.[24]

Table 4.2. Extraction of Thorium by Ether Using Various Nitrate Salting Agents [24]

(0.1 M Th(IV) in 1 M HNO$_3$ saturated with various nitrates)

M^{n+}	Li$^+$	Na$^+$	K$^+$	NH$_4^+$	Mg^{2+}	Ca^{2+}	Sr^{2+}	Ba^{2+}	Mn^{2+}	Al^{3+}	Fe^{3+}
Per cent extracted	56.5	0.67	0.15	0.36	43.8	56.9	0.18	0.08	80.9	54.1	73.6

It has been shown that if part of the chloride ion concentration involved in the process of formation of chloroferric acid is supplied as a soluble chloride salt, varying degrees of extraction are effected, depending on the nature of the cation used.[25] In general, at equal chloride concentrations, the cations of higher valency are more effective, as might be expected. This effect is illustrated in Tables 4.3 and 4.4. In the absence of added hydrochloric acid and by using aluminum chloride as a salting agent, the iron does distribute slightly. This effect may be explained by dissociation of the hydrated aluminum ions Al(H$_2$O)$_6^{3+}$ to furnish the needed protons. At a total chloride ion concentration of 6 molar, various combinations of acid and salt appear to be equally effective in attaining almost complete extraction.

Table 4.3.   **Effect of Ammonium Chloride and Hydrochloric Acid on Ferric Chloride Extraction Using Ethyl Ether** [25]

Chloride Concentration, moles/liter		Distribution Ratio	Per Cent Extracted
NH$_4$Cl	HCl		
...	5.0	17.6	94.6
2.5	2.5	0.376	26.6
4.9	0.1 [a]	0	0
5.0	...	0	0

[a] One mole of HCl present for every mole of Fe.

Table 4.4.   **Effect of Aluminum Chloride and Hydrochloric Acid on Ferric Chloride Extraction Using Ethyl Ether** [25]

Chloride Concentration, moles/liter		Distribution Ratio	Per Cent Extracted
AlCl$_3$	HCl [a]		
...	5.0	17.6	94.6
2.5	2.5	14.0	93.3
4.9	0.1	0.196	16.4
5.0	...	0.006	0.6
5.0	1.0	33.0	97.1
4.0	2.0	66.1	98.4
3.0	3.0	116	99.2

[a] Initial HCl concentration of 6 M gives optimum extraction.

REFERENCES

1. A. E. Hill, *J. Am. Chem. Soc.*, **43**, 254 (1921) ; **46**, 1132 (1924) ; **47**, 2702 (1925).
2. J. H. Hildebrand and G. H. Rotariu, *Anal. Chem.*, **24**, 770 (1952).
3. J. H. Hildebrand and R. L. Scott, *Solubility of Nonelectrolytes*, second edition, Reinhold Publishers, New York, 1950.
4. F. Feigl, *Chemistry of Specific, Selective and Sensitive Reactions*, tr. by R. E. Oesper, Academic Press, New York, 1949.
5. O. Baudisch and R. Furst, *Ber.*, **50**, 324 (1917).
6. J. Gillis, J. Hoste, and J. van Moffaert, *Chim. Anal.*, **36**, 43 (1954).
7. J. F. Steinbach, Ph.D. Thesis, University of Pittsburgh, 1954.
8. C. L. Luke and M. E. Campbell, *Anal. Chem.*, **26**, 1778 (1954).
9. S. J. Jankowski and H. Freiser, private communication.
10. D. Dyrssen, *Svensk Kem. Tidskr.*, **67**, 311 (1955).
11. P. C. Yates, R. Laran, R. E. Williams, and T. E. Moore, *J. Am. Chem. Soc.*, **75**, 2212 (1953) ; *J. Phys. Chem.*, **59**, 90 (1955)
12. W. Gordy and S. C. Stanford, *J. Chem. Phys.*, **8**, 170 (1940).
13. L. I. Katzin and J. C. Sullivan, *J. Phys. & Colloid Chem.*, **55**, 346 (1951).
14. I. Nelidow and R. M. Diamond, *J. Phys. Chem.*, **59**, 710 (1955).

15. L. I. Katzin, D. M. Simon, and J. R. Ferraro, *J. Am. Chem. Soc.,* **74,** 1191 (1952).

16. L. I. Katzin and J. R. Ferraro, *J. Am. Chem. Soc.,* **74,** 6040 (1952); J. R. Ferraro, L. I. Katzin, and G. Gibson, *J. Inorg. Nuclear Chem.,* **2,** 118 (1956).

17. L. I. Katzin and E. Gebert, *J. Am. Chem. Soc.,* **72,** 5455 (1950).

18. C. C. Templeton, U.S. Atomic Energy Commission Report, AECU-1722.

19. J. Golden and A. G. Maddock, *J. Inorg. Nuclear Chem.,* **2,** 46 (1956).

20. C. A. Blake, K. B. Brown, and C. F. Coleman, U.S. Atomic Energy Commission Report, ORNL-1964.

21. N. H. Furman, R. J. Mundy, and G. H. Morrison, U.S. Atomic Energy Commission Report, AECD-2938.

22. F. Hecht and A. Grünwald, *Mikrochemie ver. Mikrochim. Acta,* **30,** 279 (1943).

23. J. B. Hasted, D. M. Ritson, and C. H. Collie, *J. Chem. Phys.,* **16,** 1 (1948).

24. R. Bock and E. Bock, *Z. anorg. Chem.,* **263,** 146 (1950).

25. G. H. Morrison, *Anal. Chem.,* **22,** 1388 (1950).

Chapter 5

Chemical Interactions
in the Organic Phase

Chemical interactions of the extractable species in the organic phase owe their importance to their effect on the concentration of the complex and, hence, on the extent of extraction.

One of the most important types of organic phase reactions is polymerization of ion association complexes. By their very nature, virtually all ion-pair complexes tend to form higher aggregates as the concentration increases (see Chapter 4). A few typical examples include the tetramerization of chloroferric acid in isopropyl ether,[1] the polymerization of chlorogallic acid in isopropyl ether,[2] that of copper(II) thiocyanate in tributyl phosphate,[3] the polymerization of tetraphenylarsonium perrhenate in chloroform,[4] and the formation of micellar aggregates of the complex of uranyl sulfate–trioctylamine in kerosene.[5] Naturally, as polymerization tends to reduce the activity of the extractable species in the organic phase, the overall extraction equilibrium is shifted in favor of higher distribution ratios. It should follow that the extent of most ion association extractions will depend on the concentration of the metal involved as is found to be the case in practice.

Dissociation of ion association complexes may also occur in very dilute solutions, particularly in the more polar solvents such as β,β'-dichloroethyl ether.[6,7] This reaction would result in increased extraction at very low metal concentrations.[8]

Since extractable metal chelates are essentially covalent compounds, their solutions in neutral organic solvents are relatively free from chemical interaction. One noteworthy exception arises in the use of buffers that have extractable components. For example, the use of an acetic acid–sodium acetate buffer to adjust the pH of the aqueous medium could easily result in extraction of acetic acid into the organic phase. The acetic acid might react with either the chelating reagent or the chelate itself and thereby affect the course of the extraction. Such a reaction might be pictured with 8-quinolinol as

$$\text{CH}_3\text{COOH} + \left[\text{quinolinol-OH}\right] \rightleftharpoons \left(\left[\text{quinolinol-OH, N-H}^+\right], {}^-\text{OOC}-\text{CH}_3\right)$$

REFERENCES

1. R. J. Myers, D. E. Metzler, and E. H. Swift, *J. Am. Chem. Soc.*, **72**, 3767 (1950).
2. N. H. Nachtrieb and R. E. Fryxell, *J. Am. Chem. Soc.*, **74**, 897 (1952).
3. L. M. Melnick and H. Freiser, *Anal. Chem.*, **27**, 462 (1955).
4. S. Tribalat, *Anal. Chim. Acta*, **4**, 228 (1950).
5. K. A. Allen, *J. Phys. Chem.*, **60**, 943 (1956).
6. D. E. Campbell, Ph.D. Thesis, Rensselaer Polytechnic Institute, 1952; U.S. Atomic Energy Commission Report, AECU-2313.
7. G. S. Golden, B.S. Thesis, Department of Chemistry, Massachusetts Institute of Technology, 1954.
8. R. H. Herber and J. W. Irvine, Jr., *J. Am. Chem. Soc.*, **76**, 987 (1954).

Chapter 6

Quantitative Treatment
of Extraction Equilibria

To be able to accurately predict the course of a solvent extraction on the basis of the theoretical principles outlined above is an ultimate objective upon whose achievement rests a major justification of the presentation of material in this chapter. The attempt will be made to derive quantitative relationships from a consideration of the combined equilibria involved in the three stages of the process of extraction. The degree of success in the achievement will, of course, depend on the extent of information available concerning the nature of the chemical reactions involved in the particular system. In this regard, metal chelate extractions are in a distinctly advantageous position relative to ion association extraction systems. In the latter, highly complex behavior, arising largely out of the presence of high concentrations of strong electrolytes, keeps us from our ultimate objective. Metal chelate systems offer a happy contrast to the inorganic systems and yield more readily to quantitative treatment. In the following pages examples of both types will be considered.

1. CHELATE EXTRACTION SYSTEMS

Among the more commonly encountered metal extractions is that involving a weakly acidic chelating agent such as cupferron (ammonium salt of N-nitrosophenylhydroxylamine), dithizone (diphenylthiocarbazone), or thenoyltrifluoroacetone (TTA) dissolved in an organic solvent. Writing the formula for the chelating agent as HR, we can describe the reactions involved by the following equations.

(*Note:* Unless otherwise indicated, concentrations are those in aqueous phase. No activity corrections are included in these considerations.)

1. Ionization of the reagent to give the active chelating anion.

$$HR \rightleftharpoons H^+ + R^- \qquad K_i = \frac{[H^+][R^-]}{[HR]} \qquad (6.1)$$

2. Formation of the chelate. (In accord with the findings of Calvin [1] and others, the stepwise formation of chelates is shown to occur.)

$$(a) \quad M^{n+} + R^- \rightleftharpoons MR^{n-1} \qquad k_1 = \frac{[MR^{n-1}]}{[M^{n+}][R^-]}$$

$$MR^+_{n-1} + R^- \rightleftharpoons MR_n \qquad k_n = \frac{[MR_n]}{[MR^+_{n-1}][R^-]} \qquad (6.2)$$

The overall formation constant, K_f, may readily be seen to be $K_f = k_1 \cdot k_2 \cdots k_n$.

3. Competing reactions for the metal ion are those of hydrolysis and metal anion coordination.

$$(a) \quad M^{n+} + OH^- \rightleftharpoons M(OH)^{n-1}, \text{ etc.}$$

$$(b) \quad M^{n+} + X^- \rightleftharpoons MX^{n-1}, \text{ etc.} \qquad (6.3)$$

where X^- represents the anion present, e.g. Cl^-, NO_3^-, or SO_4^{2-}, etc. Finally we must consider the distribution of the chelating agent as well as the chelate between the two phases. Thus,

4. Distribution of the reagent.

$$K_{D_R} = \frac{[HR]_o}{[HR]} \qquad (6.4)$$

where subscript o refers to organic phase.

5. Distribution of the chelate.

$$K_{D_X} = \frac{[MR_n]_o}{[MR_n]} \qquad (6.5)$$

These equilibrium expressions may be used to derive an expression for D, the ratio of the stoichiometric metal concentrations in the two phases. If it is assumed that the only metal-bearing species in the organic phase is the fully formed chelate, MR_n, then

$$D \equiv \frac{|M|_o}{|M|} =$$

$$\frac{[MR_n]_o}{[M^{n+}] + [MR^{(n-1)+}] \cdots [MR_{n-1}^+] + \sum_i [M(OH)_i^{n-i}] + \sum_j [MX_j^{n-j}]}$$

$$(6.6)$$

Dividing both numerator and denominator by $[MR_n]$ and substituting appropriate values from eqs. 6.2 and 6.5 for the ratios obtained, we find

$$D = \frac{K_f K_{DX}[R^-]^n}{1 + k_1[R^-] + k_1 k_2[R^-]^2 \cdots K_f[R^-]^n(1 + x)} \qquad (6.7)$$

where

$$x = \{ \sum_i [M(OH)_i^{n-i}] + \sum_j [MX_J^{n-j}] \}/[MR_n]$$

Further substitutions of eqs. 6.1 and 6.4 give

$$D = \frac{K_f K_{DX} K_i^n}{K_{D_R}{}^n} \left[\left\{ \frac{[H^+]}{[HR]_o} \right\}^n + \frac{k_1 K_i}{K_{D_R}} \left\{ \frac{[H^+]}{[HR]_o} \right\}^{n-1} \right.$$

$$\left. \cdots \frac{k_1 \cdots k_{n-1} K_i^{n-1}}{K_{D_R}^{n-1}} \frac{[H^+]}{[HR]_o} + \frac{K_f K_i^n}{K_{D_R}{}^n} (1 + x) \right]^{-1} \qquad (6.8)$$

A useful approximation for D may be obtained from eq. 6.8 by making the following assumptions:

(a) That the metal ion forms no appreciable amounts of hydrolysis or anion coordination complexes, $x = 0$.

(b) That the chelate concentration in the aqueous phase is negligible.

$$[MR_n] \rightarrow 0 \qquad \text{or} \qquad \left\{ \frac{[H^+]}{[HR]_o} \right\}^n \gg \frac{K_f K_i^n}{K_{D_R}{}^n}$$

(c) That the concentrations of the intermediate chelate species are negligible. In this manner, eq. 6.8 simplifies to

$$D = \frac{K_f K_{DX} K_i^n}{K_{D_R}{}^n} \left\{ \frac{[HR]_o}{[H^+]} \right\}^n = K^* \left[\frac{(HR)_o}{(H^+)} \right]^n \qquad (6.9)$$

Equation 6.9 was first experimentally verified for the extraction of zinc by dithizone [2] and later for cupferron extractions.[3] The behavior of many chelate extraction systems may be characterized by eq. 6.8, which correctly predicts that the extractability of a metal depends equally heavily on the hydrogen ion concentration in the aqueous phase and on the reagent concentration in the organic phase, although it is *independent of metal concentration*. A tenfold change in the concentration of the reagent in the organic phase would be as effective as a corresponding change in the aqueous phase of one pH unit. Indeed, where metal hydrolysis formation assumes importance [$(x > 0)$—eq. 6.8], the dependence on the pH decreases although the effect of the reagent concentration remains unchanged.

Kolthoff described a modification of eq. 6.9 in which hydrolysis of the metal ion in the aqueous phase was taken into account. According to eq. 6.6, if it is assumed that the average number of hydroxyl groups coordinated to the metal is i, the total metal ion concentration in the aqueous phase may be represented by $M(OH)_i^{n-i}$. The distribution ratio then becomes

$$D \equiv \frac{|M|_o}{|M|} = \frac{[MR_n]_o}{[M(OH)_i^{n-i}]} = \frac{K^*}{K_h} \cdot \frac{[HR]_o^n}{[H^+]^{n-i}} \qquad (6.10)$$

where K_h represents the appropriate hydrolysis constant(s). A more general expression for systems involving hydrolysis is given by Connick and McVey.[4]

Equation 6.9 demonstrates the importance of chelate stability (K_f) and relative solubility of the chelate in the organic phase (K_{Dx}) to metal extractability. An acidic chelating agent (high K_a) that is relatively more soluble in water (low K_{DR}) is also desirable for optimal extraction. Although chelate stability (K_f) has been shown, in closely related compounds, to increase linearly with the basicity of the chelating agent, i.e., as K_a decreases,[1] in many instances the slope of the change is such that the values of K_a increase faster than K_f decreases so that $K_f K_a^n$ would be larger for the reagent forming less stable chelates. As a result, a reagent having a high dissociation constant such as TTA might well possess advantages over a more basic related reagent such as acetylacetone.

The effect of changing the solvent on the extractability of a particular metal may be evaluated from eq. 6.9 in terms of the changes in the K_D values. Thus,

$$\frac{D}{D'} = \frac{K_{Dx}/K_{DR}{}^n}{K'_{Dx}/K'_{DR}{}^n} = \frac{K_{Dx}/K'_{Dx}}{[K_{DR}/K'_{DR}]^n} \qquad (6.11)$$

Although the effect of changing the solvent on the value of a distribution coefficient of a particular compound may not be known, such a change may well be similar for similar compounds, i.e., a reagent and its chelates, so that

$$\frac{K_{D_X}}{K'_{D_X}} \simeq \frac{K_{D_R}}{K'_{D_R}} \qquad (6.12)$$

By incorporating this reasonable assumption in eq. 6.11, then

$$\frac{D}{D'} = \left[\frac{K'_{D_R}}{K_{D_R}}\right]^{n-1} \qquad (6.13)$$

From eq. 6.13 we may infer that a change to a solvent in which a reagent and its multivalent metal $(n > 1)$ chelates are more soluble will result in a lower D value so that extractions will require higher pH values (or higher reagent concentrations). Dithizone and its chelates are more soluble in chloroform than in carbon tetrachloride. A comparison of dithizone extractions with these solvents [5] confirms the expectation that extractions involving chloroform are in higher pH regions than the corresponding carbon tetrachloride extractions.

When the metal chelate is relatively soluble in water (i.e., K_{D_X} is small), eq. 6.9 must be modified.[5] Starting with eq. 6.6, we may write

$$D = \frac{[MR_n]_o}{[M^{n+}] + [MR_n]}$$

$$= \frac{K_{D_X}}{K_f[R^-]^n + 1} = \frac{[K_{D_X} - D]K_f K_i^n}{K_{D_R}^n} \cdot \frac{[HR]_o^n}{[H^+]^n} \qquad (6.14)$$

Equation 6.14 indicates that D rises to a maximum value equal to K_{D_X}. Steinbach and Freiser [6] encountered such cases in acetylacetone extractions and, evaluating K_{D_X}, were able to use this information to calculate values of K_f from the extraction data.* Good agreement was obtained with K_f values determined by other means which confirmed the validity of eq. 6.14.

If competing reactions of the metal ion to be extracted occur with anions such as chloride, sulfate, etc., then the course of the extraction will, of course, depend on the concentration of the anion. If the anion concentration is kept constant, then the fraction of metal combined will also be constant so that, at a given anion concentration, the extraction can be described according to eq. 6.10. The value of K^* will vary with the competing anion concentration. Such a result was found by Sandell and Cumming [7] in their study of iron(III) cupferrate extraction from hydrochloric acid–sodium chloride solutions. The

---

* The use of extraction data for the determination of K_f values can be generalized to include those systems for which K_{D_X} values are high by the use of tracer techniques to evaluate K_{D_X}. [See, for example, J. Rydberg, *Acta Chem. Scand.*, **4**, 1503 (1950); *Arkiv. Kemi*, **8**, 101 (1955).]

log K^* values were found to decrease regularly with increasing Cl^- concentration.

Extractions using acetylacetone afford an illustration of a case in which water-soluble intermediate chelate forms—($MR^{(n-1)+}$, $MR_2^{(n-2)+} \cdots$)—of eq. 6.2 affect the course of an extraction. Steinbach and Freiser [8] credit the occurrence of appreciable fractions of these intermediate chelates with the unusually small dependence on pH in the extraction of aluminum with acetylacetone.

It can be seen with the aid of eq. 6.10 that, provided the reagent concentration is maintained constant, the distribution of the metal in a given system is a function of pH alone. For this reason, curves of distribution versus pH at constant reagent concentration are of great analytical significance. Equation 6.9 may be written as

$$D = K^* \frac{[HR]_o^{\,n}}{[H^+]^n} = K^{*\prime}[H^+]^{-n} \qquad (6.15)$$

if $[HR]_o$ remains a constant.

Now, since D and the per cent extracted ($\% \, E$) are related, we can also write

$$D \equiv \frac{E}{100 - E} = K^{*\prime}[H^+]^{-n} \qquad (6.16)$$

or

$$\log E - \log (100 - E) = \log K^{*\prime} + npH \qquad (6.17)$$

Equation 6.17 represents a family of symmetrical sigmoid curves,[5] with the position of each along the pH axis depending only on the magnitude of $K^{*\prime}$ (see Fig. 6.1) and the slope of each uniquely depending on n (see Fig. 6.2). Of course, in extractions where eq. 6.17 is not strictly applicable, such as those in which hydrolysis of the metal or those in which intermediate chelate forms occur (see above), the slope of the extraction curve cannot be expected to be proportional to n but will be found to be significantly lower. Those extractions in which no care is taken to maintain a constant reagent concentration will also give rise to curves of lower slope. Naturally, since the sharpness of extraction is a function of the steepness of the slope of the extraction curve, conditions such as have just been described are best avoided.

The pH value at $\% \, E = 50$ has been designated as $pH_{1/2}$,[5] whose value is, from eq. 6.17,

$$pH_{1/2} = -\frac{1}{n} \log K^{*\prime} \qquad (6.18)$$

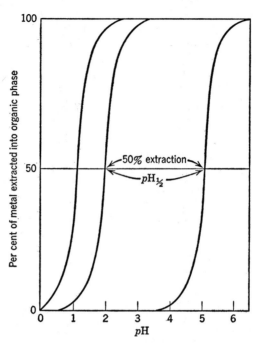

Figure 6.1. Typical theoretical extraction curves for divalent metals.[5]

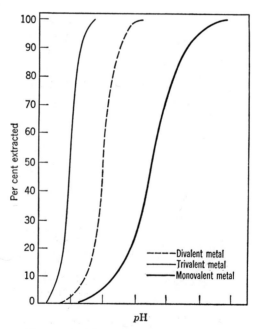

Figure 6.2. Theoretical extraction curves.

The difference in $pH_{\frac{1}{2}}$ values of two metal ions in a specific system is a measure of the separability of these two ions.

The ease of separation of two metals, both of which form extractable chelates with a particular reagent, may be readily assessed with the help of eq. 6.9. Using the subscripts 1 and 2 to denote the metals in question, we may write for β, the separation factor

$$\beta \equiv \frac{D_1}{D_2} = \frac{K_{f_1} K_{D_{X_1}}}{K_{f_2} K_{D_{X_2}}} \tag{6.19}$$

If we accept a minimum of 99% extraction of metal 1 with a corresponding maximum of 1% extraction of metal 2, then, as

$$\beta \equiv \frac{D_1}{D_2} = \frac{10^2}{10^{-2}} = 10^4 \tag{6.20}$$

the $K_f K_{D_X}$ product for metal 1 must be at least 10,000 times greater than that of metal 2 for separation with a one-stage extraction. Separations of practical value have been carried out in two or three extraction stages where the distribution ratios of the two metals differed by much smaller values. An interesting example is afforded by the separation of zirconium and hafnium by TTA in benzene.[9] The distribution ratio for zirconium was found to be twenty times larger than that for hafnium. Two extractions with 0.025 M TTA in benzene of an aqueous solution initially containing a 1:1.7 zirconium-hafnium ratio resulted in an aqueous solution having a 1:83 zirconium-hafnium ratio. Similarly, three extractions of an aqueous hafnium solution containing 5% zirconium impurity gave a hafnium solution in which the zirconium content was reduced to 0.4%.

A general separation scheme to isolate a particular element from a complex mixture may be carried out simply by adjusting the pH (and the chelating agent concentration) to a value at which the desired element, plus all those whose $pH_{\frac{1}{2}}$ values are smaller than that of this element, are completely extracted into the organic phase. This is then followed by a back extraction, or stripping, of the organic phase with an aqueous phase whose pH value has been decreased to the point where the desired element returns to this phase; the other elements whose $pH_{\frac{1}{2}}$ values are smaller still remain in the organic phase.

In an increasing number of extraction procedures for metal pairs that are difficult to separate, a supplementary "masking" chelating agent is introduced to improve the separation factor. The "masking" agent forms water-soluble complexes with the metals in competition with the extracting agent. A most outstanding example of this method is given in a study by Taylor,[10] who found EDTA to profoundly modify the extraction of metals by 8-quinolinol. Cyanide, tartrate, thiosulfate, and phenanthroline have also been used to advantage.

The effect of the presence of a masking agent on chelate extraction is illustrated in the following discussion with EDTA.

The additional equilibria which must be considered in the presence of EDTA are

(a) The ionization of EDTA (symbolized as H_4V)

$$K_A = K_1K_2K_3K_4 = \frac{[H^+]^4[V^{-4}]}{[H_4V]}$$

The concentration of unionized EDTA, H_4V, can be replaced by $\rho|EDTA|$, where $|EDTA|$ is the stoichiometric EDTA concentration and ρ, the fraction of EDTA not ionized,

$$\rho = \frac{[H^+]^4}{[H^+]^4 + K_1[H^+]^3 + K_1K_2[H^+]^2 + K_1K_2K_3[H^+] + K_1K_2K_3K_4}$$

The ionization equilibrium equation now becomes

$$K_A = \{[H^+]^4 + K_1[H^+]^3 + K_1K_2[H^+]^2$$
$$+ K_1K_2K_3[H^+] + K_1K_2K_3K_4\} \frac{[V^{-4}]}{|EDTA|}$$

(b) The formation of the metal-EDTA complex

$$K_{MV} = \frac{[MV^{n-4}]}{[M^{n+}][V^{-4}]}$$

As would be the case in an analytically significant situation, the EDTA concentration is assumed to be in large excess to the metal ion concentration. The expression for the distribution ratio, then, can be shown to be

$$D = \frac{[MR_n]_o}{[MV^{n-4}]}$$

$$= \frac{K_fK_{DX}K_i^n[HR]_o^n}{K_{DR}^nK_{MV}K_A|EDTA|[H^+]^n} \cdot \{[H^+]^4 + \cdots K_1K_2K_3K_4\} \quad (6.21)$$

Equation 6.21 makes it plain that EDTA will not only shift the $pH_{1/2}$ of the extraction to a higher value but that the slope of the extraction curve (D vs. pH) may also be different.

The separation factor of two metals in the presence of a masking agent such as EDTA would appear as

$$\beta \equiv \frac{D_1}{D_2} = \frac{K_{f_1}K_{D_{X_1}}/K_{MV_1}}{K_{f_2}K_{D_{X_2}}/K_{MV_2}} \tag{6.22}$$

A salient feature in the use of masking agents is the increased opportunities for significant alterations in the usual sequence of metal extractions. As mentioned before (Chapter 3), the stability order for metals with most chelates is fairly constant. However, the use of two reagents in conjunction will tend to exaggerate differences to the point where drastic changes may be observed. Thus, although copper gives significantly more stable chelates with both 8-quinolinol and EDTA than does the uranyl ion, in the presence of both reagents, only the uranyl ion will react with 8-quinolinol. That is to say, if K_{f_1} is greater than K_{f_2}, it might be expected that K_{MV_1} would be greater than K_{MV_2}. Interestingly enough, the ratio of K_f to K_{MV} which is of prime importance in eq. 6.22 is often larger for metal 2 than for metal 1.

2. ION ASSOCIATION EXTRACTION SYSTEMS

The problem of reducing the behavior of ion association extraction systems to analytical expressions that quantitatively describe the relation between the extent of extraction and the experimental parameters is far more difficult for many systems than it is for chelate extractions. It must not be concluded, however, that the source of the difficulty is inherent in the nature of the forces responsible for the formation of ion association complexes. Indeed, the reactions involved are as amenable to description by mass action expressions as any encountered in chelate extractions. The complications, which become most evident in oxonium systems, arise from two major factors.

First, the generally high electrolyte concentrations employed lie in a range in which great disparities exist between concentrations and activities. Concentrated electrolyte solutions represent a relatively uncharted area of solution theory, one in which activity coefficients are influenced by a large number of physical factors. Such work as has been done to evaluate activity coefficients in concentrated electrolyte solutions has served to emphasize the difficulty of applying results obtained in one solution to all other solutions. The activity coefficients are much more dependent on the specific nature of the salts in the solution. In such circumstances, when relatively small changes in concentrations may result in significant activity changes, the utility of the mass action expressions used to describe the extraction equilibria is drastically reduced, particularly since relevant activity coefficient data is known incompletely or not at all.

Second, the relatively large number of equilibria that are involved in the formation of the extractable ion association complex lead to extremely complex relationships among the extraction parameters. As an illustration might be cited the extraction of iron(III) out of hydrochloric acid into ether (see discussion below). In this system four equations are required to describe interactions of the iron and chloride ions leading to the formation of the chloro complexes from $Fe(H_2O)_5Cl^{2+}$ to $Fe(H_2O)_2Cl_4^-$, all of which can enter into solvent exchange reactions, viz., $Fe(H_2O)_2Cl_4^-$ might be considered to change through $Fe(H_2O)(ether)Cl_4^-$ to $Fe(ether)_2Cl_4^-$. When the ion association reactions that could take place in aqueous and organic phases are also considered, a truly bewildering array of reactions menaces those who attempt a general equation describing this extraction.

The complexities just referred to should not be allowed to obscure the general pattern for ion association extraction (see page 14). Several illustrative extractions of the relatively few that have received theoretical attention will now be discussed, using the general pattern of the extraction process as a guide. These examples will include the extraction of tetraphenylarsonium perrhenate, a relatively simple case, and two oxonium systems: that of iron(III), hydrochloric acid, and ether and that of uranyl nitrate and ether.

a. Extraction of Tetraphenylarsonium Perrhenate

Tetraphenylarsonium chloride is a water-soluble salt used to form chloroform-extractable complexes with permanganate, perrhenate, and pertechnetate anions. The equilibria involved in these extractions are relatively simple since high electrolyte concentrations are not necessary and the reactions involved may be described by just a few equations. The quantitative treatment is in many ways similar to that developed for chelate extractions (see previous section). Thus, for perrhenate, the following equations apply. (*Note:* Unless otherwise indicated, concentrations are those in the aqueous phase.)

1. Dissociation of the Reagent, (R_4As^+, Cl^-),

$$(R_4As^+, Cl^-) \rightleftharpoons R_4As^+ + Cl^- \qquad K_i = \frac{[R_4As^+][Cl^-]}{[(R_4As^+, Cl^-)]} \qquad (6.23)$$

where $R = C_6H_5$.

The value of K_i is probably very large.

2. Formation of the Ion Association Complex

$$R_4As^+ + ReO_4^- \rightleftharpoons (R_4As^+, ReO_4^-) \quad K_f = \frac{[(R_4As^+, ReO_4^-)]}{[R_4As^+][ReO_4^-]} \quad (6.24)$$

The value of K_f is probably very small.

3. Distribution of the Reagent

$$K_{D_R} = \frac{[(R_4As^+, Cl^-)]_o}{[(R_4As^+, Cl^-)]} \quad (6.25)$$

4. Distribution of the Complex

$$K_{D_X} = \frac{[(R_4As^+, ReO_4^-)]_o}{[(R_4As^+, ReO_4^-)]} \quad (6.26)$$

5. Reactions of the Organic Phase

Dimerization (or higher condensation) of ion-pairs can be expected at relatively low concentrations. Thus,

$$2(R_4As^+, Cl^-) \rightleftharpoons (R_4As^+, Cl^-)_2 \quad K_p = \frac{[(R_4As^+, Cl^-)_2]_o}{[(R_4As^+, Cl^-)]_o^2} \quad (6.27)$$

and

$$2(R_4As^+, ReO_4^-) \rightleftharpoons (R_4As^+, ReO_4^-)_2$$

$$K'_p = \frac{[(R_4As^+, ReO_4^-)_2]_o}{[(R_4As^+, ReO_4^-)]_o^2} \quad (6.28)$$

From these equilibrium expressions the perrhenate distribution ratio, D, may be derived.

$$D \equiv \frac{|ReO_4^-|_o}{|ReO_4^-|} = \frac{[(R_4As^+, ReO_4^-)]_o + [(R_4As^+, ReO_4^-)_2]_o}{[ReO_4^-] + [(R_4As^+, ReO_4^-)]} \quad (6.29)$$

Equation 6.29 may be simplified since the degree of ion-pairing in the aqueous phase is negligible in this case. If it may be assumed that the rhenium concentration is very small, as is usually the case analytically, then the dimer may be neglected. Hence, by substituting appropriately from eq. 6.22 to eq. 6.26, D becomes

$$D = \frac{[(R_4As^+, ReO_4^-)]_o}{[ReO_4^-]} = K_{D_X}K_f[R_4As^+] \quad (6.30)$$

From eq. 6.30 it may be concluded that the distribution ratio of the perrhenate complex is solely a function of the equilibrium concentration of the reagent cation. Tribalat [11] has evaluated the combined $K_{D_X} \times K_f$ as being approximately 2×10^6.

Chlorides are expected to affect the extraction, for the chloride concentration tends to reduce the reagent concentration. Thus in the presence of chlorides

$$[R_4As^+] = \frac{K_i[(R_4As^+, Cl^-)]_o}{K_{D_R}[Cl^-]}$$ (6.31)

To substitute in eq. 6.30

$$D = \frac{K_{D_X}K_fK_i}{K_{D_R}} \cdot \frac{[(R_4As^+, Cl^-)]_o}{[Cl^-]} \simeq 10^4 \cdot \frac{[(R_4As^+, Cl^-)]_o}{[Cl^-]}$$ (6.32)

The formal resemblance to eq. 6.9 developed for chelate extraction is most striking. The distribution is here seen to be proportional to the concentration of the reagent and inversely proportional to the chloride ion concentration. This has been confirmed by Tribalat.[11]

In a study of the distribution of tetraphenylphosphonium chloride between chloroform and water, Tribalat [12] found that dimerization of the reagent in the organic phase occurred when the initial aqueous reagent concentration was of the order of $10^{-2} M$. No further polymerization was noted up to concentrations of 0.4 M reagent.

b. Extraction of Iron(III) Chloride

Since Rothe's discovery [13] of the extractability of iron(III) from strong hydrochloric acid solutions into ethyl ether, this interesting system has attracted much attention, but as yet no theory has been developed which can provide a quantitative description of the system. Following Dodson, Forney, and Swift's demonstration [14] of the applicability of isopropyl ether to the extraction, there has been much theoretical work involving this solvent.[15-19] It has been established that the distribution of the iron is greatly dependent on the acid and chloride concentrations, increasing, within certain limits, with increasing acid concentration. A decrease in extraction at acid concentrations above 6 M is observed with ethyl ether. This decrease has been attributed to the high solubility of ethyl ether in highly concentrated hydrochloric acid and does not occur until there is a much higher acid concentration with the less soluble isopropyl ether. No decrease is observed even at 12 M HCl when β,β'-dichloroethyl ether is used.[20]

The compound extracted has been described as a solvated chloroferric acid, and a compound corresponding to the composition of $HFeCl_4 \cdot 2(C_2H_5)_2O$ has been isolated [21] from a mixture of ferric chloride, hydrochloric acid, and ethyl ether. The complex carries with it four to five molecules of water [17] which are considered to be associated with the proton as $(H_3O^+ \cdot 4H_2O)$, $FeCl_4^-$.[22] Friedman[23] found anhydrous potassium chloroferrate to dissolve in ether (2.7 moles/l) and in ethylene bromide (0.0001 moles/l) to give solutions whose spectra in the visible and ultraviolet regions were identical to the spectrum of the ether extract of chloroferric acid. From this he concluded that the iron was tetracoordinated and the chloroferrate ion not solvated. Although the treatment which follows describes the chloroferrate ion as being solvated, it should not be considered as predicated on the basis of experimental evidence contrary to that of Friedman, but rather on the authors' recognition of the vital role played by ethers and other oxonium solvents in practical extraction procedures for iron(III) in hydrochloric acid solutions.

The ion association complex is involved in organic phase interactions of two types. At extremely low iron concentrations, dissociation has been observed,[24] whereas polymerization has been postulated[17,18] at higher iron concentrations.

The reactions involved in the iron chloride extraction process may be written

1. Formation of the $FeCl_4^-$ Anion

$$Fe(H_2O)_6^{3+} + Cl^- \overset{K_1}{\rightleftharpoons} Fe(H_2O)_5Cl^{2+} + H_2O$$

$$\begin{array}{ccc} \cdot & \cdot & \cdot \\ \cdot & \cdot & \cdot \\ \cdot & \cdot & \cdot \end{array} \tag{6.33}$$

$$Fe(H_2O)_3Cl_3 + Cl^- \overset{K_4}{\rightleftharpoons} Fe(H_2O)_2Cl_4^- + H_2O$$

These may be combined to give the overall reaction

$$Fe(H_2O)_6^{3+} + 4Cl^- \overset{K_1K_2K_3K_4}{\rightleftharpoons} Fe(H_2O)_2Cl_4^- + 4H_2O \tag{6.34}$$

whence the equilibrium expression

$$K'_1 \equiv K_1K_2K_3K_4 = \frac{[Fe(H_2O)_2Cl_4^-][H_2O]^4}{[Fe(H_2O)_6^{3+}][Cl^-]^4} \tag{6.35}$$

At the high chloride concentrations employed in extractions, the $FeCl_4^-$ is probably the major species in solution.

2. Solvate Formation

At high acid concentrations when the water activity decreases and the ether activity in the aqueous phase increases, solvent exchange in the complex probably occurs

$$Fe(H_2O)_2Cl_4^- + 2R_2O \overset{K_5}{\rightleftharpoons} Fe(R_2O)_2Cl_4^- + 2H_2O \qquad (6.36)$$

where R_2O represents an ether molecule. Similarly, hydronium ions may react as follows:

$$H_3O^+ + R_2O \overset{K_6}{\rightleftharpoons} R_2OH^+ + H_2O \qquad (6.37)$$

See, however, reference 22.

3. Formation of Extractable Complex

Ion-pairing results in the formation of the extractable complex (or complexes).

$$H_3O^+ + Fe(H_2O)_2Cl_4^- \overset{K_7}{\rightleftharpoons} [(H_3O^+, Fe(H_2O)_2Cl_4^-)] \qquad (6.38)$$

$$R_2OH^+ + Fe(R_2O)_2Cl_4^- \overset{K_8}{\rightleftharpoons} [(R_2OH^+, Fe(R_2O)_2Cl_4^-)] \qquad (6.39)$$

or, more generally

$$H(S)^+ + Fe(S)_2Cl_4^- \overset{K_9}{\rightleftharpoons} [(HS^+, Fe(S)_2Cl_4^-)] \qquad (6.40)$$

where S = either H_2O or R_2O. Equation 6.40 may well represent qualitatively different reactions at different relative water and ether activities.

4. The Distribution of the Reagent and of the Extractable Complex

$$(HS^+, Cl^-) \overset{K_D}{\rightleftharpoons} (HS^+, Cl^-)_o \qquad (6.41)$$

$$[(HS^+, Fe(S)_2Cl_4^-)] \overset{K'_D}{\rightleftharpoons} [(HS^+, Fe(S)_2Cl_4^-)]_o \qquad (6.42)$$

5. Polymerization of the Ion Pair in the Ether Phase

$$n[(HS^+, Fe(S)_2Cl_4^-)]_o \overset{K_{10}}{\rightleftharpoons} [(HS^+, FeS_2Cl_4^-)_n]_o \qquad (6.43)$$

where n varies from 2 to 4.[18]

6. Dissociation of the Extractable Complex and of the Reagent in the Ether Phase

$$(HS^+, Fe(S)_2Cl_4^-)_o \overset{K_{11}}{\rightleftharpoons} (HS^+)_o + (Fe(S)_2Cl_4^-)_o \qquad (6.44)$$

$$(HS^+, Cl^-)_o \overset{K_{12}}{\rightleftharpoons} (HS^+)_o + (Cl^-)_o \qquad (6.45)$$

The overall distribution ratio

$$D \equiv \frac{|Fe|_o}{|Fe|}$$

$$= \frac{[(HS^+, FeS_2Cl_4^-)]_o + [FeS_2Cl_4^-]_o + n[(HS^+, FeS_2Cl_4^-)_n]_o}{[FeS_2Cl_4^-] + [(HS^+, FeS_2Cl_4^-)]} \qquad (6.46)$$

can now be seen to be a highly complex function of the experimental parameters. By suitable substitution of the previous equations, we obtain

$$D = K'_D K_7 [\text{HS}^+] \big[1 + K_{11} \{ K_D K_7 K_{11} [\text{HS}^+] | \text{Fe} | + K_{12} K_D [\text{HS}^+][\text{Cl}^-] \}^{-\frac{1}{2}}$$
$$+ n K_{10} (K_D K_7)^{n-1} [\text{HS}^+]^{n-1} | \text{Fe} |^{n-1} \big] \quad (6.47)$$

The two major influences on the extent of extraction are seen from eq. 6.47 to be the acidity and the total iron concentration.

In a region of relatively high iron concentration where polymerization occurs to a significant extent although dissociation is relatively unimportant, eq. 6.47 simplifies to

$$D \simeq K'_D K_7 [\text{HS}^+] \{ 1 + n K_{10} (K_D K_7)^{n-1} [\text{HS}^+]^{n-1} | \text{Fe} |^{n-1} \} \quad (6.48)$$

in which the extent of extraction is seen to increase with increasing iron concentration. In a low iron concentration region, dissociation of the complex becomes its only significant organic phase reaction, and eq. 6.47 becomes

$$D \simeq K'_D K_7 [\text{HS}^+] \big[1 + K_{11} \{ K_D K_7 K_{11} [\text{HS}^+] | \text{Fe} |$$
$$+ K_{12} K_D [\text{HS}^+][\text{Cl}^-] \}_o^{-\frac{1}{2}} \big] \quad (6.49)$$

which shows extraction increasing with decreasing iron concentration reaching a maximum of

$$D \simeq K'_D K_7 [\text{HS}^+] \{ 1 + K_{12} K_D [\text{H}^+][\text{Cl}^-] \}^{-\frac{1}{2}} \quad (6.50)$$

Iron extraction is seen to be favored by increasing acidity, regardless of the level of iron concentration. These equations do not reveal the reversal at very high acidities of the extent of extraction, but this effect may be due largely to activity and solubility effects referred to earlier.

c. Extraction of Uranyl Nitrate

The widespread interest in uranium chemistry has resulted in detailed examination of separation processes involving this metal. Uranyl nitrate extraction, because of high practical interest, has been given a great deal of attention in recent years. The extraction by ether has been subjected to a rather rigorous thermodynamic study and may be considered to be fairly completely and accurately described.

Some liberty has been taken with the classification system of extractions in listing uranyl nitrate as an ion association system, for in some solvents such as ethers and esters, uranyl nitrate exists as a coordination compound, and in the more strongly basic solvents, notably the alcohols and water, the solvent occupies all the coordination positions and consequently the species extracted is an ion association complex. Regardless of the nature of the bonding in the extractable species, uranyl nitrate extractions have enough in common with bona fide ion association systems to warrant making the exception.

The reactions involved in the distribution of uranyl nitrate between an oxonium solvent and water may be described as follows:

1. Formation of the Complex

$$UO_2(H_2O)_6{}^{2+} + 2NO_3{}^- \overset{K_f}{\rightleftharpoons} (UO_2(H_2O)_6{}^{2+}, 2NO_3{}^-) \quad (6.51)$$

or, if the water activity is low

$$UO_2(H_2O)_6{}^{2+} + 2NO_3{}^- \overset{K'_f}{\rightleftharpoons} UO_2(H_2O)_4(NO_3)_2 + 2H_2O \quad (6.52)$$

2. Distribution of the Complex

$$(UO_2(H_2O)_6{}^{2+}, 2NO_3{}^-) \overset{K_D}{\rightleftharpoons} (UO_2(H_2O)_6{}^{2+}, 2NO_3{}^-)_o \quad (6.53)$$

$$UO_2(H_2O)_4(NO_3)_2 \overset{K'_D}{\rightleftharpoons} [UO_2(H_2O)_4(NO_3)_2]_o \quad (6.53')$$

3. Reactions in the Organic Phase

$(UO_2(H_2O)_6{}^{2+}, 2NO_3{}^-)_o$

$$+ nS \overset{K_s}{\rightleftharpoons} UO_2S_n(H_2O)_{4-n}(NO_3)_2 + (n+2)H_2O \quad (6.54)$$

Or

$$UO_2(H_2O)_4(NO_3)_2 + nS \overset{K'_s}{\rightleftharpoons} UO_2(H_2O)_{4-n}S_n(NO_3)_2 + nH_2O \quad (6.54')$$

If S represents a strongly basic solvent such as butanol, then

$$(UO_2)(H_2O)_4(NO_3)_2 + 6S \overset{K''_s}{\rightleftharpoons} ((UO_2)S_6{}^{2+}, 2NO_3{}^-) + 4H_2O \quad (6.55)$$

In addition, polymerization reactions will occur at higher concentrations of uranyl nitrate where eq. 6.55 is valid.

The following expression for the distribution ratio is applicable when ether is used as the extraction solvent.

$$D \equiv \frac{|U|_o}{|U|} =$$

$$\frac{[(UO_2(H_2O)_6{}^{2+}, 2NO_3{}^-)]_o + \sum_{n=0}^{n=4} [(UO_2)S_n(H_2O)_{4-n}(NO_3)_2]}{[(UO_2)(H_2O)_6{}^{2+}] + [(UO_2(H_2O)_6{}^{2+}, 2NO_3{}^-)] + [UO_2(H_2O)_4(NO_3)_2]}$$

$$(6.56)$$

In solutions having low to moderate ionic strengths, reactions 6.51 and 6.52 proceed to a sufficiently small extent [25] so that $|U|$ simplifies to just $[(UO_2)(H_2O)_6{}^{2+}]$. To make use of equilibrium expressions of reactions in eqs. 6.51 to 6.54, D is seen to be

$$D = [NO_3{}^-]^2\gamma_{\pm}{}^3[K_f K_D(1 + K_s/a_w{}^{n+2})\gamma_o$$

$$+ K'_f K'_D(1 + K'_s/a_w{}^n)\gamma'_o] \quad (6.57)$$

where K's represent thermodynamic constants, concentrations are expressed in molality, γ_o and γ'_o are the molal activity coefficients of the complex in the ether phase, $\gamma_{\pm}$ is the mean activity coefficient of the uranyl nitrate, and a_w is the activity of the water.

At relatively low uranyl nitrate concentrations the activity of water and the activity coefficients of the complexes γ_o and γ'_o may be considered unity so that

$$D = K^*[NO_3{}^-]^2\gamma_{\pm}{}^3 \quad (6.58)$$

The following data for the distribution of uranyl nitrate between ethyl ether and water taken from the study of Glueckauf et al.[25] can be used to test eq. 6.58.

Table 6.1. Distribution of Uranyl Nitrate between Ethyl Ether and Water at 25°C [25]

Aqueous Molality	Ether Molality	D	$\gamma_{\pm}$	$D/(NO_3{}^-)^2\gamma_{\pm}{}^3$
0.348	0.00258	0.00742	0.54	1.55
0.502	0.0097	0.0193	0.57	1.65
0.626	0.0235	0.0375	0.59	1.86
0.829	0.066	0.0796	0.66	1.61
1.24	0.338	0.272	0.84	1.20
1.42	0.635	0.447	0.92	1.14

The constancy of the quantity shown in the last column, which has an average value of 1.67 ± 0.09 for solutions under 1 molal, indicates the validity of eq. 6.58 in this region. Deviations at the higher concentrations are to be expected for the reasons outlined earlier.

Equation 6.58 predicts that the addition of other nitrates as salting-out agents will improve the extraction by increasing the nitrate concentration. The fact that different nitrates vary considerably in their efficiencies as salting-out agents is a reflection of the different effects of the salts on $\gamma_{\pm}$, the activity coefficient of the uranyl nitrate. Jenkins and McKay [26] have applied Harned's equations [27] relating the activity coefficients of salts in solutions containing more than one electrolyte to the solutions of uranyl nitrate containing a second nitrate $M(NO_3)_x$. These may be written

$$\tfrac{1}{2}(\log \gamma_u - \log \gamma_u{}^0) = -\alpha_u I_n$$

$$\frac{1}{x}(\log \gamma_n - \log \gamma_n{}^0) = -\alpha_n I_u$$

(6.59)

where the superscript 0 refers to a solution of a single salt at the same ionic strength I as the mixed solution, and I_u and I_n are the respective ionic strengths of the uranyl and the second nitrate. The proportionality constants, α_u and α_n, have been shown to be a function of the total ionic strength, I, and to remain constant despite variations in I_u and I_n, so long as I remains constant. Using the ether extraction data of Furman, Mundy, and Morrison [28] and their own methyl isobutyl ketone and dibutyl carbitol extraction data, Jenkins and McKay [26] calculated values of $\gamma_{\pm}$ for uranyl nitrate in the presence of various nitrate salting-out agents, and from these values with the help of eqs. 6.59 they evaluated α_u. Values of α_u were found to depend only on the total ionic strength I rather than on either I_u or I_n and not on the extraction solvent in accord with the Harned rule (see Fig. 6.3).

Once α_u was evaluated, Jenkins and McKay used this to extrapolate to trace concentrations (superscript t) of uranium, thus

$$\tfrac{1}{2}(\log \gamma_u{}^t - \log \gamma_u{}^0) = -\alpha_u I$$

(6.60)

Their results are shown in Figs. 6.4 and 6.5.

It is interesting to observe that the order of the $\log \gamma_u{}^t$ curves up to 5 molal ionic strength

$$Li > Mg \sim Zn \sim Co \quad \text{and} \quad Cu > Ca \sim Sr \sim Na > NH_4 > K$$

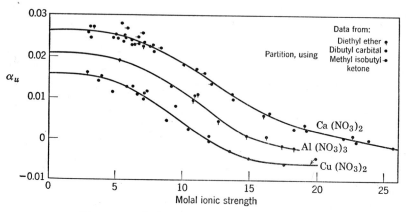

Figure 6.3. Variation of α_u with ionic strength.[26]

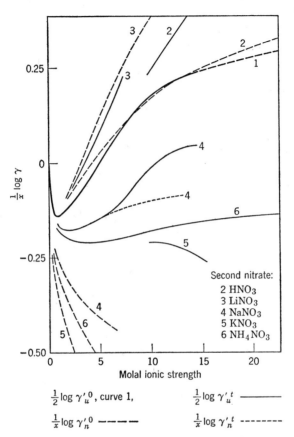

Figure 6.4. Activity coefficients of uranyl nitrate.[26]

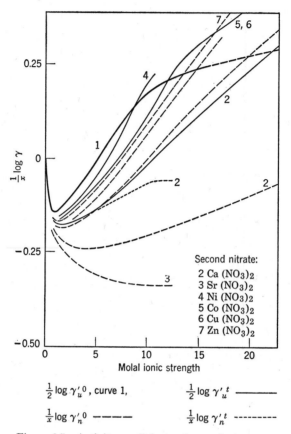

$$\frac{1}{2}\log \gamma_u'^0 \text{, curve 1,} \qquad \frac{1}{2}\log \gamma_u'^t \;\text{———}$$

$$\frac{1}{x}\log \gamma_n'^0 \;\text{————} \qquad \frac{1}{x}\log \gamma_n'^t \;\text{--------}$$

Figure 6.5. Activity coefficients of uranyl nitrate.[26]

is substantially the same as the $1/x$ log γ_n curves. This indicates that the higher the activity coefficient of the pure nitrate, the more efficient the salting-out, since all other factors being equal, the distribution ratio varies roughly as $(\gamma_u{}^t)^3$.

Above about 5 molal ionic strength, ion association of uranyl nitrate in the aqueous phase probably becomes appreciable, for the dielectric constant is quite low in concentrated salt solutions; in this region, therefore, values of activity coefficients change in extremely complex ways.

REFERENCES

1. M. Calvin and K. W. Wilson, *J. Am. Chem. Soc.*, **67**, 2003 (1945).
2. I. M. Kolthoff and E. B. Sandell, *J. Am. Chem. Soc.*, **63**, 1906 (1941).
3. N. H. Furman, W. B. Mason, and J. S. Pekola, *Anal. Chem.*, **21**, 1356 (1949).
4. R. E. Connick and W. H. McVey, *J. Am. Chem. Soc.*, **71**, 3182 (1949).
5. H. M. Irving and R. J. P. Williams, *J. Chem. Soc.*, **1949**, 1841.
6. J. Steinbach and H. Freiser, *Anal. Chem.*, **25**, 881 (1953).
7. E. B. Sandell and P. F. Cumming, *Anal. Chem.*, **21**, 1356 (1949).
8. J. Steinbach and H. Freiser, *Anal. Chem.*, **26**, 375 (1954).
9. E. H. Huffman and L. J. Beaufait, *J. Am. Chem. Soc.*, **71**, 3179 (1949).
10. R. P. Taylor, Ph.D. Thesis, Princeton University, 1954.
11. S. Tribalat, *Anal. Chim. Acta*, **3**, 113 (1949).
12. S. Tribalat, *Anal. Chim. Acta*, **4**, 228 (1950).
13. J. W. Rothe, *Stahl u. Eisen*, **12**, 1052 (1892).
14. R. W. Dodson, G. J. Forney, and E. H. Swift, *J. Am. Chem. Soc.*, **58**, 2573 (1936).
15. N. H. Nachtrieb and J. G. Conway, *J. Am. Chem. Soc.*, **70**, 3547 (1948).
16. N. H. Nachtrieb and R. E. Fryxell, *J. Am. Chem. Soc.*, **70**, 3552 (1948).
17. R. J. Myers, D. E. Metzler, and E. H. Swift, *J. Am. Chem. Soc.*, **72**, 3767 (1950).
18. R. J. Myers and D. E. Metzler, *J. Am. Chem. Soc.*, **72**, 3772 (1950).
19. D. E. Metzler and R. J. Myers, *J. Am. Chem. Soc.*, **72**, 3776 (1950).
20. J. Axelrod and E. H. Swift, *J. Am. Chem. Soc.*, **62**, 33 (1940).
21. J. Houben and W. Fischer, *J. prakt. Chem.*, **123**, 89 (1929).
22. A. H. Laurene, D. E. Campbell, S. E. Campbell, S. E. Wiberley, and H. M. Clark, *J. Phys. Chem.*, **60**, 901 (1956).
23. H. L. Friedman, *J. Am. Chem. Soc.*, **74**, 5 (1952).
24. J. Saldick, *J. Phys. Chem.*, **60**, 500 (1956).
25. E. Glueckauf, H. A. C. McKay, and A. R. Mathieson, *Trans. Faraday Soc.*, **47**, 437 (1951).
26. I. L. Jenkins and H. A. C. McKay, *Trans. Faraday Soc.*, **50**, 107 (1954).
27. H. S. Harned and B. B. Owen, *The Physical Chemistry of Electrolytic Solutions*, chapter 14, Reinhold Publishing Corp., New York, 1943.
28. N. H. Furman, R. Mundy, and G. H. Morrison, U.S. Atomic Energy Commission Report, AECD-2938.

Chapter 7

Kinetic Factors
in Extraction

Both the qualitative and quantitative descriptions of extraction discussed in previous sections are predicated upon the assumption that the two phases are in equilibrium. If this is not the case, a much more complex situation exists with which none of the previously elaborated equations, simple or complex, can cope. Although, in general, extraction under equilibrium conditions will be found most desirable, failure to attain equilibrium simultaneously for all the components of a mixture may be used to good advantage in achieving selectivity.

The rate of achievement of equilibrium, the point at which the net rate of matter across the boundary between the two liquid phases is zero, depends on two factors: (1) the rate of formation of the extractable species and (2) the rate of transfer of the species from one phase to the other. Fortunately, from the utilitarian point of view, most extractions require only a few minutes to attain equilibrium.

1. RATE OF TRANSFER

The transfer of any solute from one phase to another involves more than just the transition across the molecularly thin phase boundary. The solute molecules must first move by a diffusion process (eddy diffusion[1]) from the bulk of the solution which is in more or less violent motion through a relatively thin, stationary layer or film of the solvent on each side of the boundary.[2] The thickness of this film depends on the relative velocity of the liquid in the bulk phase but it never vanishes altogether. The rate of diffusion of the solute through this layer will depend on the size and shape of the solute as well as on the viscosity of the solvent. Provided there is interfacial turbulence, the rate of passage through the phase boundary is rapid.[1,3] Once through, the solute molecule must diffuse through another stationary layer of the second solvent before it reaches the bulk phase where mixing by agitation will adjust the concentration gradient.

There is a practical limit to the degree of agitation which can be advantageously employed in equilibrating an extraction mixture. Although shaking is desirable in reducing the thickness of the stationary films on either side of the phase boundary, it is important to remember that it is the velocity of one phase relative to that of the other which determines the film thickness. Too violent agitation serves no purpose other than imparting a high translational motion to the entire mixture without appreciable increase in the relative motion of the two phases. Likewise, the increase of the degree of dispersion of one phase in the other obviously reduces the relative velocity of the phases until, in an emulsion, this velocity is essentially zero, despite the most violent agitation. Craig has shown that simple repeated inversion of a tube containing the two phases imparted sufficient relative velocity to the phases to give equilibrium in a relatively few inversions.[4] Even with high molecular weight solutes such as the penicillins, a maximum of fifty inversions were needed for the systems to equilibrate. This was accomplished in about a minute and a half.

Unless the liquids employed are quite viscous, one may reasonably conclude that as far as the rate of transfer of material from one phase to the other is concerned, equilibration can be effected with a shaking time of several minutes.

2. RATE OF COMPLEX FORMATION

Although the metal complexes formed in most ion association extractions are essentially electrostatic in nature and are reversibly formed at extremely rapid rates, there are notable exceptions, particularly with metal chelates, where formation and dissociation can be measurably slow.

Non-equilibrium extraction has been observed in the case of the dithizonates of zinc [5,6] and copper,[7,8] in the TTA extraction of a number of metals,[9] and in the acetylacetone extraction of chromium.[10] The presence of EDTA was found to reduce the rate of equilibration in the diethyldithiocarbamate extraction of copper [11] and in the 8-quinolinol extraction of copper and iron.[12]

A kinetic study of the plutonium(IV)–TTA extraction has shown that the rate of chelate formation in the aqueous phase is the limiting step in the extraction.[13] Rubin and Hicks conclude from their study that equilibrium values of the distribution ratio, and hence reagent concentration and pH, will affect extraction rates. This might well be generally applicable to all extractions in which the rate-determining step involves chelate formation.

Since the rate of formation of metal chelates would involve the concentration of chelating agent in the aqueous phase, we might reasonably expect extraction rates to be sensitive to reagent concentrations employed. Bolomey and Wish [9] found that use of a very dilute solution (0.01 M) of TTA in benzene resulted in extractions that equilibrated very slowly, although their experience with a more concentrated solution (0.1 M) of reagent indicated higher extraction rates. Further, if the concentration of the reagent in the aqueous phase is involved in the rate, it would follow that the nature of the organic solvent used will affect the rate of extraction, for $[HR]_{aq}$ depends on K_{D_R}, the distribution coefficient of the reagent. Irving and Williams [6] in a preliminary report on the rate of extraction of zinc dithizonate found this to be thirty times faster in carbon tetrachloride than in chloroform, a factor approximately equal to the first power of the ratio of the K_D values for dithizone between water and each of the two solvents ($K_{D_{CHCl_3}}/K_{D_{CCl_4}} = 46$). This suggests that the rate-determining step involves only one dithizonate ion.

The formation of the extractable complex is not necessarily the sole chemical reaction that may be rate determining. The slow rate of extraction of copper diethyldithiocarbamate or 8-quinolinate in the presence of EDTA may well arise out of rate phenomena of the copper–EDTA complex rather than that for the extractable complexes.

The extraction curves obtained under non-equilibrium conditions will differ from theoretical curves in that they will be displaced toward higher pH values. Also, since the rate of equilibration is pH dependent, the departure of the non-equilibrium curves from theory would decrease at higher pH values. Taylor [2] reports that with a 3-minute extraction time, iron(III) 8-quinolinate begins to extract from an EDTA-containing solution about 3 pH units higher than necessary in equilibrium extraction. This great difference emphasizes the importance of extraction time and indicates the possibility of achieving thermodynamically infeasible separations by taking advantage of favorable differences in extraction kinetics. A case in point is the extraction of iron(III) from beryllium with a very dilute solution of TTA in benzene, using what for this system is a short extraction time (2 hours).[9] Another illustration is the separation of iron(III), aluminum, and many other metal ions from chromium by extraction with acetylacetone.[10] Despite the stability of the chromium acetylacetonate, the rate of its formation and extraction is negligible except at relatively high pH values (pH 6–8). Once formed, the complex remains extractable even at very low pH values.

REFERENCES

1. J. B. Lewis, *Chem. Eng. Sci. 3*, **248** (1954); *Chem. Abstracts*, **49**, 4378g; *Nature*, **178**, 274 (1956).
2. K. F. Gordon and T. K. Sherwood, in press, listed in Reference 1.
3. T. G. Hunter and A. W. Nash, *J. Soc. Chem. Ind.* (*London*), **51**, 285 (1932).
4. G. T. Barry, Y. Sato, and L. C. Craig, *J. Biol. Chem.*, **174**, 209 (1948).
5. A. Walkley, *Proc. Australian Chem. Inst.*, **9**, 29 (1942).
6. H. Irving and R. J. P. Williams, *J. Chem. Soc.*, **1949**, 1841.
7. H. Barnes, *Analyst*, **72**, 469 (1947).
8. H. Irving, G. Andrew, and E. J. Risdon, *J. Chem. Soc.*, **1949**, 541.
9. R. A. Bolomey and L. Wish, *J. Am. Chem. Soc.*, **72**, 4483 (1950).
10. J. P. McKaveney, Ph.D. Thesis, University of Pittsburgh, 1957.
11. J. L. Hague, E. D. Brown, and H. A. Bright, *J. Research Natl. Bur. Standards*, **47**, 380 (1951).
12. R. P. Taylor, Ph.D. Thesis, Princeton University, 1954.
13. B. Rubin and T. E. Hicks, U.S. Atomic Energy Commission Report, UCRL-126.

Part 2

*Apparatus
and
General
Techniques*

Chapter 8

Methods of Extraction

In most situations encountered in analytical chemistry the technique of solvent extraction is employed to separate the solute of interest from substances that interfere in the ultimate quantitative determination of the material. This is usually accomplished by selectively transferring the material from one phase in which it is dissolved or dispersed into another liquid phase, although it is sometimes possible to selectively extract interfering elements and leave the material of interest in the original phase.

In order to effect a simple separation, it is essential that the distribution ratios of the material of interest and the interference be sufficiently different. The effectiveness of separation is usually expressed by means of the separation factor, β, which is related to the individual distribution ratios as follows:

$$\beta = \frac{(c_1)_o/(c_2)_o}{(c_1)_w/(c_2)_w} = \frac{(c_1)_o/(c_1)_w}{(c_2)_o/(c_2)_w} = D_1/D_2 \tag{8.1}$$

where c_1 is the concentration of component 1 in either the organic or water phases, and c_2 is the concentration of component 2 in the respective phases.

In those situations where one of the distribution ratios is very small and the other relatively large, clean separations can be quickly and easily achieved. If the separation factor is large but the smaller distribution ratio is sufficiently large that extraction of both components occurs, it is necessary to resort to various techniques to suppress the extraction of the undesired component. These are discussed in the next chapter.

The completeness of separation required will, of course, depend on the final method of determination employed. Thus, the presence of small amounts of certain elements may not interfere if a particular method of estimation is chosen. It is necessary, therefore, to consider the entire analytical procedure when choosing a particular extraction separation.

Although most analytical separations involving extraction are based on favorable separation factors, it is occasionally necessary to resort to separations where the distribution ratios of the components of the mixture are of the same order of magnitude. In those extractions where the separation factor approaches unity, it is necessary to employ fractionation methods in which distribution, transfer, and recombination of various fractions are performed a sufficient number of times to achieve separation.[1]

In the analytical laboratory, three basic types of liquid-liquid extractions are generally utilized. The simplest is batch extraction, which consists of extracting the solute from one immiscible layer by simply shaking the two layers until equilibrium is attained. Then the layers are allowed to settle and are separated. The second type, continuous extraction, makes use of a continuous flow of immiscible solvent through the solution or a continuous countercurrent flow of both phases. In continuous extraction the spent solvent is stripped and recycled by distillation, or fresh solvent is added continuously from a reservoir. Discontinuous countercurrent distribution extraction, which is used for fractionation purposes, is the third general type and involves the use of a series of separatory funnels or more elaborate contacting vessels to achieve many individual extractions rapidly and in sequence.

With regard to apparatus there are just a few basic types; however, an infinite number of modifications of these basic designs have evolved as a result of the chemist's desire to improve a particular apparatus for his specific problem. A small sample of some of the more interesting extractors will now be described; many more can be found in the catalogs of supply houses. The reader will undoubtedly have many ideas of his own for further modification.

1. BATCH EXTRACTION

In this method a given volume of solution is contacted with a given volume of the solvent until equilibrium is attained, and the two layers are then separated. This is the simplest extraction procedure possible and is the most used of any for analytical separations. It is also the preliminary or exploratory operation employed in the study of unknown systems and is designed to yield the quantitative distribution information which will serve as a guide in the final choice of the method of extraction.

If essentially none of the interfering elements is extracted by a given solvent, the only factor to be considered is the completeness of extraction of the solute of interest. Since the distribution ratio is a concentration ratio, the actual fraction of the total solute extracted will vary with the ratio of solvent volumes, as seen in the following equations.

Let v ml of solution (phase 1) containing w g of solute be extracted with s ml of another solvent (phase 2) immiscible with the first. Let w_1 represent the weight of solute remaining in phase 1 after equilibrium has been attained.

The concentration in phase 1 is w_1/v g per ml and that in phase 2, $(w - w_1)/s$ g per ml. Therefore

$$D = c_2/c_1 = \frac{(w - w_1)/s}{w_1/v}$$

and

$$w_1 = w \left(\frac{v}{Ds + v} \right)$$

If another extraction of phase 1 is made with another portion of s ml of solvent, w_2 g will be the weight of solute remaining in phase 1. After the second extraction

$$w_2 = w_1 \left(\frac{v}{Ds + v} \right)$$

$$w_1 = w \left(\frac{v}{Ds + v} \right)$$

$$w_2 = w \left(\frac{v}{Ds + v} \right)^2$$

If the same volume of the extracting solvent is used in each successive extraction, and if w_n represents after n extractions the weight of solute remaining in phase 1, then

$$w_n = w \left(\frac{v}{Ds + v} \right)^n \tag{8.2}$$

For the most complete extraction, s should be made as small as possible and n as great as possible for a given amount of solvent; that is, the best results are obtained by a relatively large number of extractions with small amounts of solvent.

It is obvious from the treatment above that some idea of the value of the distribution ratio makes possible a much more intelligent use of the method of extraction.

If a distribution ratio is not already known, it may be obtained by simply equilibrating equal (for convenience) volumes of the solution and extracting solvent and determining the solute concentration in both phases.*

Batch extractions may be used to advantage when the distribution ratio is large, for in such cases a few extractions will effect quantitative separation. Various methods for increasing the distribution ratio as well as the selectivity of an extraction are discussed in the next chapter.

The usual apparatus for a batch extraction is a separatory funnel. The choice of any one from the large variety available is a matter of personal preference; however, the Squibb pear-shaped type is usually the most convenient for analytical extractions.

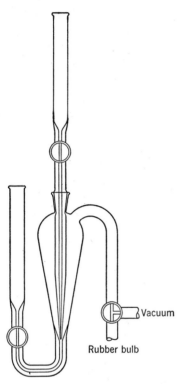

Vacuum

Rubber bulb

Figure 8.1. Batch microextractor.[2]

Another useful extractor is a glass-stoppered weighing buret which has a graduated scale for reading volumes. In extracting from one liquid to a lighter liquid, it is necessary, when using a separatory funnel, to remove the heavier liquid from the funnel after each extraction before removing the extracting solvent, as in the case of ethyl ether extractions.

This double removal may be avoided by means of the apparatus shown in Fig. 8.1,[2] which gives reasonably clean separation of the

---

* Although it is possible to obtain D from the knowledge of the initial solute concentration and an analysis of one of the phases after equilibration, it is advisable to analyze both phases, particularly to assure material balance. Since in a number of instances D has been shown to vary with the initial solute concentration, it is essential to determine D over a range of concentration.

phases and is applicable to most types of lighter-than-water solvents used to extract aqueous solutions.

The conical extraction chamber is connected at the bottom through a capillary stopcock to a side tube. The top of the chamber is connected through a three-way stopcock either to a vacuum line or to a rubber bulb. Through a ground joint at the top passes a narrow separatory funnel with a capillary stem reaching to the bottom of the extraction chamber. The liquid and the solvent are placed in the side tube, drawn into the extraction chamber by the vacuum and mixed by a stream of air.* The three-way stopcock is turned to shut off the vacuum and the phases separate. Pressure of the rubber bulb forces the liquids into the side tube, and the stopcock is closed when the interface between the two liquids reaches it. The upper stopcock to the separatory funnel is opened and the solvent phase forced into it. This stopcock is then closed to retain the solvent, and the procedure is repeated. After the final extraction, the separatory funnel containing the solvent phase is lifted out. This extractor was designed for working with small volumes but can probably be applied to larger volumes.

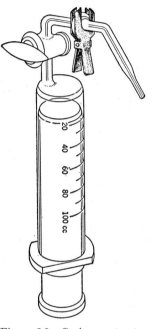

Figure 8.2. Syringe extractor for solvents of low density.[3]

Another simple extractor that avoids transfer of the aqueous phase when extracting with a solvent less dense than the aqueous phase is shown in Fig. 8.2.[3] The apparatus consists of a syringe with an eccentric tip, to which are sealed a stopcock and an outlet tube. The spherical joint provides greater flexibility and permits extraction with solvents denser than water. It is suggested that a closely fitting syringe be employed.

The aqueous phase is introduced by placing the solution in a container with a pointed bottom and then sucking it into the syringe. The aqueous phase may also be pipetted directly into the open syringe barrel, which is clamped in a nearly horizontal position; care

---

* Vacuum mixing may also be used to advantage with a simple separatory funnel, provided the organic solvent is not too volatile. Apply a vacuum through a standard taper joint connected to the top of the separatory funnel and allow air to enter through the stopcock at a rate just adequate to effect intimate mixing of the phases.

must be taken to avoid introduction of this solution into the capillary tip during insertion of the plunger. The organic solvent is next sucked in through the outlet tube by drawing out the plunger. Some air is also drawn in, the stopcock is closed, and then the syringe is shaken. The syringe is then held as shown in Fig. 8.2; and after separation of the phases, the lighter phase is forced out through the outlet tube. The eccentric tip is kept at the top so that none of the organic phase is trapped. More organic solvent is then sucked in through the delivery tip, thus rinsing the contents of the tip back into the syringe, and further extractions are performed as before.

For extraction with dense solvents, the same procedure is used as with light solvents, but the outlet tube is turned in the opposite direction from that shown, and the whole syringe is inverted to permit the dense solvent to be forced out through the outlet tube.

The use of extraction techniques in spot test analysis offers a means of separating an ion from its interferences which might well prove valuable in a manner similar to the use of masking agents as a spot test technique. Carlton [4] has devised an extraction pipette prepared from a capillary dropper pipette. The extractor consists of a capillary tip with a bulb of 2- to 3-ml capacity blown just above the capillary tip. An upper stem is attached to the upper part of the bulb, and a rubber bulb of 10-ml capacity is attached to the upper stem.

In practice, an extraction involves the addition of a few drops of extractant to one or more drops of the test solution. Mixing is accomplished by drawing the liquids into the pipette and then expelling them and quickly repeating the procedure several times. By using a rubber bulb of considerably greater capacity than that of the pipette, a large quantity of air is drawn into the pipette after the liquids have been drawn up; the bubbling of this air through the two liquid phases provides an efficient mixing of the two layers. After completion of extraction, the two phases are permitted to separate and the rubber bulb is squeezed until the lower phase has been removed. By means of this extractor, efficient separations of many substances can be carried out in a matter of 10 to 20 seconds.

Batch extraction of organometallic complexes is best performed with a separatory funnel when a heavier than water solvent such as chloroform is used. A special inverted funnel device shown in Fig. 8.3 has been found convenient for cupferron extractions using ethyl ether as the solvent. [5] The aqueous solution is forced up by mercury with the aid of a leveling bulb, not shown in the figure, and the ethereal layer is drawn off at the top. In microextractions the ethereal layers can be drawn off with a pipette.

When performing a batch extraction, it is important to follow a few simple steps to separate the phases for sampling for subsequent processing or estimation. Most extractors or separatory funnels taper off into a narrow bottom in which is sealed a stopcock. Thus, it is a relatively easy task to separate the two phases on withdrawal for further processing. It is, of course, essential to wait until the phases have completely settled after agitation. Usually this will occur in a matter of minutes, unless emulsions have formed. This problem is treated later in Chapter 9.

If only aliquots of the phases are to be used, it is necessary to notice any volume changes of the phases due to mutual solubility of the solvents. The extraction and sampling must be performed at a constant temperature, since the distribution ratio as well as volume of the solvents are influenced by temperature changes. A useful method of withdrawing the phases for sampling involves the use of three graduates. Most of the heavier phase is withdrawn into the first graduate, and then the remainder of the heavier phase and a little of the lighter phase are withdrawn into the second graduate. The remaining portion of the lighter phase is run into the third graduate, and the volumes of all three are noted. The second graduate can now be discarded and aliquots of the other two taken without danger of contamination of one by the other.

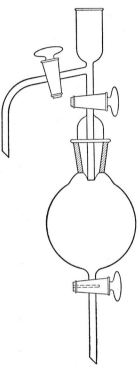

Figure 8.3. Apparatus for extractions with ether plus cupferron. After equilibrium is established, ethereal and aqueous layers are displaced upward by introducing mercury through stopcock at bottom of bulb.[5]

If droplets of aqueous phase are entrained in the organic extract, it is possible to remove them by filtering the extract through a dry filter paper. The aqueous droplets will be absorbed by the paper, which should be washed several times with fresh organic solvent. Another method commonly used in chelate extractions is the addition of a drying agent, such as sodium sulfate, to the organic extract. Perhaps the simplest technique for removal of slight traces of the aqueous phase which may contain certain impurities is the use of the backwash technique, described later.

2. CONTINUOUS EXTRACTION

Continuous extractions are particularly applicable when the distribution ratio is relatively small, so that a large number of batch extractions would normally be necessary to effect quantitative separation. Most continuous extraction devices operate on the same general principle, which consists of distilling the extracting solvent from a boiler flask and condensing it and passing it continuously through the solution being extracted. The extracting liquid separates out and flows back into the receiving flask, where it is again evaporated and recycled while the extracted solute remains in the receiving flask. When the solvent cannot easily be distilled, a continuous supply of fresh solvent may be added from a reservoir.

It should be remembered that high efficiency in continuous extraction depends on the viscosity of the phases and other factors affecting the rate of attaining equilibrium, the value of the distribution ratio, the relative volumes of the two phases, and other factors. One practical method of improving the efficiency is to insure as high an area of contact as possible between the two liquids. As the extracting solvent passes through the solution, fritted-glass discs, small orifices, baffles, and stirrers may be used to bring the two immiscible layers in closer contact.

The efficiency of continuous extraction processes may be conveniently evaluated by a method devised by Bewick, Currah, and Beamish,[6] in which the values of the "half-extraction volume," V, are compared. This is the volume in milliliters of extracting solvent required to decrease the amount of extracted constituent to one-half its former value.

This value is obtained in the following manner, using the extractor shown in Fig. 8.9. A series of aliquots of the extract is drawn off, and the amount of extracted constituent in each is determined. The logarithm of these values is plotted against the number of aliquots (or the volume in milliliters) of the extracting solvent. A straight line is usually obtained. Two points on the rectilinear part of the plot are now chosen, such that the value of the extracted constituent corresponding to one of them is equal to half the value corresponding to the other; the difference of the corresponding abscissas converted to milliliters of solvent gives the value of the half-extraction volume, V. This value thus makes possible a numerical comparison of changing conditions in continuous extractions, and the distribution of the solute between the two liquid phases during a continuous extraction may be estimated from it.

The half-extraction volume, V, may be used to obtain the distribution factor, k, from the relation

$$k = \frac{0.693W}{V} \qquad (8.3)$$

where k is the concentration of solute in the extracting solvent divided by the concentration of solute in the original solution. The volume in milliliters of original solution is W.

The difference between the distribution factor, k, and the distribution ratio, D, should be emphasized. The former is the number characteristic of the easily reproducible conditions of the continuous extraction, and the latter is the value obtained for equilibrium with respect to the passage of the dissolved constituent between the two phases under specific conditions. The distribution factor for a particular system closely approaches the distribution ratio if the value of the latter is low.

Many different types of apparatus providing continuous contacting of the two liquids for extraction purposes have been reported in the literature. Because of the great diversity of types and special features, no attempt is made here to cover all the types.

a. Extraction with Light Solvents

In analytical work the simpler the apparatus the better, since it is often necessary to recover both phases for subsequent chemical steps. Continuous extractors can conveniently be arranged according to whether the solvent is lighter than or heavier than the phase being extracted. An example of the former type is a modified tall form of Friedrich extractor designed by Heberling and Furman [7] and shown in Fig. 8.4. This apparatus is particularly useful for the ether extraction of aqueous solutions of inorganic substances; and has been used successfully for the extraction of uranyl nitrate from aqueous solutions containing salting-out agents. In order to achieve rapid transfer of the solute from the aqueous to the solvent phase, the solvent is dispersed in the aqueous phase by means of a sintered-glass disc. The pressure required to force the solvent through the sintered disc is obtained by distilling the solvent and condensing it far enough above the disc to obtain the necessary hydrostatic head. A coarse sintered-glass vertical dispersing disc with a 66-cm-long, 6-mm-out-

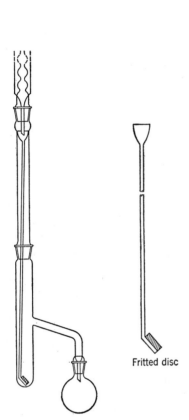

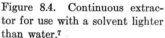

Fritted disc

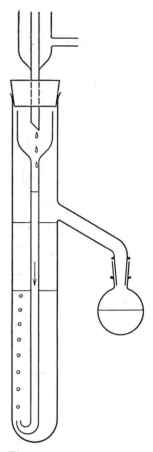

Figure 8.4. Continuous extractor for use with a solvent lighter
than water.[7]

Figure   8.5.   Kutscher-
Steudel extractor for use
with solvents lighter than
water.[8]

side-diameter tube ending in a funnel at the top to catch the solvent
is used. A further modification for a more precise separation involves
the use of two of these extractors in series; a fresh aqueous phase containing a salting-out agent is used in the second extractor. This has
resulted in analyses of samples for uranium accurate to 1 part in 3000.

Another simple extractor for solvents lighter than water is the
Kutscher-Steudel type [8] shown in Fig. 8.5. It is similar to the Heberling extractor and employs a small orifice to disperse the solvent
in the aqueous phase. The condensed solvent drips into the central
tube and passes out through the bottom. It extracts as it rises through
the heavier phase, and the extract flows into the side tube.

An extractor for solvents lighter than water, where fresh solvent is added rather than the spent solvent recycled, is the Schmall extractor [9] shown in Fig. 8.6. This type of extractor is useful with solvents such as tributyl phosphate, which cannot be easily distilled and recycled. The sample is placed in the Erlenmeyer flask and a magnetic stirring bar introduced. The flask is then mounted on a magnetic stirrer. The separator column is inserted and attached to the reservoir at the ball joint. Water is added through the funnel, to bring the volume in the flask to the tip of the delivery tube, and the stirrer is set in motion. The reservoir is filled with solvent, and its flow is regulated with the separator stopcock. The extract passes through the sidearm and is collected in an Erlenmeyer flask. This

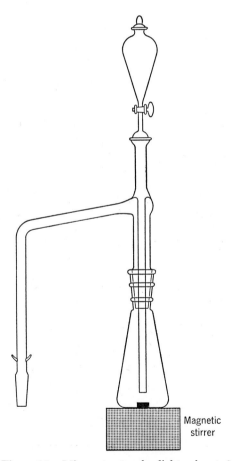

Magnetic stirrer

Figure 8.6. Microextractor for light solvents.[9]

extractor has been used in the extraction of organic acids and bases in connection with the assay of salts of these acids and bases.

The microextractor of Wayman and Wright [10] is used for the extraction of small volumes and minimizes losses difficult to avoid with small separatory funnels or with suction pipettes. It is particularly applicable when the distribution ratio is unfavorable. The extractor for use with solvents lighter than water is shown in Fig. 8.7. The solvent boiling in A is condensed and falls into B where it builds up sufficient pressure to force bubbles of solvent through the extraction chamber, C. This chamber is wave-shaped, as shown at E', to delay the solvent in its passage through the aqueous solution and thereby prolong the time of contact. It is claimed that in one case a 90-minute continuous extraction was found to be better than 20 successive batch extractions.

A small-scale continuous extractor for operation at superatmospheric pressures has been designed to improve extractions when the distribution ratio is unfavorable.[11] The increased boiling point of the liquids

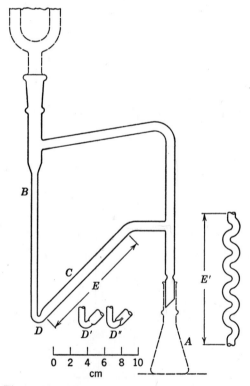

Figure 8.7. Microextractor for light solvents.[10]

in the system under these conditions permits operation in what may be a more favorable temperature range.

One of the few extractors designed specifically for the continuous extraction of metals using chelating agents is that of Meinke and Anderson.[12]   The apparatus has been used for the extraction of thorium complexed with TTA into benzene.   The extractor is particularly useful for the separation of radioactive materials with chelating agents since most operations are automatic and a minimum of shielding is required.   Figure 8.8 illustrates the continuous extractor, which consists of a 50-ml sintered-glass funnel of medium porosity, extended above the sintered disc to a total height of 25 cm

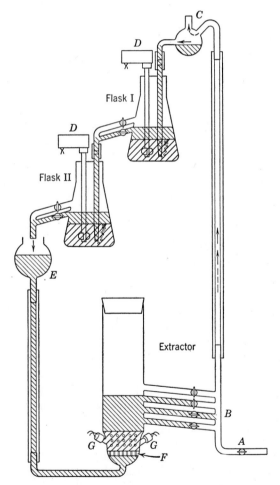

Figure 8.8.   Continuous apparatus for extraction of chelates.[12]

by the addition of 50-mm glass tubing. Several overflow tubes of 7-mm glass tubing sealed onto the side of the extractor allow the adaptation of the extractor to varying amounts of solution to be extracted.

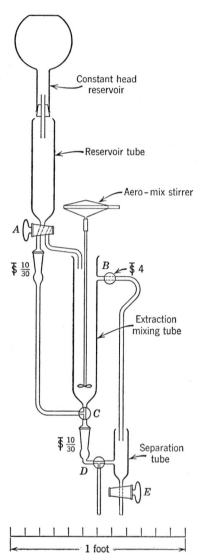

Figure 8.9. Continuous extractor for obtaining "half extraction volumes"; [6] C and D are $\bar{S}$ three-way stopcocks.

The inlet tube below the sintered-glass disc, F, is connected to the 200-ml chelate reservoir, E, with flexible tubing. The tubes sealed onto the extractor at G permit the insertion of micro pH electrodes into the solution to be extracted. A small collar of rubber tubing effectively seals the electrodes and tubes. The stopcock at A controls the flow of nitrogen gas, which is used to lift the extract from the extractor to the small trap bulb, C, where it then falls by gravity into flask I. The trap bulb eliminates spattering which would occur if the solution were directly discharged into flask I. Flasks I and II are standard 500-ml Erlenmeyer flasks with attached overflow side tubes of 7-mm glass tubing. Small stirring motors, D, furnish sufficient agitation for the stripping and washing taking place in these flasks.

The apparatus illustrated in Fig. 8.9, designed for the study of continuous liquid-liquid extractions of inorganic and organometallic compounds with various immiscible solvents, is convenient also for routine use in standard analytical separations.[6] The parts are interchangeable, so that only one portion, the extraction mixing tube, need be replaced in order to convert from the extraction of a large to a small volume of liquid. The apparatus may be used with solvents either heavier or lighter than the liquid being extracted. When used with light extracting solvents, the vertical delivery and reservoir tubes are filled with the solvent. In order to have a constant head of solvent in the reservoir tube, a 500-ml flask fitted with a one-hole stopper and a short length of tubing is held inverted over this tube. The solution to be extracted is measured into the extraction mixing tube to about 3.75 cm below the outlet tube at B. Stirring is begun, tap C is opened partially into the extraction tube, and the solvent flow rate is regulated by tap A. The extracting solvent passes through tap B, and the removal from the settling tube is controlled by tap E.

When the apparatus is used with heavy extracting solvents, taps A, B, C, and E are closed and the solution to be extracted is measured into the extraction tube. Tap D is opened horizontally. The stirrer is started and the extracting solvent permitted to drop into the top of the extraction tube. When about a 2.5-cm layer of clear solvent has collected at the bottom of the extraction tube, tap C is partially opened and the liquid drawn off at the desired rate. The rate of flow of solvent is regulated by A. Tap E is used to measure the extract into the desired container. This apparatus has been used to measure half-extraction volumes for evaluating continuous extractions as described on page 86.

b. Extraction with Heavy Solvents

Many continuous extractions for separation purposes involve the use of an organic solvent that is heavier than the phase being extracted. A number of the extractors described in the previous section can easily be adapted for use under these conditions. Thus, the extractor shown in Fig. 8.10 [13] is similar to the extractor of Furman,[7] except that the funnel tube is replaced with a cylindrical tube inside the extractor. The heavier solvent condenses and passes through the phase to be extracted and then flows to the outer part of the extractor. It then flows through the sidearm and is ready for stripping and recycling.

The Wehrli extractor [14] for heavier solvents, shown in Fig. 8.11, is another modification whereby the solvent containing the extracted solute is returned to the distilling flask through the narrow tube leaving the bottom of the extraction chamber.

A microextractor for use with heavier solvents is shown in Fig. 8.12 and is a companion apparatus to the one shown in Fig. 8.7.[10] The operation of the apparatus is obvious, the extract returning through

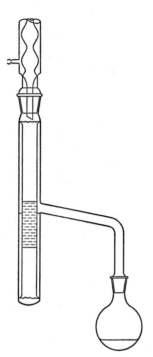

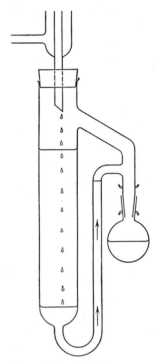

Figure 8.10. Continuous
extractor for use with a solvent heavier than water.[13]

Figure 8.11. Wehrli extractor for solvents heavier than
water.[14]

the sidearm. The advantage of this extractor is the minimizing of
losses when using small volumes.

An apparatus for extraction with solvents which are heavier than
water and which cannot easily be distilled is that of Schmall, Pifer,
and Wollish,[9] shown in Fig. 8.13. It consists of an extracting cylinder
that is flared at the top. A U-shaped capillary delivery tube is fused to
the bottom of the extracting cylinder. At the upper bend of the delivery
tube a stopcock permits regulation of the solvent flow. The end of the
delivery tube has a ground-glass joint, onto which a stopcock attach-
ment can be fitted. A solid glass plug is carefully inserted into the
extracting cylinder, on top of which a glass ring and subsequently a
perforated porcelain or glass disc are brought into place. A mechanical stirrer is centered within the extraction chamber, and the blades
are allowed to revolve about 1 inch above the perforated disc. A
separatory funnel acts as a reservoir and extends into the flared top
of the extraction chamber.

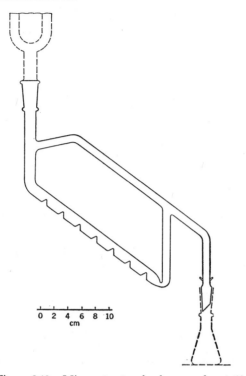

Figure 8.12. Microextractor for heavy solvents.[10]

The chamber is filled with a solvent heavier than water to a level equal to the height of the delivery tube. An aqueous solution of the sample is transferred on top of the solvent layer, and the stirrer is immediately set in operation. The total aqueous phase should exceed 25 ml, and the solvent interface should not extend below the glass disc when the stirrer is not in motion. The extract is collected in an Erlenmeyer flask.

c. Continuous Countercurrent Extraction

This type of extraction involves a process whereby the two liquid phases are caused to flow counter to each other. It is used to great advantage for separating materials for isolation or purification purposes, and it is also used extensively in engineering problems.

One of the few examples of countercurrent extractors used for analytical purposes is the micro rotary extractor of Spence and Streeton,[15] which can be operated on either a continuous or batch basis. The extractor consists of two coaxial cylinders, the inner one of which rotates. When two liquids pass through the annular space,

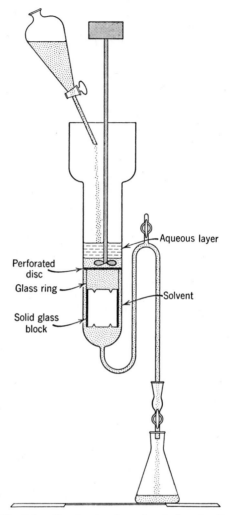

Figure 8.13. Schmall extractor for solvents heavier than water.[9]

in countercurrent flow, vortices are set up in the continuous phase, and when the rate of rotation of the inner cylinder is sufficiently great, the disperse phase is broken up into small droplets that are carried into the vortices, which then appear to form symmetrical pairs, the individual members of which rotate in opposite directions. When the column is operated in this way and when one of the liquids contains a component extractable by the other, a state of equilibrium is ultimately reached in which each vortex represents a stationary state, and a limited number of vortices can be regarded as constituting one equivalent theoretical extraction stage. The efficiency of extraction on the microscale increases as the radius of the inner cylinder and the width of the annular space decrease.

The extractor consists of a motor-driven rotor and a stator made of glass tubing of uniform bore with side tubes for aqueous feed, solvent feed, extract, and raffinate as shown in Fig. 8.14. Polyethylene bearings A and B are used at the bottom and top of the rotor. Control of flow of the various liquids into and out of the column at rates of a few milliliters per hour are accomplished by positive discharge by means of piston pipettes of about 75-ml capacity. An intermediate vessel C is used for sample volumes of the order of 1 ml and can be removed for continuous operation.

The metering pipettes are charged with aqueous feed and with solvent feed, respectively, and the column is allowed to fill with aqueous phase. When the flow control mechanism is operating, the rotor is started and the speed is adjusted to give well-defined vortices as

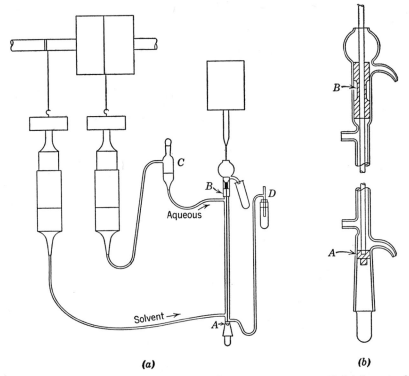

(a) *(b)*

Figure 8.14. Continuous countercurrent micro rotary extractor:[15] (a) layout of extractor; (b) details of extractor. Reproduced by permission of the Society for Analytical Chemistry, from *The Analyst,* **77,** 578 (1952).

the solvent rises in the column. The peripheral speed of the rotor exceeds about 60 cm per second for most solvents. After starting the rotor it is necessary to adjust the level of the interface to a point immediately above the aqueous feed point by raising or lowering the raffinate collecting vessel, D.

Although the extractor is not a substitute for the ordinary separatory funnel when simple batch extractions are to be carried out, it has the advantage of being operable countercurrently with many equivalent theoretical stages. Thus, it is suitable mainly for routine determinations or single determinations when high extraction efficiency is essential for solutes of low distribution ratios. The extractor has been used successfully for the extraction of uranium by dibutyl tetraethylene glycol, β,β'-dibutoxydiethyl ether, and methyl isobutyl ketone.

Further information on the subject of continuous countercurrent extraction may be found in *Liquid Extraction*, by R. E. Treybal.[16]

3. EXTRACTION OF SOLIDS

The separation of solutes by extraction is best performed by liquid-liquid distribution procedures; however, there may be some situations where it is more convenient to extract (selectively dissolve) a particular material present in a solid sample. Then the solute cannot be easily modified to enhance or suppress extraction, and removal is dependent chiefly on the solubility of the substance in a particular solvent. Solid-liquid extractions find their chief application in problems involving biological or natural samples, although a number of inorganic salts may be separated in this fashion. An example of this is the separation of calcium from strontium by extraction of the anhydrous nitrates with such solvents as absolute alcohol and ethyl ether. Another separation involving the extraction of solids is the separation of sodium from potassium by extracting sodium perchlorate with ethyl acetate or some other suitable solvent.

Extraction for solids is an operation that frequently requires a considerable amount of time, except when the desired solute is adsorbed only on the surface of the solid. Thus, a continuous process is most often preferred. Since the diffusion of a solute through the body of a solid is a slow process, it is essential that the material be finely ground for most intimate contact.

The simplest apparatus for the extraction of a solid could be any vessel, such as a beaker, in which the solid is treated with the solvent and the extract then decanted. This technique is employed in the separation of inorganic salts and is essentially a leaching operation.

When complete removal of the solute from a solid sample can be accomplished only by prolonged treatment with the solvent, a continuous extraction should be employed. The two basic types of con-

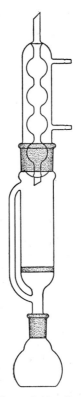

Figure 8.15. Soxhlet extractor for solid-liquid extractions.

Figure 8.16. Continuous-infusion extractor for solid-liquid extractions.

tinuous extractors for solids are the discontinuous-infusion type and the continuous-infusion type. The well-known "Soxhlet" [17] is an example of the former and is shown in Fig. 8.15, and a simple extractor of the latter class is shown in Fig. 8.16. A better method of insuring a layer of fresh solvent over the solid sample is provided by the apparatus in Fig. 8.17, in which the sample can never run dry. When the short drip tube is removed at the ball joint A, the apparatus for continuous supply of the solvent by distillation can be attached by B and C.

Both the discontinuous- and continuous-infusion types of extractors usually employ a filter of some sort. An extraction thimble is employed with the Soxhlet extractor; however, filter paper, cloth, fine-wire screen, etc., can be used. In the continuous type, filter paper,

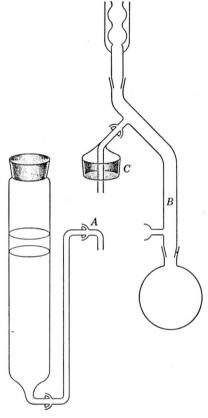

Figure 8.17. Continuous apparatus for extraction of solids. From L. C. Craig and D. Craig in *Technique of Organic Chemistry*, edited by A. Weissberger, Vol. III, Part I, second edition, Interscience Publishers, Inc., New York, 1956.

a sintered-glass filter, a plug of cotton or glass wool, etc., are used. There are many variations of both types of extractors, depending on the specific problem under consideration.

Batt and Alber [18] have made a general study of the extraction of solids and have concluded that the semimicro Soxhlet extractor has several advantages over the macro apparatus. Among other things it requires a shorter extraction time. They also concluded that the continuous-infusion types of extractors are superior to the siphoning type. A number of different extractors were included in their study.

4. COUNTERCURRENT DISTRIBUTION: EXTRACTION FOR FRACTIONATION

Discontinuous countercurrent distribution extractions have been applied with great success to the fractionation of organic compounds, particularly where the distribution ratios are of the same order of magnitude. This technique, however, has not been used to any great extent to separate metals for analytical determination, and a new and promising area of research awaits development. Craig[19] has been mainly responsible for the development of the method and its application to a number of organic and biochemical problems, and the chapter by L. C. Craig and D. Craig in *Technique of Organic Chemistry*, edited by A. Weissberger, should be consulted for further details.[1]

The method is based on the carrying out of many individual extractions rapidly and in sequence; it permits direct application of the binomial expansion for interpreting the results quantitatively. Fractionation is accomplished by distribution, transfer, and recombination of various fractions. To demonstrate the method, a simple experiment described by Craig,[1] involving the use of equal volumes of the two phases and a solute whose distribution ratio is 1 in the solvent pair, is presented. It must be assumed that when two solutes are extracted reversibly in a given two-phase system, each will behave independently of the other. Also, it is assumed that the distribution ratios are constant over the concentration range employed. For most substances, these conditions may be approached in actual practice by using sufficiently dilute solutions.

A series of contacting tubes numbered 0, 1, 2 $\cdots$ r, as shown in Fig. 8.18, is employed. One gram of the solute is dissolved in tube L_0, and tube U_0 containing the solvent is placed over it. The two phases in tube 0 are equilibrated and, after they have separated, the upper phases are shifted so that U_0 is over L_1 and U_1 is over L_0, resulting in one transfer. Since the distribution ratio is 1 and the volumes of the two phases are equal, half the solute has been transferred to tube 1 in the upper layer. The total in both layers combined, of each tube, 0 or 1, is therefore 0.500 g.

For the second transfer, both tubes are equilibrated and the upper layers of both shifted so that U_0 is over L_2, U_1 is over L_1, and U_2 is over L_0. The total fraction of solute in each tube, both layers combined, is given in Fig. 8.18 on the line opposite the second transfer.

The process may be continued until n transfers have been performed.

The figure represents an expansion corresponding to $(X + Y)^n = 1$, where Y represents the fraction remaining in the lower phase and X represents the fraction being transferred; here $X = Y$. The letter n corresponds to the number of transfers made. The numbers of the tubes $0, 1, 2 \cdots r$ correspond to the rth term of the binomial expansion.

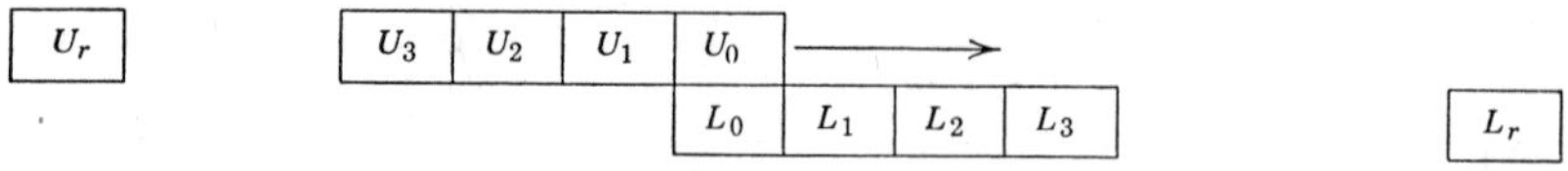

Transfer No. \ Tube No.	0	1	2	3	-------	r
0	1.0					
1	0.50	0.50				
2	0.25	0.50	0.25			
3	0.125	0.375	0.375	0.125		
4	0.0625	0.25	0.375	0.25	0.0625	
n						

Figure 8.18. Countercurrent distribution. From L. C. Craig and D. Craig in *Technique of Organic Chemistry,* edited by A. Weissberger, Vol. III, Part I, second edition, Interscience Publishers, Inc., New York, 1956.

The fraction or percentage of solute in a single tube to be found in each phase is fixed by the distribution ratio. Thus, eq. 8.4 gives the relation of the fraction X to be found in the upper phase

$$X = \frac{D}{D + 1} \tag{8.4}$$

to the distribution ratio, D, at equilibrium. The fraction Y in the lower phase is also fixed by eq. 8.5, since unit quantity was taken initially.

$$Y = 1 - \frac{D}{D + 1} = \frac{1}{1 + D} \tag{8.5}$$

The binomial expansion in terms of the distribution ratio, D, as applied to the stepwise countercurrent extraction therefore becomes

$$\left(\frac{1}{1 + D} + \frac{D}{D + 1}\right)^n = 1 \tag{8.6}$$

when equal volumes of the two phases are used. The expression applies equally well for unequal volumes when D throughout the expression is multiplied by the ratio of the two volumes. Thus, the percentage of the original solute to be found in each tube is fixed for a given D when the number of transfers is fixed.

When carried out as in Fig. 8.18, the amount of substance present in each tube can be calculated directly by the binomial theorem, since the fraction in the rth tube is that of the rth term of the binomial theorem. Equation 8.7 gives a general formula for calculating the fraction $T_{n,r}$ of substance present in the rth tube for n transfers.

$$T_{n,r} = \frac{n!}{r!(n-r)!} \left(\frac{1}{D+1}\right)^n D^r \tag{8.7}$$

The extraction data can be represented graphically in a convenient fashion by plotting the fraction or percentage present in a tube against the serial number of the tube.[19, 20] Curve 1 of Fig. 8.19 shows a distribution curve for a distribution ratio of 1 and for eight transfers.[1] The curve is perfectly symmetrical. For higher numbers of transfers, the curve becomes the normal curve of error. Curves 2 and 3 are obtained with distribution ratios 0.333 and 3.0, respectively.

A series of separatory funnels may be used to perform this type of extraction; however, certain special devices are more convenient when high numbers of transfers are required for the separation of complicated mixtures.[21] Variations in the fundamental procedure permit the use of a simpler apparatus and are based on the use of withdrawal steps.[21, 22, 23]

A glass countercurrent distribution apparatus designed by Craig[24] and used for extractions involving large numbers of transfers is shown in Fig. 8.20. The right figure shows a single unit. The equilibration chamber, A, is a glass tube approximately 12 in. long with a 0.5-in. inside diameter. The two phases are inserted together with the solute through opening E. Equilibration is accomplished by tilting back and forth at an angle of about 35°. The unit tubes interlock with exit tube D inserted into the opening of the adjoining tube as shown in the left side of the figure. After the layers have separated, the tubes are tilted to an angle slightly more than 90°, where the upper phase will decant through tube B into chamber C. On righting the tubes to the position shown in the figure on the right, the contents of C will flow through D into the next adjoining tube in the series. In the decanting position, the heavier layer remains in A because its volume is such that none will flow out through B, although practically all the lighter layer flows out. With an apparatus containing 108 units it is possible to

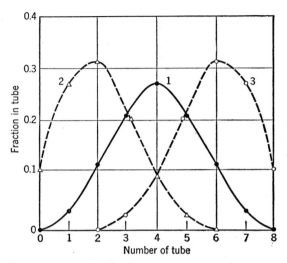

Figure 8.19. Countercurrent distribution curves: curve 1 for distribution ratio of 1, curve 2 for distribution ratio of 0.333, curve 3 for distribution ratio of 3.0. From L. C. Craig and D. Craig, *Technique of Organic Chemistry*, edited by A. Weissberger, Vol. III, Part I, second edition, Interscience Publishers, Inc., New York, 1956.

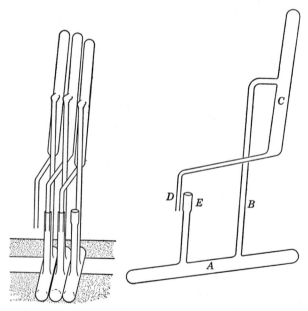

Figure 8.20. Countercurrent distribution extractors for simultaneous transfers by decantation. Individual unit at right.[24]

make 40 transfers in 1 hour. A modified automatic countercurrent distribution has more recently been developed.[25]

REFERENCES

1. L. C. Craig and D. Craig in *Technique of Organic Chemistry*, edited by A. Weissberger, Vol. III, Part I, second edition, Interscience Publishers, Inc., New York, 1956.
2. P. L. Kirk and M. Danielson, *Anal. Chem.*, **20**, 1122 (1948).
3. A. I. Medalia and R. W. Stoenner, *Anal. Chem.*, **23**, 545 (1951).
4. J. K. Carlton, *Anal. Chem.*, **22**, 1072 (1950).
5. N. H. Furman, W. B. Mason, and J. S. Pekola, *Anal. Chem.*, **21**, 1325 (1949).
6. H. A. Bewick, J. E. Currah, and F. E. Beamish, *Anal. Chem.*, **20**, 740 (1948).
7. N. H. Furman, R. J. Mundy, and G. H. Morrison, U.S. Atomic Energy Commission Report, AECD-2861.
8. F. Kutscher and H. Steudel, *Z. physiol. Chem.*, **39**, 474 (1903).
9. M. Schmall, C. W. Pifer, and E. G. Wollish, *Anal. Chem.*, **24**, 1446 (1952); **26**, 1670 (1954).
10. M. M. Wayman and G. F. Wright, *Ind. Eng. Chem., Anal. Ed.*, **17**, 55 (1945).
11. W. J. Chute and G. F. Wright, *Anal. Chem.*, **21**, 193 (1949).
12. W. W. Meinke and R. E. Anderson, *Anal. Chem.*, **24**, 708 (1952).
13. S. Palkin, A. G. Murray, and H. R. Watkins, *Ind. Eng. Chem.*, **17**, 612 (1925).
14. S. Wehrli, *Helv. Chim. Acta*, **20**, 927 (1937).
15. R. Spence and R. J. W. Streeton, *Analyst*, **77**, 578 (1952).
16. R. E. Treybal, *Liquid Extraction*, McGraw-Hill Book Co., Inc., New York, 1951.
17. F. Soxhlet and J. Szombathy, *Dinglers Polytech. J.*, **232**, 461 (1879).
18. W. G. Batt and H. K. Alber, *Ind. Eng. Chem., Anal. Ed.*, **13**, 127 (1941).
19. L. C. Craig, *J. Biol. Chem.*, **155**, 519 (1944).
20. B. Williamson and L. C. Craig, *J. Biol. Chem.*, **168**, 687 (1947); S. Stene, *Arkiv Kemi, Mineral: Geol.*, **18A**, No. 18 (1944).
21. L. C. Craig, *Anal. Chem.*, **22**, 1346 (1950).
22. Jantzen, Das fractionierte Distillieren und das fractionierte Verteilen, Dechema Monographie, Vol. V, No. 48, Verlag Chemie, Berlin, 1932.
23. M. T. Bush and P. M. Densen, *Anal. Chem.*, **20**, 121 (1948).
24. L. C. Craig and O. Post, *Anal. Chem.*, **21**, 500 (1949).
25. L. C. Craig, W. Hausmann, E. H. Ahrens, and E. J. Harfenist, *Anal. Chem.*, **23**, 1236 (1951).

Chapter 9

Techniques in Extraction

1. CHOICE OF SOLVENT

Perhaps the most important consideration in the selection of a solvent for use in a particular extraction procedure is the extractability of the element of interest. The distribution ratio of the solute must, of course, be high if a separation is to be readily attained. By the same token the extraction of other solutes must be low if a separation is to be achieved. The role of the solvent in extraction is described in Chapter 4, and it has been shown that many other factors in addition to the nature of the solvent influence the extractability of a particular solute.

In addition to a consideration of the solubility of the solute in a particular solvent, the ease of recovery of the solute from the solvent is important for subsequent analytical processing. Thus, the boiling point of the solvent or the ease of stripping by chemical reagents enters into selection of a solvent when the possibility of a choice exists. Similarly, the degree of miscibility of the two phases, the relative specific gravities, viscosities, and tendency to form emulsions should be considered.

From the point of view of safety, the toxicity and the flammability of the organic solvent obviously enter into the choice.

Sometimes it is possible to achieve many of the desired characteristics of a solvent by employing a mixed solvent system. Thus, mixtures of alcohols and ether are commonly used in the thiocyanate extraction of elements such as cobalt, iron, etc. Similarly, a mixture of dibutoxytetraethylene glycol and ether is used to extract thorium from nitrate solutions.

Another method of varying the composition of the extracting solvent is to use organic diluents. Various organic compounds such as kerosene and other hydrocarbons are employed to dilute tributyl phosphate for extraction purposes. Likewise trichloroethylene serves as a diluent for tertiary amines for the extraction of zinc from hydrochloric acid solutions.

2. STRIPPING

Stripping is the removal of the extracted solute from the organic phase for further preparation for the estimation step of the analysis. In many colorimetric procedures involving an extraction, the concentration of the solute of interest is determined directly on the organic phase after extraction by measuring the optical density of the solution of the colored complex. In the extraction of radioactive materials, a direct determination may be made on the phase containing the extracted radioisotope by one of several methods of radioactive counting described on page 119.

Where other conventional methods of estimation are to be employed, or where further separation steps are required, it is necessary to remove the solute from the organic phase to a more suitable medium. Depending on the volatility of the organic solvent, the simplest procedure is to add a small volume of water to the extract to hold the solute and to evaporate the volatile solvent on a steam bath. This is particularly useful when performing ether extractions. Care should be taken, however, to avoid loss of a volatile solute during evaporation. Sometimes adjustment of acidity of the solution, change in the valence state, etc., may be employed to avoid loss of the solute. The addition of acid to the water before evaporation of volatile solvents in which chelate complexes are dissolved helps to break the complex, thereby causing the metal ions to enter the water solution. It is sometimes necessary to destroy residual organic matter in the aqueous solution after evaporation of the organic solvent, and this is usually accomplished by adding a few milliliters of sulfuric acid and evaporating to fumes of sulfur trioxide. Further fuming in the presence of nitric and perchloric acids is useful.

When the extracting solvent is non-volatile, it is necessary to strip the solute from the solvent by chemical means, the usual procedure being to shake the solvent with a volume of water containing acids or other reagents under conditions whereby the extractable complex is destroyed. The metal ions are then quantitatively back-extracted into the stripping aqueous phase. The conditions employed depend on the specific extraction under consideration; however, those conditions exercised to promote the extraction are reversed so that the solute will favor the new aqueous phase.

It must be pointed out that from the safety point of view, the most dangerous step in extraction procedures is the stripping of volatile solvents by evaporation. The flammability of the solvent must be considered in this operation, and the use of water and steam baths, wherever possible to avoid an open flame, is strongly recommended.

3. BACKWASHING

An auxiliary technique used with batch extractions to effect quantitative separations of elements is that of backwashing. The combined organic phases from several extractions of the original aqueous phase contain practically all the element desired and possibly some of the impurities that have been extracted to a much smaller extent, depending on their relative distribution ratios. This combined organic phase, when shaken with one or more small portions of a fresh aqueous phase containing the optimum reagent concentration, salting-out agent, etc., will result in a redistribution of the impurities, as well as of the major component, between the two phases. Under optimum conditions most of the element desired will remain in the organic layer, since its distribution ratio is high. The bulk of the impurities, however, will be back-extracted to the fresh aqueous phase, since their distribution ratios are much smaller. This technique is analogous in many respects to the reprecipitation step in a gravimetric precipitation procedure. With the proper conditions most of the impurities can be removed by this backwashing operation, with negligible loss of the main component, thereby attaining a selective separation.

4. TREATMENT OF EMULSIONS

By mixing or agitating certain combinations of immiscible liquids, an emulsion may result whereby one liquid is dispersed in a continuum of the other. From the point of view of liquid-liquid extraction, the stability or permanence of the dispersion is its most important property since it is necessary to separate the phases for further steps in the analytical procedure. For an emulsion to "break" or separate into its phases, both sedimentation and coalescence of the droplets of the dispersed phase must occur. In general, settling will be slower the greater the viscosity of the continuous phase, the smaller the density difference, and the smaller the drop size. The method of agitation undoubtedly influences the particle size, and analytical extractions involving solvents with a tendency to form emulsions are best performed with a continuous type of extractor. Usually the droplets of solvent which continuously pass through the solution are relatively large, thereby minimizing emulsification. Even though the amount of solute extracted at a single passage may be small, the continuous extraction can be allowed to run for a period of time, and separation will be accomplished without the complications of emulsions. In batch extractions, gentle inversion, rather than vigorous shaking, will often accomplish equilibration with a minimum of emulsification.

One of the main factors causing coalescence is interfacial tension; ordinarily, the greater the interfacial tension, the greater the tendency to coalesce. Interfacial tension will be low for liquids of high mutual solubility and will be lowered by the presence of emulsifying agents. These surface active agents exert a great influence, and it is generally recognized that the liquid in which the emulsifying agent is soluble has a greater tendency to form the continuous phase. High viscosity of the continuous phase hinders coalescence by decreasing the rate at which the thin film between drops is removed. It is often possible to employ mixed organic solvents whose combined properties are less favorable for the formation of emulsions yet favor extraction of the solute of interest. Sometimes a diluent organic solvent may be added to the organic solvent to avoid emulsification.

The presence of a small amount of a solid phase at the interface often prevents coalescence of emulsions, and filtration of both phases serves to prevent trouble. Another method for reducing the tendency for emulsification is the addition of neutral salts, which possibly increases the surface tension or the density. Another way of avoiding emulsification is to allow only a small amount of the aqueous solution to come in contact with a relatively large amount of the organic solvent. Finally, causing the emulsion to flow through a porous substance which has a large ratio of surface to volume but contains relatively large capillary openings, which is preferentially wetted by the dispersed phase, will frequently induce coalescence, possibly owing to mechanical destruction of the surface film surrounding the dispersed phase droplets.

Fortunately, emulsion problems are not often encountered in most extraction separations employed for analytical purposes. New extraction systems, however, may be developed where the effect may present a serious problem. A good treatment of emulsions in extraction has been given by Treybal.[1]

5. VARIATION OF OXIDATION STATE

A useful method of increasing the selectivity of an extraction involves modification of the oxidation states of some of the ions present in solution in order to prevent the formation of a metal complex necessary for extraction. Thus, the extraction of iron from chloride solutions can be prevented by reduction to iron(II), which does not extract. Similarly, reduction of cerium(IV) to cerium(III) prevents extraction of this element from nitrate solutions. Conversely, it is important in the preparation of a solution for extraction to adjust an ion to the proper valence state required for formation of the complex in order to insure complete extraction of that element. Also, variation of the valence states of certain elements in the organic extract after extraction serves as a method of stripping the solvent of these elements by destroying the extractable complex.

These variations in oxidation state are accomplished by the addition of the appropriate oxidizing or reducing agents, depending on the chemistry of the particular elements of interest and the nature of the extraction system.

6. USE OF MASKING (SEQUESTERING) AGENTS

Masking agents are themselves metal-complexing agents (not necessarily chelating agents) which serve to prevent particular metals from taking part in their "usual" reactions and thus remove their interference without the necessity of an actual separation. Since the "masked" metal must remain in solution, the complex obviously must be water-soluble. For this reason, we find that masking agents give rise to charged (most often negatively) complexes.

In solvent extraction, masking agents are used to prevent certain metals from forming extractable complexes and thus to greatly increase the selectivity of the extraction methods in which masking is employed. The application of masking agents, which include cyanide, tartrate, citrate, fluoride, and EDTA, is restricted largely to metal chelate extraction systems, since in the highly acidic solutions encountered in many inorganic extraction systems most masking agents, being weak bases, do not function effectively.

An example of the usefulness of masking agents is found in the extraction of aluminum in the presence of iron with 8-quinolinol into chloroform. Iron interference is prevented by the addition of an alkali cyanide prior to extraction to form the very stable ferrocyanide ion.

Similarly, nickel may be extracted with dimethylglyoxime in the presence of cobalt if cyanide is first used to mask the cobalt. The $Ni(CN)_4{}^{2-}$ is destroyed by hydrogen peroxide or formaldehyde but the $Co(CN)_6{}^{3-}$ is very stable. Thiosulfate and thiocyanate have been used to increase the selectivity of dithizone extractions. In some instances a combination of masking agents are employed in order to obtain a further increase in selectivity.

Masking is of course necessitated by the presence of foreign metals which would otherwise react with the extracting agent in the same pH region, or possibly a lower one, as would the metal of interest. The masking agent forms sufficiently strong complexes with the interfering metals to prevent their reactions with the extraction agent, either altogether or at least until the pH is much higher than the value needed for quantitative extraction of the metal of interest. Very often the metal of interest also forms a complex with the masking agent, with the result that a somewhat higher pH range is needed for the extraction. To illustrate these variations using 8-quinolinol, masking with cyanide renders iron(III) completely unextractable, although aluminum or cerium extract as they would in the absence of this masking agent. In the dithizone extraction of silver, a higher pH range for the copper extraction is necessary if chloride ion is present.

Ethylenediaminetetraacetic acid, which is proving a most useful masking agent, has been applied to dithizone, 8-quinolinol, carboxylic acids, acetylacetone, and diethyldithiocarbamate extractions; EDTA forms anionic complexes with quite a number of metal ions, including even those of the alkaline earths. Representative stabilities are shown in Table 9.1.

The action of this masking agent can be modified by using one of its metal complexes. Thus, whereas EDTA or its sodium salt serves to prevent the extraction of copper by 8-quinolinol, use of the calcium complex permits quantitative copper extraction at pH 6.0.[2] This behavior, which deserves wider attention and application, may be explained in terms of the data presented in Table 9.1. The effective log K_f value of the copper-EDTA complex in the presence of calcium is $19 - 11 = 8$. This lower value results in a better competitive position of the extraction complexing agent.

Other complexing agents which have been applied as masking agents include o-phenanthroline for iron(II), dimethylglyoxime for nickel, and 4-sulfobenzenearsonic acid for thorium. It should be mentioned that interfering anions may be masked by using masking cations. Thus, if F^- interferes with a $UO_2{}^{2+}$ extraction, an excess of aluminum or boron can be added to "mask" the fluoride.

Table 9.1.[4]   Formation Constants of Metal EDTA Complexes at 20°C
in 0.1 N KNO$_3$

$$K_f = \frac{[MY]}{[M^n][Y^{4-}]}$$

where Y = ethylenediaminetetraacetate anion

Metal	log$_{10}$ K_f	Metal	log$_{10}$ K_f
Sc	23.1	Al	16.13
In	24.95	Hg	22.
Zr	~25.	Cu(II)	18.80
Th	23.2	VO^{2+}	18.77
Tl(III)	23.	Ni	18.62
Bi	~26.	Y	18.09
Fe(III)	25.1	Pb	18.04
Ga	20.27	Zn	16.50
Lu	19.83	Cd	16.46
Tm	19.32	Co(II)	16.31
Dy	18.30	Fe(II)	14.
Eu	17.35	Mn	14.04
Nd	16.61	Ca	10.96
Ce	15.98	Mg	9.
La	15.50	Ba	8.

Another point of interest in connection with the use of masking agents is the possibility that a longer equilibration time may be required, since some complexing agents, notably EDTA, form chelates whose rates of dissociation are somewhat slow. This has been observed in the extraction of iron and copper 8-quinolinates [2] and of copper(II) thiocarbamate [3] where the presence of EDTA made necessary either longer extraction times or higher pH values for complete extraction.

The applicability of a particular masking agent to an extraction system of interest can be gaged by considering the complex formation constants of the metals with both the masking agent and the extraction agent.

7. USE OF SALTING-OUT AGENTS

A technique that has resulted in spectacular results in the enhancement of extraction of metals, particularly in the oxonium type of extractions, is the use of salting-out agents. The addition of inorganic salts to the aqueous phase increases the distribution ratio of many metal complexes in favor of the extracting phase. The salting-out effect may be explained in part by the pronounced effect of the salt that is added on the activity of the distributing species, as well as the strong ability of these ions to bind water around them, thereby depleting the aqueous phase of water molecules for use as a solvent. The theory of salting-out is discussed in Chapter 4.

Large amounts of inorganic salts are usually required to produce a marked enhancement in extraction, the aqueous phase often being saturated with the added salt. When using these agents it is essential that the added salt does not extract to any appreciable extent into the organic phase. It is obvious, of course, that the presence of large concentrations of added cations in the aqueous phase prevent further use of this phase for subsequent analytical processing unless the added salt can be easily removed or destroyed, as ammonium salts can be.

Although enhancement of the extraction of the metal of interest occurs with the use of the salting-out agents, it should be remembered that extraction of impurities in the system may also occur. Therefore, it is necessary to choose an agent that produces a favorable separation factor between the element of interest and the impurities. The magnitude of enhancement of extraction by the added salt depends on the charge as well as the ionic size of the added cation for a given anion. Thus, polyvalent cations provide better salting-out agents, and for a given charge, the smaller the cationic size, the greater the effect on extraction. It must be remembered, however, that anomalies sometimes result from specific interaction effects. Aluminum or ferric salts are strong salting-out agents, whereas ammonium salts are much weaker but analytically more convenient.

The aqueous phase is prepared for extraction simply by adding the solid salt until saturation is reached. It is often advisable, however, to keep slightly below the saturation point, for upon contact with the organic phase some water may be removed, resulting in some crystallization of the salt. When performing a batch extraction, a strong salting-out agent should be employed, since a good removal is desired in as few extractions as possible. With continuous extractions a weaker agent should be used to minimize the extraction of impurities. Over a period of time the element of interest will be completely removed with little of the impurities being extracted. Ammonium salts are particularly useful when the aqueous phase is to be further analyzed, since they may be destroyed after the extraction by repeated evaporations of the aqueous phase with nitric and hydrochloric acids. Care must be taken to avoid spattering.

Salting-out agents have been used with great success in separations involving the nitrate, halide, and thiocyanate systems. There are many great potentialities for the use of this technique in other extraction systems, and many substances that are only slightly extracted may be sufficiently modified so that useful analytical separations will result. This is indeed a fertile field for future research.

REFERENCES

1. R. E. Treybal, *Liquid Extraction,* McGraw-Hill Book Co., Inc., New York, 1951.
2. R. P. Taylor, Ph.D. Thesis, Princeton University, 1954.
3. J. L. Hague, E. D. Brown, and H. A. Bright, *J. Research Natl. Bur. Standards,* **47,** 380 (1951).
4. G. Schwarzenbach, R. Gut, and G. Anderegg, *Helv. Chim. Acta,* **37,** 937 (1954).

Chapter 10

Completion of Analysis

The use of solvent extraction in analytical chemistry provides a convenient method for separating a particular element or substance from the remainder of the sample, or conversely, for removing interfering substances. The final step in an analysis involves quantitative estimation of the element of interest. Colorimetric and radiochemical methods of estimation uniquely complement solvent extraction since they may be used directly on the organic extract. These will be discussed below.

In most other instances it is necessary to strip the solute from the extracting phase before estimating its concentration. The choice of the method of estimation to be employed is large, any of the conventional methods being applicable. Thus, gravimetric, volumetric, polarographic, spectrographic, and any other methods are applicable, depending on the amount of material available and the chemistry of the element involved. The effect of certain impurities that have not been completely removed by extraction may be eliminated by the choice of the appropriate estimation method.

1. RADIOISOTOPES AND SOLVENT EXTRACTION

a. Use of Solvent Extraction in Radiochemistry

Solvent extraction is particularly well suited to the purification of many radioisotopes, since after several extractions of a substance, the final product is usually relatively free from extraneous impurities which may be present when coprecipitation or other separation procedures are employed. Also, if the isotope of interest has a short half life, a rapid separation is essential and extraction procedures have proved invaluable.

The requirements of radiochemical purity are unique in that the use of radioactive tracers in research is based on the measurement of the activities of the nuclides used to label the element or compound involved. What is measured is the activity of the tracer plus a natural background count. The latter when subtracted from the former yields a net activity proportional to the number of unstable atoms in the sample. It is essential, therefore, to eliminate the presence or contribution of all radioactive impurities. This is preferably accomplished before the actual experiment is even started; however, the use of suitable chemical or physical procedures may be employed before the final assay. The nature and origin of the various radioactive contaminants in tracer materials are treated in detail by Cohn.[1]

Since these radioactive impurities are usually of significance only because of their contribution to the measured activity, it is sometimes possible to eliminate or quantitatively evaluate their effects by physical means based on the half lives, types of radiations, and energies of radiation of the species involved. Usually, however, physical methods are not effective, and chemical separations must be employed before final measurement of the sample.

Methods for the chemical removal of radioactive contaminants depend on the chemical characteristics of the species involved. When the various components are present in macroscopic amounts, conventional analytical techniques are employed. If, however, a relatively negligible mass of active materials must be segregated, special methods of separation are required. This type of problem is similar to that encountered in the isolation of carrier-free isotopes, produced by nuclear transmutation and usually obtained in amounts detectable only by their characteristic nuclear radiations. Under these circumstances solvent extraction performs an outstanding service and has been used extensively in radiochemistry. Garrison and Hamilton[2] provide a detailed treatment of the subject of the production and isolation of carrier-free isotopes, and included are many procedures involving extraction. Another area where solvent extraction has been invaluable is in the separation of fission products.

Although a number of novel separations have resulted from the application of solvent extraction to radiochemistry and are included in the appropriate sections of this book, most of the radiochemical extractions are based on previously developed conventional analytical extractions. In view of this general similarity, specific modifications of extraction procedures for radiochemical separations have not been stressed in this book. Instead, a number of references are included for perusal by those interested. Many procedures are presented in U.S. Atomic Energy Commission progress reports of laboratories such as Oak Ridge National Laboratory (ORNL), Argonne National Laboratory (ANL), University of California Radiation Laboratory (UCRL), Massachusetts Institute of Technology Laboratory for Nuclear Science (MIT), and the Brookhaven National Laboratory (BNL). Many of these reports are unclassified or have been declassified and are available from the Office of Technical Service of the U.S. Atomic Energy Commission at Oak Ridge, Tennessee.

Certain review articles have appeared in the radiochemical literature referring to a considerable number of solvent extraction steps.[3-6]

In addition, there are several compilations of radiochemical procedures, made in the past ten years, which include among them numerous procedures using solvent extraction.[7,8,9]

Finally, the use of solvent extraction in the chemistry of fission products [10,11,12] and the actinide elements [13,14] has been described at the International Conference on the Peaceful Uses of Atomic Energy at Geneva in 1955.

b. Use of Radioisotopes in Solvent Extraction

One of the most useful techniques for obtaining fundamental distribution data necessary for the development of methods of separation involves the use of radioisotopes. With the wide choice of radioisotopes available, it is possible to investigate the separation of almost all of the elements encountered in most analytical problems. Batch extractions may be easily performed with tracers to determine the optimum conditions for extraction of the element of interest, as well as the behavior of impurities under those conditions. Measurement of the activity of the tracers in both the aqueous and organic phases can be made directly in a matter of minutes, so that a complete study to develop an analytical method of separation is a relatively simple task. The high sensitivity of methods of measurement of radioactivity permits determination of very small solute concentrations in one of the phases in those extractions where the distribution ratio is very large or very small.

In addition, it is possible with the use of radioactive tracers to investigate the effect of the initial concentration of the extractable solute on the distribution ratio, particularly in the trace concentration range. Most information on liquid-liquid extraction accumulated to date involves the use of macro, and in a few instances micro, amounts of solute. According to the distribution law (see page 8), the ratio of the equilibrium concentrations of a species in two phases is constant at a given temperature. Some variation of the distribution ratio with varying initial concentration of the solute has been observed in a number of extractions. With the advent of carrier-free tracers, however, it has become possible to study the validity of the distribution law at extremely low concentrations, i.e., submicro amounts. Thus, it has been found [15] that radioiron extraction from hydrochloric acid solutions to ethyl ether in the range of iron(III) of 10^{-3} to $10^{-1} M$ increases with increasing iron(III) concentration. Below $10^{-4} M$ iron(III), the distribution ratio becomes constant as would be expected if a simple Nernst distribution occurs. Grahame and Seaborg,[16] however, have found no appreciable difference in the distribution of gallium using carrier-free tracer and macro amounts. It is apparent that further investigation must be made on the distribution of submicro amounts of materials so that effective methods of separations may be developed for application to analysis of trace impurities.

Finally, a more practical application of radioisotopes is their use as a control in studies of the efficiency of an analytical separation involving liquid-liquid extraction. When the effectiveness of a given separation is quantitatively determined, it is possible to carry out appropriate corrections to the assay values, thereby making the use of simplified procedures reliable.

In general, conventional laboratory apparatus used for solvent extraction may be employed in tracer studies, and the batch technique using separatory funnels provides the most applicability. Haas and Zebroski [17] have described procedures for carrying out continuous countercurrent extractions suitable for remote manipulation of radioactive solutions. These procedures are particularly applicable to studies of the behavior of radioactive or biological solutions when the amount of material handled should be minimized. An apparatus for the continuous extraction of chelates containing radioactive tracers is shown in Fig. 8.8. Since all manipulations are adaptable to remote control and most of the functions are automatic, the extractor can be well shielded for use with highly radioactive material.

Many excellent treatments of the various methods and instruments for measuring radioactivity for analytical purposes may be found in the literature;[18] therefore just a few special techniques particularly applicable to solvent extraction studies are presented here. The selection of any particular method is, of course, dependent on the nature of the nuclide being investigated.

Liquid-counting techniques are particularly useful in the determination of distribution ratios, especially when the radioisotope is a gamma emitter. Fortunately most radioisotopes do emit gamma photons. Since absorption effects are negligible for gamma rays in most liquids, it is possible to measure the activity in the various phases directly after extraction without further treatment or separation. Among the methods for measuring gamma activity in liquids, a well-type thallium activated sodium iodide crystal, used with a scintillation counter, provides a simple and convenient tool. Aliquots of the phases are placed in small screw-cap vials and lowered into the well of the crystal for measurement. Alternatively, the solution may be placed in a small beaker which can be set on a standard sodium iodide crystal. Another method for measuring liquids containing gamma-emitting nuclides involves measurement with a high-pressure ionization chamber.[19] The voltages developed across a high-value resistor by collection of the ions formed are measured with a vibrating reed electrometer. Aliquots of the phases are placed in glass vials and lowered into the steel thimble of the chamber, and the gamma activity is noted.

The measurement of beta particles emitted by the radioisotope whose distribution is being determined can be accomplished by the use of a dip-type Geiger counter; however, the method suffers from several disadvantages. Absorption of beta activity by the liquid, as well as by the glass walls of the counter, greatly limits the sensitivity of the method. This is particularly bad in the measurement of a very high or low distribution ratio, where most of the activity is located in one of the phases, and measurement of the low activity in the other phase is desired. Isolation of the radioactive solute by precipitation or solvent evaporation can be performed before measurement with a thin end-window Geiger counter. The procedure, however, is time-consuming; losses may occur, and errors may arise from absorption and backscattering effects. Fortunately, most radioisotopes emit both beta and gamma radiations, and measurement of the gamma activity is a relatively simple matter as described earlier. There is a small number of nuclides that are pure beta emitters, and in extractions involving them, a Geiger technique must be employed.

In addition to measuring a distribution ratio of a single radioisotope in an extraction procedure by the methods described, it is sometimes possible to determine the behavior of a number of gamma-emitting nuclides in an extraction procedure without resorting to chemical separation. Gamma scintillation spectrometry [20,21] permits the measurement of mixtures of radioisotopes based on characteristic differences in the energies of the gamma photons. This technique is particularly useful in evaluating the behavior of impurities along with that of the solute of interest.

2. COLORIMETRY AND SOLVENT EXTRACTION

Many complexes of metals in aqueous solution are colored; when extracted with an organic solvent, the colored extract may be used directly for estimation of the concentration of the metal. Thus, separation and estimation are combined into a simple procedure when colorimetric or spectrophotometric techniques are employed. These techniques are particularly applicable with many chelate complexes, although a number of colored inorganic complexes such as chloroplatinous acid, iodobismuth acid, "molybdenum blue," and some heteropoly acids may be treated in this fashion. In addition to estimating elements after an extraction separation in analysis, the colorimetric technique is quite useful in the determination of distribution ratios of various elements in the development of new extraction procedures.

The use of colorimetric and spectrophotometric methods for the estimation of the concentration of an element is based on the fact that the constituent forms a colored solution. Such a solution shows differential absorption of light of different wavelengths. This is quantitatively expressed by the well-known Lambert-Beer law, which relates the degree of absorbance of monochromatic light to the concentration of the colored substance in solution and the depth of the solution. The two approaches to the determination of concentration of the colored substance in solution involve either duplicating the color with that of a standard solution (colorimetry), or measurement of the absorption of light by the solution (spectrophotometry).

Although rapid visual color comparison techniques serve adequately for many routine problems, spectrophotometric methods have a number of advantages over these. The most important advantage is the flexibility of the wavelength of light used, since the degree of absorbance depends greatly on this wavelength. Thus, by proper choice of wavelength, maximum sensitivity and selectivity can be obtained. Also, the usable range is extended to the ultraviolet and infrared regions of the spectrum.

Another advantage is the higher precision obtainable by photoelectric spectrophotometry, which incidently is more rapid than colorimetric methods. There are many excellent books which should be consulted for greater detail.[22]

A promising development is the use of the technique of **flame** spectrophotometry for the estimation of the metal in the organic extract.[23, 24] This offers a number of advantages including that of greater sensitivity than can be achieved in aqueous solutions and minimization of interferences.

REFERENCES

1. W. E. Cohn, *Anal. Chem.,* **20,** 498 (1948).
2. W. M. Garrison and J. G. Hamilton, *Chem. Rev.,* **49,** 237 (1951); U.S. Atomic Energy Commission Report, UCRL-1067.
3. J. J. Katz and W. M. Manning, *Annual Reviews of Nuclear Science,* Vol. 1, Annual Reviews, Inc., Stanford, Calif., 1952, p. 245.
4. P. C. Stevenson and H. G. Hicks, *Annual Reviews of Nuclear Science,* Vol. 3, Annual Reviews, Inc., Stanford, Calif., 1953, p. 221.
5. L. E. Glendenin and E. P. Steinberg, *Annual Reviews of Nuclear Science,* Vol. 4, Annual Reviews, Inc., Stanford, Calif., 1954, p. 69.
6. H. L. Finston and J. Miskel, *Annual Reviews of Nuclear Science,* Vol. 5, Annual Reviews, Inc., Stanford, Calif., 1955, p. 269.
7. W. W. Meinke, U.S. Atomic Energy Commission Reports, AECD-2738 and AECD-2750.
8. J. Kleinberg, U.S. Atomic Energy Commission Reports, LA-1566 and LA-1721.
9. M. Lindner, U.S. Atomic Energy Commission Report, UCRL-4377.
10. F. R. Bruce, *Proceedings of the International Conference on the Peaceful Uses of Atomic Energy,* Vol. 7, United Nations, New York, 1956, p. 100.
11. J. M. Fletcher, *Proceedings of the International Conference on the Peaceful Uses of Atomic Energy,* Vol. 9, United Nations, New York, 1956, p. 459.
12. A. T. Gresky, *Proceedings of the International Conference on the Peaceful Uses of Atomic Energy,* Vol. 9, United Nations, New York, 1956, p. 509.
13. E. K. Hyde, *Proceedings of the International Conference on the Peaceful Uses of Atomic Energy,* Vol. 7, United Nations, New York, 1956, p. 281.
14. H. A. C. McKay, *Proceedings of the International Conference on the Peaceful Uses of Atomic Energy,* Vol. 7, United Nations, New York, 1956, p. 314.
15. J. W. Irvine, Jr., private communication.
16. D. C. Grahame and G. T. Seaborg, *J. Am. Chem. Soc.,* **60,** 2524 (1938).
17. W. O. Haas and E. L. Zebroski, U.S. Atomic Energy Commission Report, KAPL-P-243.
18. E. Bleuler and G. L. Goldsmith, *Experimental Nucleonics,* Reinhart Publishing Co., Inc., New York, 1952; G. Friedlander and J. W. Kennedy, *Nuclear and Radiochemistry,* John Wiley & Sons, Inc., New York, 1955; A. C. Wahl and N. A. Bonner, *Radioactivity Applied to Chemistry,* John Wiley & Sons, Inc., New York, 1951.
19. C. J. Borkowski, *Anal. Chem.,* **21,** 348 (1949).
20. R. E. Connally and M. B. Leboeuf, *Anal. Chem.,* **25,** 1095 (1953).
21. G. H. Morrison and J. F. Cosgrove, *Anal. Chem.,* **27,** 810 (1955).
22. E. B. Sandell, *Colorimetric Determination of Traces of Metals,* second edition, Interscience Publishers, Inc., New York, 1950; W. R. Brode, *Chemical Spectroscopy,* John Wiley & Sons, Inc., New York, 1943.
23. J. A. Dean, *Anal. Chem.,* **27,** 1224 (1955).
24. J. A. Dean and J. H. Lady, *Anal. Chem.,* **27,** 1533 (1955); **28,** 1887 (1956).

Part 3

Extraction Systems

In this section the various systems are treated in such a manner as to present an overall picture of the possible separations afforded and the extent of interferences encountered in particular systems. Two categories of extractable species, namely ion association complexes and chelates, have been used as the basis of the order in which the extraction systems are described. It might be noted that, for convenience, a few examples of coordination compounds such as germanium tetrachloride and mercuric bromide have been grouped with the ion association systems.

Solvent extraction of metals utilizing chelating agents offers striking contrast to the conditions employed in many ion association systems. In general, the distribution coefficient of the extraction reagent itself is rather large. Hence, a common practice is the use of a solution of the extraction agent in the organic extraction solvent. Second, since the formation constants of the extractable metal chelates are in general much higher than those of the inorganic complexes, the chelating reagent concentrations employed are orders of magnitude below those of reagents used in ion association extractions. An unfortunate contrast between chelating agents and inorganic extraction agents is the susceptibility of many of the former to decomposition (sensitivity to light, oxidation, etc.). It is important to purify solvents to be used in chelate extraction so that oxidizing and acid impurities are minimized.

As discussed in Chapter 6, the course of metal chelate extractions is highly dependent on the pH of the aqueous phase and the concentration of the reagent in the organic phase. Also, so long as there is sufficient reagent, it is largely independent of the concentration of the metal to be extracted. Much of the selectivity achieved in these extractions depends on adequate control of pH. In recent years, the use of masking agents has brought about greatly improved selectivity.

It might be well to consider the relative merits of ion association and chelate systems at this point. By and large, the advantages of chelate systems are the relatively greater ease of measurement of the extracted component, which often has a characteristic absorption spectra, and their applicability to more metals. On the other hand, the chelating agents are more expensive than those required in the ion association systems and sometimes are somewhat unstable. Ion association systems are, in the main, better adapted for extraction of large quantities of metals than chelate systems. Both types may be used for extraction of low levels of metal concentrations. Many exceptions to these remarks will be found, and the value of becoming familiar with characteristics of the individual systems described below cannot be overemphasized.

Chapter 11

Ion Association Systems

1. FLUORIDE SYSTEM

Only a few studies have been performed on the extraction of elements as fluoride complexes as shown in Table 11.1. This may be attributed in part to the difficulties involved in the manipulation of HF solutions, which require vessels constructed of polyethylene or other suitable materials. Elements that are extracted appreciably include Nb(V), Ta(V), Sn(II), Sn(IV), and Re(VII), while As(III), As(V), Mo(VI), Se(IV), Te(IV), W(VI), P(V), V(III), V(V), Sb(III), and Ge(IV) are partially extracted.

A study by Kitahara[1] of the extraction of various elements from HF solutions of varying concentrations to ethyl ether revealed that both Sn(II) and Sn(IV) are completely extracted, whereas As(III), Sb(III), Se(IV), and Mo(VI) are only partially extracted. No extraction was observed with Ni, Cr, Co, Mn, K, Ti, Zr, Ga, Ag, U, Bi, Te, Cd, or Os. A 4:1 volume ratio of organic to aqueous phases was employed. More recently, Bock[2] made an intensive study of the same system using equal volumes of phases and found that only Nb(V), Ta(V), and Re(VII) were extracted greater than 50%; Sn(II), Sn(IV), As(III), As(V), Te(IV), Ge(IV), P(V), Se(IV), V(III), V(V), Mo(VI), and Sb(III) were partially extracted. Extractions were performed on aqueous phases containing 0.1 moles per liter of metal and over the concentration range of 1–20 M HF. In all cases extraction increased with increasing HF concentration. Hydrofluoric acid is extracted approximately 38% to ethyl ether from aqueous solutions containing 10–20 M HF.

125

Table 11.1.   Fluoride Extractions

Element	Oxidation State	Solvent System (before mixing) Aqueous Phase	Organic Phase	Per Cent Extraction	Reference
Aluminum	Al(III)	20 M HF	Ethyl ether	0.2	2
Antimony	Sb(III)	3.5 M HF	Ethyl ether [a]	0.4	1
	Sb(III)	20 M HF	Ethyl ether	6.3	2
	Sb(V)	20 M HF	Ethyl ether	0.1	2
Arsenic	As(III)	4.6 M HF	Ethyl ether [a]	62	1
	As(III)	20 M HF	Ethyl ether	37.7	2
	As(V)	20 M HF	Ethyl ether	13.6	2
Beryllium	Be(II)	20 M HF	Ethyl ether	4.0	2
Cadmium	Cd(II)	20 M HF	Ethyl ether	1.4	2
Chromium	Cr(III)	20 M HF	Ethyl ether	<0.1	2
Cobalt	Co(II)	20 M HF	Ethyl ether	1.7	2
Copper	Cu(II)	20 M HF	Ethyl ether	1.3	2
Gallium	Ga(III)	20 M HF	Ethyl ether	<0.05	2
Germanium	Ge(IV)	20 M HF	Ethyl ether	6.7	2
Indium	In(III)	20 M HF	Ethyl ether	<0.05	2
Iron	Fe(II)	20 M HF	Ethyl ether	<0.1	2
	Fe(III)	20 M HF	Ethyl ether	<0.1	2
Manganese	Mn(II)	20 M HF	Ethyl ether	1.3	2
Mercury	Hg(II)	20 M HF	Ethyl ether	2.7	2
Molybdenum	Mo(VI)	10 M HF, 6 M H$_2$SO$_4$, 2.2 M NH$_4$F	Methyl isobutyl ketone [b]	9.7	5
	Mo(VI)	3.5 M HF	Ethyl ether [a]	9.1	1
	Mo(VI)	20 M HF	Ethyl ether	9.3	2
Nickel	Ni(II)	20 M HF	Ethyl ether	0.7	2
Niobium	Nb(V)	9 M HF, 6 M H$_2$SO$_4$	Diisopropyl ketone [b]	90	3
	Nb(V)	6 M HF, 6 M H$_2$SO$_4$	Diisobutylcarbinol [b]	98	4
	Nb(V)	10 M HF, 6 M H$_2$SO$_4$, 2.2 M NH$_4$F	Methyl isobutyl ketone [b]	96	5
	Nb(V)	20 M HF	Ethyl ether	65.8	2
Phosphorus	P(V)	20 M HF	Ethyl ether	14.8	2
Protactinium	Pa(V)	8 M HCl, 0.6 M HF, sat. AlCl$_3$	Diisopropyl ketone	~100	6
Rhenium	Re(VII)	20 M HF	Ethyl ether	61.8	2
Selenium	Se(IV)	4.6 M HF	Ethyl ether [a]	3.1	1
	Se(IV)	20 M HF	Ethyl ether	12.9	2
Silicon	Si(IV)	20 M HF	Ethyl ether	<0.1	2
Silver	Ag(I)	20 M HF	Ethyl ether	0.05	2
Tantalum	Ta(V)	10 M HF, 6 M H$_2$SO$_4$, 2.2 M NH$_4$F	Methyl isobutyl ketone [b]	99.6	5
	Ta(V)	0.4 M HF, 3.7 M HCl	Diisopropyl ketone [b]	81 ($\beta_{Ta/Nb}$ = 91)	3
	Ta(V)	0.4 M HF, 3.9 M HNO$_3$	Diisopropyl ketone [b]	79 ($\beta_{Ta/Nb}$ = 880)	3
	Ta(V)	0.4 M HF, 4.5 M H$_2$SO$_4$	Diisopropyl ketone [b]	95 ($\beta_{Ta/Nb}$ = 160)	3
	Ta(V)	0.4 M HF, 4.6 M HClO$_4$	Diisopropyl ketone [b]	90 ($\beta_{Ta/Nb}$ = 290)	3
	Ta(V)	20 M HF	Ethyl ether	79.3	2
Tellurium	Te(IV)	20 M HF	Ethyl ether	23	2
Thallium	Tl(I)	20 M HF	Ethyl ether	<0.05	2
Tin	Sn(II)	4.6 M HF	Ethyl ether [a]	100	1
	Sn(II)	20 M HF	Ethyl ether	4.9	2
	Sn(IV)	1.2–4.6 M HF	Ethyl ether [a]	100	1
	Sn(IV)	20 M HF	Ethyl ether	5.2	2
Titanium	Ti(IV)	20 M HF	Ethyl ether	<0.05	2
Tungsten	W(VI)	10 M HF, 6 M H$_2$SO$_4$, 2.2 M NH$_4$F	Methyl isobutyl ketone [b]	~26	5
	W(VI)	20 M HF	Ethyl ether	0.5	2
Uranium	U(VI)	20 M HF	Ethyl ether	1.1	2
Vanadium	V(III)	20 M HF	Ethyl ether	12	2
	V(V)	20 M HF	Ethyl ether	8.5	2
Zinc	Zn(II)	20 M HF	Ethyl ether	0.9	2
Zirconium	Zr(IV)	20 M HF	Ethyl ether	2.9	2

[a] 4:1 volume ratio of organic to aqueous phase.
[b] Organic phase pre-equilibrated with pure aqueous phase.

The differences in the extraction values for Sn reported in these two studies may be due to the formation of different species depending on the method of preparation of the fluorides of this metal for use in the distribution studies.

It is interesting to note that fewer elements are extracted to any appreciable extent as fluorides in the acid–ethyl ether system than in the comparable chloride, bromide, thiocyanate, and nitrate systems. Tantalum and Nb can be separated from mineral acid–hydrofluoric acid aqueous solutions by preferential extraction of the Ta into diisopropyl ketone.[3]   Using an aqueous phase $6\,M$ in HCl and $0.4\,M$ in HF, elemental halogens, Fe(III), Ga(III), Sb(V), As(III), Se(VI), and Te(VI), extract to a large extent.   Antimony(III) extracts slightly and As(V) and Te(IV) somewhat better, but Se(IV) does not extract appreciably.   Silicon, Sn(IV), Ti(IV), Mn(II), Zr(IV), and Hf(IV) do not extract.   Using $6\,M$ H_2SO_4 and $0.4\,M$ HF, only elemental halogens, Se(IV), and Te(VI) extract with Ta.   Niobium can also be extracted from a solution $6\,M$ in H_2SO_4 and $9\,M$ in HF. Niobium can be separated from Pa by extracting from a solution $6\,M$ in H_2SO_4 and $6\,M$ in HF with diisobutylcarbinol.[4]

Both Ta and Nb are completely extracted from aqueous solutions $10\,M$ in HF, $6\,M$ in H_2SO_4, and $2.2\,M$ in NH_4F, using methyl isobutyl ketone as solvent.[5]   Titanium, U, Zr, Fe, Al, Mn, Sn, and Ga are not extracted but Mo and W are partially extracted.   Thorium and Ce are precipitated from aqueous solution as insoluble fluorides.

REFERENCES: Fluoride System

1. S. Kitahara, *Bull. Inst. Phys. Chem. Research (Tokyo)*, **25**, 165 (1949).
2. R. Bock and M. Herrmann, *Z. anorg. u. allgem. Chemie*, **284**, 288 (1956).
3. P. C. Stevenson and H. G. Hicks, *Anal. Chem.*, **25**, 1517 (1953).
4. F. L. Moore, *Anal. Chem.*, **27**, 70 (1955).
5. G. W. C. Milner, G. A. Barnett, and A. A. Smales, *Analyst*, **80**, 380 (1955).
6. J. Golden and A. G. Maddock, *J. Inorg. Nuclear Chem.*, **2**, 46 (1956).

2. CHLORIDE SYSTEM

The extraction of iron from HCl solutions to ethyl ether has been in the past the most studied of the extraction systems involving inorganic substances.   As early as 1892 Rothe[1] recognized the possibilities of this process, and the work of Speller,[2] Langmuir,[3] and Kern[4] led to the first procedures for the separation of this metal from many others.

Other investigators have revealed the extractability of many other chlorides under various conditions of acidity, salt concentration, solvent, and oxidation state, as shown in Table 11.2, and a fair number of these separations lend themselves to analytical application.

Elements that extract well as chloride complexes include Sb(V), As(III), Ga(III), Ge(IV), Au(III), Fe(III), Hg(II), Mo(VI), Nb(V), Pt(II), Po(II), Pa(V), Tl(III), and Sc(III). Other elements that are partially extracted include Sb(III), As(V), Co(II), In(III), Te(IV), Sn(II), and Sn(IV).

Many oxygenated solvents such as ethyl ether, isopropyl ether, β,β'-dichloroethyl ether, diisopropyl ketone, methyl amyl ketone, *n*-butyl alcohol, diisopropylcarbinol, ethyl acetate, amyl acetate, *n*-butyl acetate, and tributyl phosphate have been effectively employed.

The effect of variation of acid concentration of the aqueous phase on the extraction of a number of elements is shown in Fig. 11.1. Oxidation also produces great changes, decreasing the extractability of arsenic and tin on the one hand, and increasing that of iron, antimony, and thallium on the other.

The following illustrative separations were made possible by variation of the factors mentioned earlier. Edwards and Voigt [5] found that the distribution ratio of Sb(V) between isopropyl ether and 6.5 to 8.5 *M* HCl was greater than 200, whereas that of Sb(III) was only 0.016. Thallium(III) can be extracted from HCl solutions so dilute that very little Fe or Ga accompanies it and the principal contaminant

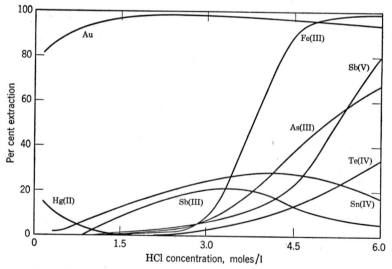

Figure 11.1. Effect of hydrochloric acid concentration on the extractability of chlorides by ethyl ether.[35]

Table 11.2   Chloride Extractions

Element	Oxidation State	Solvent System (before mixing) Aqueous Phase	Solvent System (before mixing) Organic Phase	Per Cent Extraction	Reference
Antimony	Sb(V)	6 M HCl	Ethyl ether	81	19
	Sb(V)	6.5–8.5 M HCl	Isopropyl ether	99.5	5
	Sb(V)	1–2 M HCl, 0.0032 M oxalic acid, 0.0021 M citric acid	Ethyl acetate	83	20
	Sb(III)	6 M HCl	Ethyl ether	6	19
	Sb(III)	6.5–8.5 M HCl	Isopropyl ether	1.6	5
Arsenic	As(V)	6 M HCl	Ethyl ether	2–4	7
	As(III)	6 M HCl	Ethyl ether	68	19
	As(III)	11 M HCl	Benzene	94	21
Cobalt	Co(II)	4.5 M HCl	2-Octanol	9.1($\beta_{Co/Ni} = 70$)	13
	Co(II)	0.85 M CaCl$_2$	2-Octanol	9.1($\beta_{Co/Ni} = 10$)	13
Gallium	Ga(III)	6 M HCl	Ethyl ether	97	7
	Ga(III)	7 M HCl	Isopropyl ether	>99.9	8
	Ga(III)	3 M HCl	Tributyl phosphate	99.9	22
Germanium	Ge(IV)	6 M HCl	Ethyl ether	40–60	7
	Ge(IV)	10.5 M HCl	Carbon tetrachloride	99.5	23
	Ge(IV)	11 M HCl	Benzene	99.6	21
Gold	Au(III)	10% HCl	Ethyl acetate	100	9
	Au(III)	6 M HCl	Ethyl ether	95	19
	Au(III)	pH 2–6 in HCl, sat. KCl	n-Butyl alcohol	Spot test	24
Indium	In(III)	8 M HCl	Ethyl ether [a]	3.02	25
Iron	Fe(III)	6 M HCl	Ethyl ether	99	19
	Fe(III)	7.75–8.0 M HCl	Isopropyl ether	99.9	26
	Fe(III)	9 M HCl	β,β'-Dichloroethyl ether	99	27
	Fe(III)	8 M HCl	Methyl amyl ketone	100	28
Lithium	Li(I)	Chloride in small volume of water	Amyl alcohol	0.66 g/10 ml	16
			2-Ethylhexanol	3 g/100 ml	17
Mercury	Hg(II)	0.125 M HCl	Ethyl acetate	80	29
	Hg(II)	0.1 M HCl	n-Butyl acetate + trichloro-acetic acid (3 M)	82–89	29
	Hg(II)	6 M HCl	Ethyl ether	0.2	19
Molybdenum	Mo(VI)	6 M HCl	Ethyl ether	80–90	7
	Mo(VI)	7.75 M HCl	Isopropyl ether	21	26
	Mo(VI)	5 M HCl	Amyl acetate	99	30
Nickel	Ni(II)	4.5 M HCl	2-Octanol	0.14($\beta_{Co/Ni} = 70$)	13
	Ni(II)	0.85 M CaCl$_2$	2-Octanol	0.99($\beta_{Co/Ni} = 10$)	13
Niobium	Nb(V)	11 M HCl	Diisopropyl ketone [b]	90	31
Platinum	Pt(II)	3 M HCl, 1 ml of 10% SnCl$_2$	Ethyl ether	>95	11
Polonium	Po(II)	6 M HCl	20% tributyl phosphate	80–90	11
Protactinium	Pa(V)	6 M HCl, 8 M MgCl$_2$	β,β'-Dichloroethyl ether	90	11, 12
	Pa(V)	6 M HCl	Diisopropylcarbinol [b]	99.9	32
	Pa(V)	6 M HCl	Diisopropyl ketone	99	36
Scandium	Sc(III)	8 M HCl	Tributyl phosphate	98	33
Tellurium	Te(IV)	6 M HCl	Ethyl ether	34	19
Thallium	Tl(III)	6 M HCl	Ethyl ether	90–95	34
Tin	Sn(IV)	6 M HCl	Ethyl ether	17	19
	Sn(II)	6 M HCl	Ethyl ether	15–30	7
Vanadium	V(V)	7.75 M HCl	Isopropyl ether	22	26

[a] 30:20 volume of organic to aqueous phase.
[b] Organic phase pre-equilibrated with pure aqueous phase.

is Hg(II).[6] Gallium can be separated from many impurities by extraction with ethyl ether [7] or isopropyl ether.[8]

The extraction of gold from HCl solutions increases up to an acid concentration of about 10%. Among the organic solvents examined by Lenher,[9] ethyl acetate and other aliphatic esters were the most effective, but as in other systems [10] the introduction of chlorine atoms into the oxygenated solvent impaired extraction. The same solvent can be used for the extraction of Pt from HCl solutions containing $SnCl_2$.[11] As much as 90% Pa can be selectively extracted by β,β'-dichloroethyl ether from 6 M HCl made 8 M with respect to $MgCl_2$,[11, 12] whereas less than 2% of U, Mn, Zr, or Ti are extracted. Polonium can be separated from Pb and Bi by extraction from 6 M HCl with 20% tributyl phosphate in dibutyl ether.[11] Cobalt may be separated from Ni in the presence of high concentrations of HCl or $CaCl_2$ using 2-octanol as solvent.[13]

The solubility of LiCl in a variety of organic solvents forms the basis of a simple separation from other alkali metal chlorides. Sodium and potassium chlorides are precipitated from a small volume of aqueous solution by the addition of alcohol and ether.[14] Acetone has been used successfully,[15] as well as amyl alcohol,[16] 2-ethylhexanol,[17] and dioxane.

REFERENCES: Chloride System

1. J. W. Rothe, *Chem. News,* **66,** 182 (1892).
2. F. N. Speller, *Chem. News,* **83,** 124 (1901).
3. A. C. Langmuir, *J. Am. Chem. Soc.,* **22,** 102 (1900).
4. E. F. Kern, *J. Am. Chem. Soc.,* **23,** 685 (1901).
5. F. C. Edwards and A. F. Voigt, *Anal. Chem.,* **21,** 1204 (1949).
6. H. M. Irving, *Quart. Rev. Chem. Soc., London,* Vol. V, No. 2, 200 (1951).
7. E. H. Swift, *J. Am. Chem. Soc.,* **46,** 2378 (1924).
8. N. H. Nachtrieb and R. E. Fryxell, *J. Am. Chem. Soc.,* **71,** 4035 (1949).
9. V. Lenher and C. H. Kao, *J. Phys. Chem.,* **30,** 126 (1926).
10. E. Glueckauf and H. A. C. McKay, *Nature,* **165,** 594 (1950).
11. W. W. Meinke, U.S. Atomic Energy Commission Report, AECD-2738.
12. A. G. Maddock and G. L. Miles, *J. Chem. Soc.,* **1949,** S 248, 253.
13. L. Garwin and A. M. Hixson, *Ind. Eng. Chem.,* **41,** 2303 (1949).
14. S. Palkin, *J. Am. Chem. Soc.,* **38,** 2326 (1916); R. C. Wells and R. E. Stevens, *Ind. Eng. Chem., Anal. Ed.,* **6,** 440 (1934).
15. M. H. Brown and J. H. Reedy, *Ind. Eng. Chem., Anal. Ed.,* **2,** 304 (1930).
16. F. A. Gooch, *Chem. News,* **55,** 18 (1887).
17. E. R. Caley and H. D. Axilrod, *Ind. Eng. Chem., Anal. Ed.,* **14,** 242 (1942).
18. A. Sinka, *Z. anal. Chem.,* **80,** 430 (1930).
19. F. Mylius and C. Hüttner, *Ber. deut. chem. Ges.,* **44,** 1315 (1911).
20. C. E. White and H. J. Rose, *Anal. Chem.,* **25,** 351 (1953).
21. M. Green and J. A. Kafalas, *J. Chem. Phys.,* **22,** 760 (1954).

22. W. Bennet and J. W. Irvine, *Mass. Inst. Technol. Lab. of Nuclear Sci., Prog. Rept.*, Feb. 1953.
23. W. Fischer, W. Hurre, W. Freese, and K. G. Hackstein, *Angew. Chem.*, **66**, 165 (1954).
24. P. W. West and T. C. McCoy, *Anal. Chem.*, **27**, 1820 (1955).
25. H. M. Irving and F. J. C. Rossotti, *Analyst*, **77**, 801 (1952).
26. R. Dodson, G. Forney, and E. Swift, *J. Am. Chem. Soc.*, **58**, 2573 (1936).
27. J. Axelrod and E. Swift, *J. Am. Chem. Soc.*, **62**, 33 (1940).
28. V. I. Kuznetsov, *J. Gen. Chem. (U.S.S.R.)*, **17**, 175 (1947).
29. P. W. West and M. A. Duff, private communication.
30. R. P. Taylor, "Study of Solvent Extraction of Molybdenum," Thesis, Rutgers University, 1950.
31. H. G. Hicks and R. S. Gilbert, U.S. Atomic Energy Commission Report, MTA-33.
32. F. L. Moore, U.S. Atomic Energy Commission Report, ORNL-1675.
33. D. F. Peppard, J. P. Faris, P. R. Gray, and G. W. Mason, *J. Phys. Chem.*, **57**, 294 (1953).
34. A. A. Noyes, W. C. Bray, and E. B. Spear, *J. Am. Chem. Soc.*, **30**, 515, 559 (1908).
35. E. B. Sandell, *Colorimetric Determination of Traces of Metals*, second edition, Interscience Publishers, Inc., New York, 1950, p. 34.
36. J. Golden and A. G. Maddock, *J. Inorg. Nuclear Chem.*, **2**, 46 (1956).

3. BROMIDE SYSTEM

Extraction from aqueous HBr solutions to ethyl ether has been investigated by Wada and Ishii[1,2] for the purpose of developing methods of separations for a variety of elements. More recently Bock, Kusche, and Bock[3] made an intensive study of the distribution of many metal bromides in the same system at various HBr concentrations with results as shown in Table 11.3. It can be seen that Au(III), Ga(III), In(III), Tl(III), Sb(V), Sn(II), Sn(IV), and Fe(III) extract well into ethyl ether. Arsenic(III), Sb(III), Se(IV), and Mo(VI) extract to a lesser extent, and Cu(II) and Zn(II) extract only slightly. All other elements, with the exception of Tl(I), Ir(IV), Re(VII), and Cu(I), extract to a negligible extent.

A number of studies on the separation of specific elements by bromide extraction have been performed by various investigators. Among these are the extraction of Tl(I) and Ga(III) bromides with ethyl ether,[4] and the extraction of $HgBr_2$ into benzene.[5] It has also been found that Re(VII) extracts to the extent of several per cent to ethyl ether, whereas only traces of Re(IV) are extracted.[6] Platinum is extracted from bromide solutions with ethyl ether if $SnCl_2$ is added.[7] Miller[8] investigated the distribution of Tl(III) and developed an analytical method. The extraction of In was applied to analytical

Table 11.3.   Extractability of Metal Bromides into Ethyl Ether [3]

Percentage of element extracted from solutions having an initial metal concentration of 0.1 moles/l; extraction at room temperature using equal volumes of phases.

Element	\multicolumn{8}{c}{Molarity of Hydrobromic Acid}

Element	0	0.1	1	2	3	4	5	6
Cu(II)			0.5		1.5		4.2	6.2
Au(III)			99.5		>99.9			
Zn(II)			1.3	5.0		4.9		3.6
Hg(II)	94.0	58.3	3.4		2.3			1.5
Ga(III)				0.9	1.5	54.8	96.7	95
In(III)			15	85.2	98.6	99.9	99.4	93.5
Tl(III)			>99.9	>99.9		>99.9		99.0
Sn(II)			32	64	79	84	78	36
Sn(IV)			11.5	45.2	73.6	85.4	77.4	45.1
As(III)			3.0		6.7	22.8	63.1	72.9
Sb(III)				37.9	22.3	14.9	9.0	6.1
Sb(V)							95.4	79.6
Se(IV)			0.3			3.5	18.3	31
Mo(VI)				0.16		28	25.0	54.1
Fe(III)			>0.1	1.4	55.0	97.1	97.1	94.6
Cd(II)			0.4					0.9
V(IV)			~0.001					~0.001
Te(IV)			0.7					2.2
Co(II)			0.01					0.08
Ni(II)			>0.03					>0.03

procedures by Vanossi[9] and Hudgens and Nelson.[10]   Kosta and Hoste[11] suggested the use of isopropyl ether for the separation of In from Zn.

McBryde and Yoe[12] found that Au(III) is completely extracted into isopropyl ether from 2.5 to 3 M HBr solution.   Under these conditions small amounts of Fe and Os extract.   The other platinum metals, Pd, Pt, Rh, Ir, and Ru, do not extract.

The extractability of the bromides of Cu(I), Cu(II), Zn, Ni, Co(II), Fe(II), Fe(III), Al, Mn(II), Sn(II), and Sn(IV), using methyl ethyl ketone and methyl isobutyl ketone as solvents, has been studied using aqueous solutions containing HBr and/or NH_4Br.[13]   The latter solvent is more useful than the former by virtue of its greater scope, whereby higher concentrations of acid may be used, resulting in more efficient extractions.   In comparison with the results for ethyl ether,[3] the metals extracted with methyl isobutyl ketone show the same degrees of difference of behavior between themselves but seem to be more efficiently extracted by the ketone.   Separation of Fe(III) from Mn(II), Al, Co(II), and Ni(II) can be achieved under suitable conditions.

REFERENCES: Bromide System

1. I. Wada and R. Ishii, *Bull. Inst. Phys. Chem. Research* (*Tokyo*), **13,** 264 (1934).

2. I. Wada and R. Ishii, *Sci. Papers Inst. Phys. Chem. Research* (*Tokyo*), **34**, 787 (1938).

3. R. Bock, H. Kusche, and E. Bock, *Z. anal. Chem.*, **138**, 167 (1953)

4. H. M. Irving and F. J. C. Rossotti, *Analyst*, **77**, 801 (1952).

5. M. S. Sherrill, *Z. physik. Chem.*, **43**, 705 (1903).

6. H. Bode, *Dissertation Hannover*, 1949.

7. L. Wöhler and A. Spengel, *Z. Chem. u. Ind. Kolloide*, **7**, 243 (1910).

8. C. C. Miller, *J. Chem. Soc.*, **1941**, 72.

9. R. Vanossi, *Anales asoc. quím. argentina*, **38**, 363 (1950).

10. J. E. Hudgens and L. C. Nelson, *Anal. Chem.*, **24**, 1472 (1952).

11. L. Kosta and J. Hoste, *Mikrochim. Acta*, **416**, 790 (1956).

12. W. A. E. McBryde and J. H. Yoe, *Anal. Chem.*, **20**, 1094 (1948).

13. A. R. Denaro and V. J. Occleshaw, *Anal. Chim. Acta*, **13**, 239 (1955).

4. IODIDE SYSTEM

Among the elements that extract well as iodide complexes are Sb(III), Cd, Au(III), In(III), Pb(II), Hg(II), Sn(II), Tl(III), and small amounts of Tl(I). Elements that are partially extracted include As(III), Bi, Cu, Mo(VI), Te(IV), and Zn. See Table 11.4. Solvents that have been used thus far include ethyl ether, methyl isobutyl ketone, and methyl isopropyl ketone. Many new and useful separations should result through the use of other solvents which have been used extensively in other halide systems.

An examination of the extractability of various elements from aqueous 6.9 M HI solutions with a fourfold volume ratio of ethyl ether [1] reveals the complete extraction of Sb(III), Hg(II), Cd, Au, and Sn(II). Extraction of Bi is 34.2% complete; Zn, 10.6%; Mo(VI), 6.5%; Te(IV), 5.5%; and In, 7.8%. The following elements are found not to extract at all under these conditions: K, Cs, Ba, Ca, Fe(II), Ni, Cr, Co, Mn, Ti, Zr, Pb, Th, Al, Ga, Be, U, V, Pt, Pd, Ir, Os, and Ru.

The use of HI solutions presents a problem, for the acid decomposes readily on keeping. The free acid, however, can be replaced by H_2SO_4 to which the appropriate amount of KI has been added. [2] The concentration of iodide, and, more important, that of the acid, can be varied over quite wide limits without reducing the efficiency of extraction.

When 1.5 M KI in 1.5 N H_2SO_4 with ethyl ether as solvent is used, the extraction percentages of various elements are as follows: Be and Fe(II), 0%; Al, 0.1%; Mo(VI), W(VI), 1.0%; Bi and Cu, 10%; Zn and Hg, about 33%; Sb, 50%; Cd, In, and Sn(II), 100%.

West and Carlton [3] have studied the qualitative aspects of iodide extraction and have found that Bi, Hg, Fe, Pb, Cu, Pd, Cd, Rh, Au, and Ru are at least partially extracted into one or more of the following solvents: butyraldehyde, n-amyl alcohol, methyl n-amyl ketone, methyl isobutyl ketone, methyl n-propyl ketone, methyl isopropyl ketone, and ethyl acetate. Methyl isopropyl ketone was found to be the most desirable solvent. Lead is completely extracted from iodide solutions which contain 5% HCl. Under these conditions Zn, Cd, Cu, As(III), Sb(III), Sn(IV), Rh, Ru, and Pt are partially extracted into methyl isopropyl ketone. Rhodium and Ru are extracted quite well in the presence of Pb, although otherwise their extraction is slight.

Small amounts of Sb are completely extracted from iodide solutions by benzene,[4] and Bi can be extracted by methyl isobutyl or methyl isopropyl ketones.[5]

An interesting study of the extraction of iodides indicates the possibility of separating the alkali metals. Bock and Hoppe [6] found that the polyiodides of the alkali halides extract well into nitromethane. The distribution ratios increase in the order Li < Na < K < Rb < Cs and are dependent on the concentration of free iodine added to the system.

Table 11.4. Iodide Extractions

Element	Oxidation State	Solvent System (before mixing)		Per Cent Extraction	Reference
		Aqueous Phase	Organic Phase		
Antimony	Sb(III)	6.9 M HI	Ethyl ether [a]	100	1
	Sb(III)	1.5 M KI, 1.5 N H$_2$SO$_4$	Ethyl ether	<50	2
	Sb(III)	1 drop 10% KI, 5 drops 1:3 H$_2$SO$_4$	Benzene	Spot test	4
Arsenic	As(III)	6.9 M HI	Ethyl ether [a]	62	1
Bismuth	Bi(III)	6.9 M HI	Ethyl ether [a]	34.2	1
	Bi(III)	1.5 M KI, 1.5 N H$_2$SO$_4$	Ethyl ether	<10	2
	Bi(III)	5 drops KI slightly acid	Methyl isobutyl ketone	Spot test	5
Cadmium	Cd(II)	6.9 M HI	Ethyl ether [a]	100	1
	Cd(II)	1.5 M KI, 1.5 N H$_2$SO$_4$	Ethyl ether	100	2
Copper	Cu(II)	1.5 M KI, 1.5 N H$_2$SO$_4$	Ethyl ether	<10	2
Gold	Au(III)	6.9 M HI	Ethyl ether [a]	100	1
Indium	In(III)	1.5 M KI, 1.5 N H$_2$SO$_4$	Ethyl ether	100	2
	In(III)	6.9 M HI	Ethyl ether [a]	7.8	1
Lead	Pb(II)	Excess of KI in 5% HCl	Methyl isopropyl ketone	97	3
Mercury	Hg(II)	6.9 M HI	Ethyl ether [a]	100	1
	Hg(II)	1.5 M KI, 1.5 N H$_2$SO$_4$	Ethyl ether	33	2
Molybdenum	Mo(VI)	6.9 M HI	Ethyl ether [a]	6.5	1
Tellurium	Te(IV)	6.9 M HI	Ethyl ether [a]	5.5	1
Thallium	Tl(I) [b]	0.51 M HI	Ethyl ether	99.9	2
	Tl(III)	0.51 M HI	Ethyl ether	100	2
Tin	Sn(II)	6.9 M HI	Ethyl ether [a]	100	1
	Sn(II)	1.5 M KI, 1.5 N H$_2$SO$_4$	Ethyl ether	100	2
Zinc	Zn(II)	6.9 M HI	Ethyl ether [a]	10.6	1
	Zn(II)	1.5 M HI, 1.5 N H$_2$SO$_4$	Ethyl ether	33	2

[a] 4:1 volume ratio of organic to aqueous phase.
[b] Small amounts of Tl.

REFERENCES: Iodide System

1. S. Kitahara, *Bull. Inst. Phys. Chem. Research (Tokyo)*, **24**, 454 (1948).
2. H. M. Irving and F. J. C. Rossotti, *Analyst*, **77**, 801 (1952).
3. P. W. West and J. K. Carlton, *Anal. Chim. Acta*, **6**, 406 (1952).
4. P. W. West and W. C. Hamilton, *Anal. Chem.*, **24**, 1025 (1952).
5. P. W. West, P. Senise, and J. K. Carlton, *Anal. Chim. Acta*, **6**, 488 (1952).
6. R. Bock and T. Hoppe, *XV International Congress of Pure and Applied Chemistry, Lisbon, Sept. 1956* (in press).

5. THIOCYANATE SYSTEM

The use of alkali thiocyanates as complexing reagents for the colorimetric estimation of a number of metals has been known for some time. Thus, the red color of $FeSCN^{2+}$ has long been employed for the colorimetric estimation of $Fe(III)$ and, in the presence of excess of thiocyanate, iron can be extracted as a stable red complex into oxygen-containing solvents. Extractable yellow complexes for use in colorimetry are similarly formed by $U(VI)$, Bi, Nb, and Re; $Co(II)$ forms a blue complex and $Ru(III)$ forms a pink complex. In the presence of reducing agents and thiocyanate, W and Mo are also solvent-extractable, possibly as $(WO)SCN$ (purple) and $Mo(SCN)_5$ (amber to red). Cobalt, Ni, and Cu in the presence of pyridine (py) give water-insoluble complexes which dissolve in chloroform to give pink, blue, and green solutions of which the last, containing $Cu(py)_2(SCN)_2$, has been used in colorimetry.[1] Similar complexes are formed by Zn, Cd, and many other metals which can serve as the basis for their solvent extraction.[2]

More recently, advantage has been taken of the use of thiocyanate complexing as a method of chemical separation. Several of the rare earth elements have been separated, based on the slightly different solubilities of their thiocyanates in butanol.[3] Conversely, a separation of thorium from the rare earths is attained by extracting aqueous solutions of these substances containing NH_4SCN with 1-pentanol.[4] One of the most effective separations using the thiocyanate system is the extraction of Sc with ethyl ether using NH_4SCN.[5] Another interesting application is the separation of Hf from Zr, utilizing differences in extractability by ether [6,7] or by hexone [8] of the thiocyanate complexes of these metals.

An intensive study of the distribution of many metal thiocyanates to ethyl ether at various NH_4SCN concentrations has been made by Bock,[9] and the results are shown in Table 11.5. It can be seen that Be, Zn, Co, Sc, Ga, In, Ti(III), Fe(III), Sn(IV), and Mo(V) ex-

Table 11.5.   Extractability of Metal Thiocyanates into Ethyl Ether [9]

Percentage of element extracted from solutions having an initial metal concentration of 0.1 M and 0.5 M HCl; extraction at room temperature using equal volumes of phases.

Molarity of Ammonium Thiocyanate

Element	0.5	1	2	3	4	5	6	7
Be(II)		3.8	24.3	49.7		84.1		92.2
Zn(II)		96.0		97.4		94.8		92.8
Co(II)		3.6	37.7	58.2		74.9		75.2
Al(III)				1.1		9.0	19.4	
Sc(III)		12.7	55.4	79.8	84.6			89.0
Ga(III)	18.3	65.4		90.5				99.3
In(III)	26.0	51.5	75.1	75.3		68.3		47.6
Ti(III)	14.7	58.8	80.5	84.0		79.8		76.3
Ti(IV)								13.0
Fe(III)		88.9		83.7		75.5		53.3
Sn(IV)		99.3		99.9		>99.9		>99.9
V(IV)	10.7	15.0	13.1	8.7				2.2
Mo(V)		99.3	97.2					97.3
U(VI)		45.1	41.4	29.4		13.8		6.7
Cu(I)		2.9				0.4		
Ge(IV)		<0.3						<0.5
As(III)		0.4 [a]						0.4 [a]
As(V)		0.1					0.03	
Sb(III)		Hydrolysis		Hydrolysis		Hydrolysis		2.2
Bi(III)		0.3						0.1
Cd(II)		0.1 [b]						0.2 [c]
Cr(III)		0.06 [b]						3.4 [b]
Pd(II)		1.7						<0.1
Ni(II)		0.01 [d]						0.003 [d]
Hg(II)		0.15 [d]						0.15 [d]
Li(I)								0.04 [d]

[a] 0.8 M HCl used.
[b] 10:1 volume ratio of ether to water used.
[c] 6:1 volume ratio of ether to water used.
[d] Neutral aqueous solution extracted with a 10:1 volume ratio of ether to water.

tract well into ethyl ether. Aluminum, V(IV), and U(VI) extract to a lesser extent, and Li, Cu, Cd, Hg(II), Ge, As(III), As(V), Sb(III), Bi, Cr, Ni, and Pd extract very slightly. Although Be, Zn, Ga, Fe(III), Sc, U, and V(IV) can be extracted from neutral solutions at their particular optimum thiocyanate concentrations, best results are obtained for most metals at an HCl concentration of 0.5 M in the aqueous phase. At this acidity the extraction of Co, Be, Sc, and Ga greatly increases with higher concentrations of NH_4SCN, and the extraction of Al increases moderately. The extraction of Zn and Fe, on the other hand, is good at low thiocyanate concentrations and drops off slightly at higher concentrations, whereas Sn(IV) and Mo(V) extract well over a wide range of thiocyanate concentration. The extractions of Ti(III) and In reach a maximum at approximately 3 M NH_4SCN, and U(VI) and V(IV) extractions reach a maximum at 1–1.5 M.

The extraction of thiocyanic acid (HSCN) formed from the NH_4SCN and HCl added to the aqueous phase increases with increasing thiocyanate concentration and reaches a value of 98.3% at 7 M NH_4SCN and 0.5 M HCl.

Lowering the temperature of extraction has been shown to increase the distribution of Fe, Cr, Al, and Ti, and it is possible that the same effect occurs with other metals.

A number of solvents may be used effectively in the thiocyanate system, including ethyl ether, amyl alcohol, methyl isobutyl ketone, and butyl acetate. The presence of certain anions must be avoided in performing metal thiocyanate extractions, owing to the formation of complexes and precipitates which do not extract. In the extraction of Fe and Zr, for example, both chloride and nitrate are permissible; however, sulfate and phosphate seriously interfere.

By the proper choice of acid concentration, thiocyanate concentration, organic solvent, valence state of the metal, etc., it is possible to effect various separations among these elements.

The extraction of metal thiocyanate complexes with tributyl phosphate as a solvent can be used for the removal of Fe in the analysis of steel.[10,11] The advantages of using this solvent include non-volatility, non-flammability, and rapid extraction. Also, butyl phosphate is more effective than ether in removing Fe.

REFERENCES: Thiocyanate System

1. T. Moeller and R. E. Zogg, *Anal. Chem.*, **22**, 612 (1950).
2. J. A. Hunter and C. C. Miller, *Analyst*, **81**, 79 (1956).
3. D. B. Appleton and P. W. Selwood, *J. Am. Chem. Soc.*, **63**, 2029 (1941).
4. G. F. Asselin, L. F. Audrieth, and E. W. Cummings, *J. Phys. & Colloid Chem.*, **54**, 640 (1950).
5. W. Fischer and R. Bock, *Z. anorg. Chem.*, **249**, 146 (1942).
6. W. Fischer and W. Chalybaeus, *Z. anorg. Chem.*, **254**, 79 (1947).
7. W. Fischer, W. Chalybaeus, and C. Zumbusch, *Z. anorg. Chem.*, **255**, 277 (1948).
8. C. J. Barton, Sr., L. G. Overholser, and W. R. Grimes, U.S. Atomic Energy Commission Report, Y-611.
9. R. Bock, *Z. Anal. Chem.*, **133**, 110 (1951).
10. M. Aven and H. Freiser, *Anal. Chim. Acta*, **6**, 412 (1952).
11. L. Melnick and H. Freiser, *Anal. Chem.*, **25**, 856 (1953).

6. NITRATE SYSTEM

The principle of solvent extraction has long been applied by many investigators as a means of separating numerous elements from uranium in nitrate solutions. In 1842 Peligot[1] found that uranyl nitrate dissolved readily in ethyl ether and used this solvent in the purification of U from pitchblende. Pierle [2] separated U from V by evaporating a solution of U ore to dryness with excess of nitric acid, moistening the residue with additional nitric acid and extracting with ethyl ether. Hoffman [3] concentrated the rare earth elements in the analysis of U ores by treating an aqueous solution of the nitrates with a large volume of ethyl ether. The rare earth elements remain in the aqueous layer whereas the bulk of the U is removed by ether. With the discovery of the enhancement of the extraction by means of salting-out agents,[4,5] the process has assumed great importance in recent years in connection with the analytical chemistry of U and problems incidental to atomic energy development.

It is noteworthy that neptunyl and plutonyl nitrates behave in the same way as uranyl nitrate.[6] Moreover, after removal of sulfate ions with barium ions and salting-out with HNO_3 and NH_4NO_3, all the Am in the yellow solution obtained by oxidizing Am(III) with persulfate can be solvent extracted,[7] thus indicating by analogy to U the existence of sexavalent americium and the $AmO_2{}^{2+}$ ion.

In addition to U(VI), Am(VI), Np(VI), and Pu(VI), other elements which extract well as nitrate complexes include Ce(IV), Au(III), Fe(III), Sc(III), Pa(IV), and Th(IV) as shown in Table 11.6. Elements that are partially extracted include P, Cr(VI), As(V), Hg(II), Tl(III), and Bi(III).

The distribution ratios of a number of these elements using ethyl ether are very dependent on HNO_3 concentration [8,9] as shown in Fig. 11.2 for Au(III), U(VI), Ce(IV), and Th(IV). In addition, salting-out agents and temperature produce striking effects. Thus, Sc is extracted from $8\,M$ HNO_3 to the extent of 0.1%, but when the aqueous phase is satuated with $LiNO_3$ at $35°C$, more than 83% can be extracted. The effects of various salting-out agents on the extraction of Th(IV) can be seen in Table 11.6, and the use of these salts in the extraction of U(VI) can be seen in Fig. 4.1.

Solvents that have been used extensively in the extraction of elements as nitrate complexes include ethyl ether, tributyl phosphate, and methyl isobutyl ketone. Tributyl phosphate provides a good solvent for the extraction of cerium, thallium, and uranium nitrates from HNO_3 solutions.[10] Cerium(IV) can be extracted completely from $8\text{--}10\,M$ HNO_3 containing $3\,M$ $NaNO_3$ if $NaBrO_3$ is added to reoxidize any metal reduced by the solvent during extraction. The lanthanides can be fractionated using tributyl phosphate and $8\text{--}15.6\,M$ HNO_3.[11] A study has been made of the distribution ratios of samarium, gadolin-

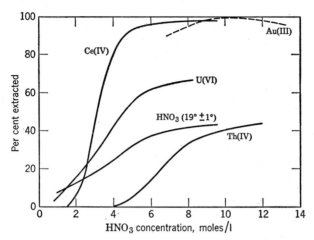

Figure 11.2. Effect of nitric acid concentration on the extractability of nitrates by ethyl ether.[8]

ium, dysprosium, and yttrium nitrates between HNO_3 and tributyl phosphate at various acidities (8.5–17.2 M HNO_3) and rare earth concentrations to assist in the development of methods of fractionation.[29] It has been found that the dependence of extraction on rare earth concentration increases with acidity and with the atomic number of the rare earth.

Templeton[12] has made extensive studies of the distribution of $Th(NO_3)_4$ between water and a variety of alcohols and methyl ketones; he found that the extractability of rare earth nitrates by n-hexyl alcohol increased in the order $Ce < La < Pr < Nd < Sm$. It is thus feasible to separate Nd and La by solvent extraction.[13] Bock and Bock[8] have similarly studied the effects of various solvents on the separation of Th from La and found methyl isobutyl ketone and diethyl ketone to be most effective ($\beta > 12,000$).

An interesting variation of nitrate extractions is the separation of Ca from Sr based on the extraction of the anhydrous nitrates with such solvents as absolute alcohol and ether,[14] acetone,[15] and the monobutyl ether of ethylene glycol.[16] The calcium nitrate is dissolved, leaving most of the strontium (and barium) nitrate.

The extraction behavior of the actinide elements has been extensively studied in connection with various atomic energy programs, and one of the reviews of the subject is that by Hyde.[17] An interesting study by McKay[18] of the separation of actinides using tributyl phosphate shows that differences in the extractability between the different oxidation states makes possible a number of separations of the lower

Table 11.6.   Nitrate Extractions

Element	Oxidation State	Solvent System (before mixing)		Per Cent Extraction	Reference
		Aqueous Phase	Organic Phase		
Americium	Am(VI)	HNO_3, NH_4NO_3	Ethyl ether	100	7
Arsenic	As(V) as Na_2HAsO_4	8 M HNO_3	Ethyl ether	14.4	8
Bismuth	Bi(III)	8 M HNO_3	Ethyl ether	6.8	8
Boron	B(III)	0–2 N HNO_3, 120 g $Cu(NO_3)_2/100$ g H_2O	Dibutyl carbitol	61–64	20
Calcium	Ca(II)	Anhydrous nitrate	1:1 absolute alcohol–absolute ether	0.37 g $Ca(NO_3)_2$ per ml	14
	Ca(II)	Anhydrous nitrate	Acetone	0.212 g/ml	15
	Ca(II)	Anhydrous nitrate	Monobutyl ether of ethylene glycol	0.243 g/ml	16
Cerium	Ce(IV)	1 M HNO_3	Tributyl phosphate	98–99	10
	Ce(IV)	8–10 M HNO_3, 3 M $NaNO_3$	Tributyl phosphate	98–99	10
	Ce(IV)	8 M HNO_3	Ethyl ether	96.8	8
	Ce(IV)	9 M HNO_3	Methyl isobutyl ketone	78	21
Chromium	Cr(VI) as $K_2Cr_2O_7$ (decomposed)	8 M HNO_3	Ethyl ether	>15	8
Gold	Au(III)	8 M HNO_3	Ethyl ether	97	8
Iron	Fe(III)	pH 0, 120 g $Cu(NO_3)_2/100$ g H_2O	Dibutyl carbitol	60	20
Mercury	Hg(II)	8 M HNO_3	Ethyl ether	4.7	8
Neptunium	Np(VI)	8–9 M HNO_3	Dibutyl carbitol	89	22
	Np(VI)	6–9 M HNO_3	Ethyl ether	82	22
	Np(VI)	6–9 M HNO_3	Methyl isobutyl ketone	78	22
Phosphorus	P(V) as $(NH_4)_2PO_4$	8 M HNO_3	Ethyl ether	20.4	8
Plutonium	Pu(VI)	HNO_3, sat. NH_4NO_3	Ethyl ether		6
Protactinium	Pa(V)	6 M HNO_3	Diisopropyl ketone	60	23
	Pa(V)	6 M HNO_3	Diisopropylcarbinol	89.5	24
Rare earths	R.E.(III)	~20% $LiNO_3$ solution	Ethyl ether	~0.1 [a]	25
	R.E.(III)	~20% $LiNO_3$ solution	Pentanone	~0.1 [a]	25
	R.E.(III)	Concentrated R.E. nitrates at low acid concentration	Tributyl phosphate	~0.1 [a]	26
Scandium	Sc(III)	1 M HNO_3, sat. $LiNO_3$ at 35°C	Ethyl ether	83	8
Thallium	Tl(III)	8 M HNO_3	Ethyl ether	7.7	8
Thorium	Th(IV)	8 M HNO_3	Ethyl ether	34.6	8
	Th(IV)	1 M HNO_3, sat. $LiNO_3$	Ethyl ether	56.5	8
	Th(IV)	1 M HNO_3, sat. $NaNO_3$	Ethyl ether	0.67	8
	Th(IV)	1 M HNO_3, sat. KNO_3	Ethyl ether	0.15	8
	Th(IV)	1 M HNO_3, sat. NH_4NO_3	Ethyl ether	0.36	8
	Th(IV)	1 M HNO_3, sat. $Mg(NO_3)_2$	Ethyl ether	43.8	8
	Th(IV)	1 M HNO_3, sat. $Ca(NO_3)_2$	Ethyl ether	56.9	8
	Th(IV)	1 M HNO_3, sat. $Zn(NO_3)_2$	Ethyl ether	80.9	8
	Th(IV)	1 M HNO_3, sat. $Al(NO_3)_3$	Ethyl ether	54.1	8
	Th(IV)	1 M HNO_3, sat. $Fe(NO_3)_3$	Ethyl ether	73.6	8
	Th(IV)	3 M HNO_3, 3 M $Ca(NO_3)_2$, 0.3 M Th(IV)	20% n-butyl phosphate–80% n-butyl ether	91	27
	Th(IV)	3 M HNO_3, 3 M $Ca(NO_3)_2$, 0.6 M Th(IV)	20% n-butyl phosphate–80% n-butyl ether	74	27
	Th(IV)	0.3 M HNO_3, 6 M NH_4NO_3	Dibutoxytetraethylene glycol and ethyl ether (2:1 by volume)	90	28
Uranium	U(VI)	8 M HNO_3	Ethyl ether	65	8
	U(VI)	Saturated solutions of various salting-out agents	Ethyl ether	33–99.6 [b]	5
	U(VI)	1 N HNO_3, 3/4 sat. NH_4NO_3	Pentaether	99.7	30
Zirconium	Zr(IV)	8 M HNO_3	Ethyl ether	~8	8

[a] Fractional extraction to separate individual rare earths.
[b] See Fig. 4.1 for effects of various salting-out agents on extraction of U.

Table 11.7. Extraction of Important Fission Products by Solvents [19]

Distribution Ratio

Fission Product	Methyl Isobutyl Ketone [a]	Tributyl Phosphate [b]
Cesium	$<10^{-4}$	$<10^{-4}$
Total rare earths	0.01	0.0004
Gross beta emitters	0.03	0.001
Cerium	0.03	0.01
Zirconium	0.04	0.01
Ruthenium	1.0	0.001

[a] $1.5\ M\ Al(NO_3)_3$–$0.25\ M\ HNO_3$.
[b] $3\ M\ HNO_3$–30% TBP (80% saturated with U).

actinides. Uranyl nitrate, the most extractable hexavalent nitrate, can for example be extracted away from $Th(NO_3)_4$, the least extractable tetravalent nitrate, using 5% tributyl phosphate/diluent. A similar extraction of U from Pu is possible if the Pu is first reduced to the trivalent state, e.g., by ferrous ion, using 20% tributyl phosphate/diluent. Under such reducing conditions, Np becomes tetravalent and therefore extracts with the U; Am and the higher actinides, on the other hand, being trivalent, accompany the Pu. Reoxidation of the Pu to the tetravalent or hexavalent state would render it extractable again, and hence separable from Am, etc.

Methyl isobutyl ketone has been employed as a solvent for U and Pu recovery from fission products.[19] In this extraction the separation of the desired products from the fission products is influenced by solvent purity, salting strength, acidity, temperature, and the presence of minor components in the system. The uranium concentration and contacting times are not significant factors.

Tributyl phosphate is used, in a manner similar to methyl isobutyl ketone, as a solvent in Pu and U recovery processes.[19] It may also be used to separate Th from fission products. The distribution ratio of tributyl phosphate–extractable materials depends on the concentration of uncomplexed tributyl phosphate in the organic phase. Thus, one of the most important variables in fission product extraction by tributyl phosphate is the degree of solvent saturation with elements such as U, Pu, or Th, which are more strongly complexed by tributyl phosphate than the fission products. Table 11.7 shows typical values of fission product distribution ratios in methyl isobutyl ketone and tributyl phosphate extractions.

Limited work has been done on the separation of fissionable materials from fission products by the use of other solvents such as penta-ether, isopropyl ether, dibutyl cellosolve, and many alcohols.[19]

REFERENCES: Nitrate System

1. E. Peligot, *Ann. Chim. Phys.*, (3), **5**, 1 (1842).
2. C. A. Pierle, *Ind. Eng. Chem.*, **12**, 60 (1920).
3. J. I. Hoffman, *J. Wash. Acad. Sci.*, **38**, 233 (1948).
4. F. Hecht and A. Grünwald, *Mikrochemie ver. Mikrochim. Acta*, **30**, 279 (1943).
5. N. H. Furman, R. J. Mundy, and G. H. Morrison, U.S. Atomic Energy Commission Report, AECD-2938.
6. E. Glueckauf and H. A. C. McKay, *Nature*, **165**, 594 (1950).
7. L. B. Asprey, S. G. Stephanou, and P. A. Penneman, *J. Am. Chem. Soc.*, **72**, 1425 (1950).
8. R. Bock and E. Bock, *Z. anorg. Chem.*, **263**, 146 (1950).
9. A. Norström and L. G. Sillen, *Svensk Kem. Tidskr.*, **60**, 227 (1948).
10. J. C. Warf, *J. Am. Chem. Soc.*, **71**, 3257 (1949).
11. D. F. Peppard, J. P. Faris, P. R. Gray, and G. W. Mason, *J. Phys. Chem.*, **57**, 294 (1953).
12. C. C. Templeton, *J. Am. Chem. Soc.*, **71**, 2187 (1949).
13. C. C. Templeton and J. A. Peterson, *J. Am. Chem. Soc.*, **70**, 3967 (1948).
14. R. Fresenius, *Z. anal. Chem.*, **32**, 189 (1893).
15. M. M. Tillu and N. S. Telang, *J. Indian Chem. Soc.*, **19**, 231 (1942).
16. H. H. Barber, *Ind. Eng. Chem., Anal. Ed.*, **13**, 572 (1941).
17. E. K. Hyde, *Proceedings of the International Conference on the Peaceful Uses of Atomic Energy*, Vol. 7, United Nations, New York, 1956, p. 281.
18. H. A. C. McKay, *Proceedings of the International Conference on the Peaceful Uses of Atomic Energy*, Vol. 7, United Nations, New York, 1956, p. 314.
19. F. R. Bruce, *Proceedings of the International Conference on the Peaceful Uses of Atomic Energy*, Vol. 7, United Nations, New York, 1956, pp. 100, 128.
20. B. S. Weaver and C. E. Larson, U.S. Atomic Energy Commission Report, AECD-3936.
21. L. E. Glendenin, K. F. Flynn, R. F. Buchanan, and E. P. Steinberg, *Anal. Chem.*, **27**, 59 (1955).
22. J. Kooi, *Proceedings of the International Conference on the Peaceful Uses of Atomic Energy*, Vol. 7, United Nations, New York, 1956, p. 309.
23. W. W. Meinke, U.S. Atomic Energy Commission Report, AECD-2738
24. F. L. Moore, *Anal. Chem.*, **27**, 70 (1955).
25. W. Fischer, G. Braune, W. Dietz, O. Juberman, G. Krause, K. Niemann, and G. Siekemeir, *Angew. Chem.*, **66**, 317 (1954).
26. J. Bochinski, M. Smutz, and F. Spedding, U.S. Atomic Energy Commission Report, ISC-438.
27. M. R. Anderson, U.S. Atomic Energy Commission Report, ISC-116.
28. D. F. Peppard *et al.*, *J. Am. Chem. Soc.*, **75**, 4576 (1953).
29. A. C. Topp and B. Weaver, U.S. Atomic Energy Commission Report, ORNL-1811.
30. D. F. Musser, D. P. Krause, and R. H. Smellie, Jr., U.S. Atomic Energy Commission Report, AECD-3907.

7. PERCHLORATE SYSTEM

The perchlorates of the alkali metals K, Rb, and Cs are insoluble in various alcohols and in ethyl acetate; the perchlorates of Tl and ammonium are sparingly soluble in these solvents, but the perchlorates of all other metals are soluble. Thus, it is possible to separate moderately small amounts of K in the presence of much Na, as well as most other elements whose perchlorates are soluble under the conditions employed. The solubility of potassium perchlorate in ethyl alcohol, n-butyl alcohol, and ethyl acetate is respectively 9.4, 3.6, and 1.3 mg per 100 ml of solution at 25°C.[1]

The alkali salts are converted into perchlorates by evaporation to dryness with perchloric acid, and the residue is extracted with a suitable organic solvent. The sodium perchlorate is soluble in the solvent, leaving most of the potassium perchlorate.

More recently it has been claimed that uranium perchlorate can be extracted from perchloric acid solutions using ethyl ether.[2]

REFERENCES: Perchlorate System

1. H. H. Willard and G. F. Smith, *J. Am. Chem. Soc.*, **45**, 286 (1923).
2. K. Käärik, *Radiometer Polarographics*, **2**, 105 (1953).

8. HETEROPOLY ACID SYSTEM

A characteristic property of heteropoly acids is their solubility in organic solvents. Thus, the possibility presents itself of effecting separations of elements by the formation of a complex of this type, followed by extraction with a suitable solvent. Elements capable of forming this type of complex which can be extracted include Mo, As, P, W, V, and Si.

Liquid-liquid extraction can be used to effect separations of heteropoly acids in a variety of applications. For example, tungstophosphoric acid can be completely extracted with 1-pentanol from $6 N$ H_2SO_4 solutions. Under these conditions Mo is extracted to an appreciable extent, and As and Fe to a lesser extent. Many other elements are not extracted. Molybdophosphoric acid can be extracted into ethyl ether as a means of purifying the acid.[1] If molybdophosphoric acid is shaken with ethyl ether, three layers form. The volume of the viscous, deep yellow bottom layer is proportional to the amount of P present.[2] A similar method can be applied to the measurement of As.[3]

With regard to the solvent used in the extraction of heteropoly acids, esters, ketones, aldehydes, and ethers are good extractants, but carbon disulfide, carbon tetrachloride, chloroform, benzene, and toluene are not.[4] Thus, oxygen-containing materials appear to be good solvents.[5]

By extracting into ethyl acetoacetate it is possible to concentrate molybdophosphoric acid and to separate it from molybdosilicic acid.[6] Molybdosilicic acid can also be measured after removal of molybdophosphoric acid with ethyl acetate.[7] Butyl acetate can also be used for this separation.[8]

2-Methyl-1-propanol has been used to extract molybdophosphoric acid.[9,10,11] 3-Methyl-1-butanol has also been used;[12] however, it has been found that 1-octanol extracts less extraneous material than 1-butanol.[13] A method for the determination of P in steel involves extraction of molybdophosphoric acid with a 20%-by-volume solution of 1-butanol in chloroform.[14]

A method for the determination of arsenic is based on extraction with 1-butanol.[15]

Molybdovanadophosphoric acid has been extracted with 3-methyl-1-butanol and ethyl ether[16] and mixtures of 1-butanol and ethyl ether or 1-butyl acetate, 1-butanol, and ethyl ether.[17]

A mixture of 1-butanol and chloroform selectively extracts molybdophosphoric acid in the presence of As and Si.[18,19] The procedure can be extended by treating the residual aqueous solution with a mixture of 1-butanol and ethyl ether to extract molybdoarsenic acid and finally with 1-butanol to extract molybdosilicic acid.[20,21]

Microgram quantities of P can be extracted into ether[22] or isobutanol.[23]

REFERENCES: Heteropoly Acid System

1. H. Wu, *J. Biol. Chem.,* **43,** 189 (1920).
2. H. Copaux, *Compt. rend.,* **173,** 656 (1921).
3. M. Poussigues, *Ann. chim. anal. et chim. appl.,* **5,** 265 (1923).
4. A. G. Scroggie, *J. Am. Chem. Soc.,* **51,** 1057 (1929).
5. J. F. Keggin, *Proc. Roy. Soc. (London),* **144,** 75 (1934).
6. K. Stoll, *Z. anal. Chem.,* **112,** 81 (1938).
7. J. Hure and T. Ortis, *Bull. soc. chim. France,* **1949,** 834.
8. T. Kato *et al., Technol. Repts. Tôhoku Imp. Univ.,* **15,** No. 1, 70 (1950).
9. R. J. L. Allen, *Biochem. J.,* **34,** 858 (1940).
10. I. Berenblum and E. Chain, *Biochem. J.,* **32,** 287 (1938).
11. C. Sideris, *Ind. Eng. Chem., Anal. Ed.,* **14,** 762 (1942).
12. C. Rainbow, *Nature,* **157,** 268 (1946).
13. F. L. Schafer, J. Fong, and P. L. Kirk, *Anal. Chem.,* **25,** 343 (1953).
14. C. Wadelin and M. G. Mellon, *Anal. Chem.,* **25,** 1668 (1953).
15. C. Wadelin and M. G. Mellon, *Analyst,* **77,** 708 (1952).
16. N. V. Maksimova and M. T. Kozlovskii, *Zhur. Anal. Khim.,* **2,** 353 (1947).
17. J. Kinnunen and B. Wennerstrand, *Chemist-Analyst,* **40,** 35 (1951).

18. K. T. H. Farrer and S. J. Nuir, *Australian Chem. Inst. J. & Proc.*, **11**, 222 (1944).
19. R. V. Mervel, *Zovodskaya Lab.*, **11**, 135 (1945).
20. R. I. Akkseev, *Zovodskaya Lab.*, **11**, 122 (1945).
21. N. A. Filippova and L. I. Kuznetsova, *Zovodskaya Lab.*, **16**, 536 (1950).
22. N. S. Ging, *Anal. Chem.*, **28**, 1330 (1956).
23. C. H. Lueck and D. F. Boltz, *Anal. Chem.*, **28**, 1168 (1956).

9. CARBOXYLIC ACIDS

Solutions of carboxylic acids in organic solvents have been found to be effective in extracting several metals out of alkaline aqueous solutions.

Johnson [1] found that benzoates of Fe(III), Al, Be, Ga, In, and Sc are extracted by ethyl acetate, butyl, or amyl alcohol. The benzoates are formed in the aqueous phase at a pH of 7 using a solution of 25% sodium benzoate.

West and coworkers,[2] employing a 5% n-capric acid ($C_9H_{19}COOH$) solution in ethyl acetate, found Cu(II) to be quantitatively extracted in the pH range from 6.3 to 10.3. Manganese, Fe, Ni, Pd, Co, and Ru were the only positive interferences (precipitates of Ni and Co did not dissolve in the organic phase but were gathered by this phase and eventually settled in the interface). When commercial butyraldehyde was used as the solvent, no extraction of Ni or Pd occurred but the other ions interfered, as did Rh(III). With butyric acid in benzene, only Cu, Mn, and Fe extracted. Although not extracted when alone, Ru(III) was found to extract in the presence of Cu(II).

Sundaram and Banerjee,[3] using butyric acid, were able to extract over 90% of Be into chloroform from an aqueous phase held at a pH of 9.3 to 9.5. Other solvents were less effective. With ethyl acetate, ether, and benzene, 70–80% Be extraction was obtained. With chloroform (50 ml), the optimal amount of acid was found to be 10–15 ml; higher concentrations resulted in decreased extraction. With ether no such maximum was observed. Addition of salts such as KCl or KNO_3 (3 g to the mixture) improved the extraction by about 75%. Iron(III) and Al(III) will be completely extracted by chloroform under the same conditions that apply for Be extraction. These metals will not interfere with Be extraction if an excess of the disodium salt of EDTA is added prior to the extraction.[4]

Plutonium(IV) was found to form extractable complexes with salicylic acid, 3,5-dinitrobenzoic acid, and cinnamic acid.[5] The extraction of La, Th(IV), and U(VI) with these acids and with methoxybenzoic acid, using hexone or chloroform as solvents, has also been studied.[6]

Best separations were achieved with cinnamic acid in chloroform which gave partial separation of Th from U and complete separation of La from the other two.

More recently, perfluorocarboxylic acids in ethyl ether have been found to be capable of metal extraction.[7] With perfluorobutyric acid (C_3F_7COOH), Fe(III), Al, Cr(III), U(VI), and Be are separated from monovalent and other divalent cations. With perfluorooctanoic acid $(C_7F_{15}COOH)$, divalent ions such as Ca, Mg, Fe(II), Pb, and Zn can be separated from monovalent ions. Extractions are said to be optimum at a pH just less than that at which the metal hydroxide would precipitate. Fluoride and sulfate are found to hinder extraction.

Biffen[8] describes a method of extracting calcium stearate from graphite using trichlorobenzene at its boiling point, 165°C. At this temperature, at least 0.5 g of the soap is soluble in 10 ml solvent. Application to other, more soluble metal stearates such as those of Al and Mg was suggested.

REFERENCES: Carboxylic Acids

1. S. E. J. Johnson as reported by E. B. Sandell, *Colorimetric Determination of Traces of Metals,* second edition, Interscience Publishers, Inc., New York, 1950, p. 537.
2. P. W. West, F. C. Lyons, and J. K. Carlton, *Anal. Chim. Acta,* **6,** 400 (1952).
3. A. K. Sundaram and S. Banerjee, *Anal. Chim. Acta,* **8,** 526 (1953).
4. S. Banerjee, A. K. Sundaram, and H. D. Sharma, *Anal. Chim. Acta,* **10,** 256 (1954).
5. B. G. Harvey, H. G. Heal, A. G. Maddock, and E. L. Rowley, *J. Chem. Soc.,* **1947,** 1010.
6. B. Hök-Bernström, *Svensk Kem. Tidskr.,* **68,** 1 (1956); *Acta Chem. Scand.,* **10,** 163 (1956).
7. G. F. Mills and H. B. Whetsel, *J. Am. Chem. Soc.,* **77,** 4690 (1955).
8. F. M. Biffen, *Ind. Eng. Chem., Anal. Ed.,* **6,** 169 (1934).

10. ALKYLPHOSPHORIC ACIDS

The di-*n*-butyl ester of phosphoric acid $\left[(C_4H_9O)_2P{\nearrow}^{OH}_{\to O} \right]$, either alone or in a mixture with the monoester as in commercial "butylphosphoric acid," has been found to extract trace levels of Zr quantitatively from aqueous solutions 1 M in either HNO_3, HCl, $HClO_4$, or H_2SO_4.[1] A 0.06 M solution of the dibutylphosphoric acid (containing some monobutylphosphoric acid[2]) in di-*n*-butyl ether used for the Zr extraction left 98% of the tracer quantity Nb present in the aqueous phase. Extraction time influenced the amount of Nb but not the amount of Zr extracted. The per cent of Nb extracted increased from 2 to 10% as

Table 11.8. Extraction Properties of Carrier-Free Concentrations of Fission Product Elements with Mixed Butylphosphoric Acids [1]

Conditions: Aqueous phase, $1\,M$ HNO_3, 5-minute mixing; volume ratio (organic/aqueous), 1:1.

Elements Extracted

Concentration of DBPA,[a] M	< 5% by DBPA	5–95% by DBPA	> 95% by DBPA
0.06	Cs, Sr, La, Ce(III), Ag,[b] Cd, Ge, Se(IV), Te(IV), Sb(III),[c] Sb(V), As(V), Pd,[b] Ru, Rh, Nb	Y, 15%; Sn(IV),[b] 50%; Mo,[b] 15%	Zr, In
0.6	Cs, Sr, La, Ag,[b] Cd, Ge, Se(IV), Te(IV), Sb(III),[c] Sb(V), As(V), Pd,[b] Ru, Rh	Mo,[b] 23%; Nb, 60%; Ta,[c] 85%	Zr, Nb,[c] Y, In, Sn(IV)[b]

[a] Di-n-butylphosphoric acid solution in which the mole ratio of di-n-butylphosphoric acid to mono-n-butylphosphoric acid is 4.5:1.
[b] Silver, Sn, Pd, and Mo were not carrier-free; their concentrations were 0.5, 3, 8, and 8μg/ml, respectively.
[c] No H_2O_2 present.

Table 11.9. Extraction Properties of Macro Quantities of Fission Product Elements with Mixed Butylphosphoric Acids [1]

Conditions: Aqueous phase, 1 mg element per milliliter, $1\,M$ H_2SO_4, $2.5\,M$ $(NH_4)_2SO_4$, $0.004\,M$ oxalic acid, 6% H_2O_2; volume ratio (organic/aqueous), 1:1; mixing time, 15 minutes with $0.06\,M$ DBPA and 5 minutes with $0.6\,M$ DBPA.

Elements Extracted

Concentration of DBPA,[a] M	<5% by DBPA	5–95% by DBPA	>95% by DBPA
0.06	Cs, Sr, Y, La, Ce(III), Ag, Cd, Ge, Se(IV), Te(IV), Sb(III),[b] Sb(V), As(V), Pd, Ru, Rh, Mo, Nb	Sn(IV), 15%; In, 85%	Zr, I_2
0.6	Cs, Sr, La, Ce(III), Ag, Cd, Ge, Se(IV), Te(IV), Sb(III),[b] Sb(V), As(V), Pd, Ru, Rh, Mo	Sn(IV), 50%; Ta, 35%	Zr, Nb,[b] Y, Ho, In, I_2

[a] Di-n-butylphosphoric acid solution in which mole ratio of di-n-butylphosphoric acid to mono-n-butylphosphoric acid is 4.5:1.
[b] No H_2O_2 present.

extraction time increased from 1 to 5 minutes. Addition of 3% H_2O_2 reduced Nb extraction to less than 1% (even with 10-minute extraction times) without affecting Zr extraction. Similar results are obtained with macro quantities of Zr and Nb.

The use of a more concentrated dibutylphosphoric acid solution resulted in quantitative extraction of both Zr and Nb in the absence of H_2O_2. The addition of H_2O_2 did not affect Zr extraction but reduced that of Nb to 93%. Tables 11.8 and 11.9 indicate the behavior of both trace and macro quantities of other elements. In addition to the separation of Zr and Nb from each other and from nearly all other fission products, this system seems capable of separating the Y group from the La group of rare earths.

Precautions against emulsion formation must be taken with this reagent. Higher homologs such as the octylphosphoric acids, since they are less soluble in water, are reported to be free of the emulsion difficulty.[3]

REFERENCES: Alkylphosphoric Acids

1. E. M. Scadden and N. E. Ballou, *Anal. Chem.*, **25**, 1602 (1953).
2. D. C. Stewart and H. W. Crandall, *J. Am. Chem. Soc.*, **73**, 1377 (1951).
3. K. B. Brown, private communication.

11. TRIALKYLPHOSPHINE OXIDES

$$(C_nH_{2n+1})_3P \rightarrow O$$

In a comparative study at the Hanford Laboratories and at the Oak Ridge National Laboratory of the uranium-extracting ability of a homologous series of organophosphorus compounds, phosphine oxides were found to be the strongest.[1,2] The compounds studied were prepared by the systematic replacement of the ester groups in a trialkyl phosphate with alkyl groups bonded directly to the phosphorus atom and included trialkyl phosphates, dialkyl(alkyl phosphonates), alkyl-(dialkyl phosphonates), and trialkylphosphine oxides. Phosphine oxides are extremely stable compounds.

Uranium may be quantitatively extracted from a solution containing 0.1 M nitrate ion at pH 1.0 using a 0.1 M alkylphosphine oxide solution in kerosene or carbon tetrachloride when n-octyl, n-decyl, n-dodecyl, or 3,5,5-trimethylhexylphosphine oxides are employed.[3] Although the extent of extraction is drastically reduced in the presence of sulfate or phosphate anions, increase of the nitrate anion concentration to 0.3 M results in good extraction, even with sulfate or phosphate concentrations as high as 0.5 M. Uranium may also be extracted from solutions containing chloride ion in concentrations higher than 0.5 M, using 0.05 M tridecylphosphine oxide in kerosene, and is essentially independent of acidity in the range between 0.05 and 4 M H$^+$.

Uranium cannot be stripped from the organic phase by water and is only poorly stripped by oxalic, acetic, or dilute hydrochloric acid. Phosphoric and hydrofluoric acids, concentrated sulfate solutions at pH 2, and sodium carbonate solutions are effective stripping agents.

Vanadium(V) can be extracted quantitatively (95%) from nitrate solutions of pH 1.5–2.0, using 0.6 M trioctylphosphine oxide in kerosene. Chloride ion does not improve the extraction whereas sulfate and carbonate inhibit it. Since V(IV) is not extractable, V may be effectively stripped from the organic phase by a reducing agent such as 0.25 M oxalic acid.

The phosphine oxides, like tributyl phosphate, extract HNO$_3$ and, to lesser extents, HCl, H$_2$SO$_4$, and H$_3$PO$_4$. Very poor extraction of Fe(III), Al, and Th was obtained from chloride, sulfate, nitrate, or phosphate solutions using trioctylphosphine oxide in kerosene.

The great potentiality of the alkylphosphine oxides as analytical extractants is evident from initial studies of J. C. White,[4] who examined the extraction characteristics of most metal ions in acid media using a 0.1 M solution of either tri-n-octylphosphine oxide or 2-ethyl-n-hexylphosphine oxide in cyclohexane. With tri-n-octylphosphine oxide, the following ions were completely extracted from 1 M HCl: Cr(VI), Au(I), Hf(IV), Fe(III), Mo(VI), Sn(IV), U(VI), and Zr(IV). Ions that were partially extracted under these conditions include: Sb(III), Bi(III), Cd(II), In(III), Hg(II), Pt(II), and Zn(II). Increase of the HCl concentration to 7 M resulted in complete extraction of Sb (III), Cr(VI), Ga(III), Au(I), Hf(IV), Fe(III), Mo(VI), Sn(IV), Ti(IV), U(VI), V(IV), and Zr(IV). White also examined extraction behavior from sulfuric, perchloric, and nitric acid media. As might be anticipated from the presence of the ethyl group in a position to exert adverse steric influence, tris-2-ethyl-n-hexylphosphine oxide extracts fewer metals than does the n-octyl compound. A 0.1 M solution of tris-2-ethyl-n-hexylphosphine oxide will completely extract the following ions from a 1 M HCl solution: Au(I), Sn(IV), and U(VI). With a 7 M HCl solution the ions completely extracted include Ga(III), Hf(IV), Fe(III), Mo(VI), Sn(IV), U(VI), and Zr(IV).

REFERENCES: Trialkylphosphine Oxides

1. U.S. Atomic Energy Commission Report, HW-23160.
2. U.S. Atomic Energy Commission Report, ORNL-1260; ORNL-1338.
3. C. A. Blake, K. B. Brown, and C. F. Coleman, U.S. Atomic Energy Commission Report, ORNL-1964.

4. J. C. White, Oak Ridge National Laboratory, paper presented at Pittsburgh Conference on Analytical Chemistry and Applied Spectroscopy, March 1957.

12. HIGH MOLECULAR WEIGHT AMINES

A number of high molecular weight amines have been used to extract metals. First used to extract strong acids, HCl and H_2SO_4,[1] they have been shown by a group at Oak Ridge to be extractants of major importance for both analytical and large-scale separations of metals. Methyldioctylamine $\{[CH_3(CH_2)_6CH_2]_2NCH_3\}$ in xylene solution was shown to selectively extract Nb from Ta out of concentrated HCl.[2] Tribenzylamine $[(C_6H_5CH_2)_3N]$ dissolved in either chloroform or dichloromethane was also effective in Nb and Ta separation out of either concentrated HCl or H_2SO_4 solutions, although HCl is the more desirable medium [3] because of the lower Ta extraction. Both methyldioctylamine and tribenzylamine have shown themselves to be effective for the selective extraction of Zn at a Zn concentration of 20 mg/ml from many of the metals of the first transition series from dilute HCl solutions.[4] In 2 N HCl, using a solution of 8 g methyldioctylamine per 100 ml of trichloroethylene, Zn was quantitatively extracted (100.0%), and smaller percentages of Cr(III) (3.2%), Mn(II) (0.07%), Fe(III) (76%), Ni(II) (0.2%), Cu(II) (9.5%), and Co(II) (0.4%) were extracted. At higher concentrations of HCl, the extraction of most of the metals increased markedly so that from 10 N HCl 7.6% Cr(III), 31.8% Mn, 93.4% Fe(III), 0.9% Ni, 72% Cu and 85.4% Co were removed; Zn removal remained essentially quantitative. Several organic solvents were used in the methyldioctylamine extractions of Zn and Co. The extent of extraction of these metals was greatest with trichloroethylene (out of 3N HCl, 99.7% Zn, 1.6% Co), almost as much with xylene (99.3% Zn, 0.44% Co), and considerably less with chloroform (84.9% Zn, 0.006% Co). Since tribenzylamine was found to form an insoluble addition product with HCl in trichloroethylene and xylene, it could only be used in chloroform solution.

Recent reports of the Oak Ridge group attest the interest in long-chain secondary and tertiary amines for the extraction of U[5,6,7] and Th.[8] Uranium can be selectively extracted from a solution of pH 0.85 containing about 1 g/l U, 6 g/l Fe(III), 3 g/l Al, 50 g/l SO_4, 2 g/l PO_4, and 1.7 g/l F with a 0.1 M amine solution in kerosene. Amines such as di-(2-butyloctyl) amine, bis-(1-isobutyl-3,5-dimethylhexyl) amine, N-benzyl-1-(3-ethylpentyl)-4-ethyloctylamine, tri-n-octylamine, and trilaurylamine in kerosene, to name a few of the better of the more than 200 compounds screened, efficiently and selectively extract U from most contaminants. An increase in the pH up to 1.5 increases the U distribution ratio, although further pH increase has no further significant effect. The extent of extraction of Mo from sulfate solutions are as high or higher than those for U[5] so that any Mo present will also be extracted with U. If V(V) is present, the Mo and V are coextracted (probably as a heteropoly acid) with a mole ratio of Mo to V of 2:1.[7] Vanadium(IV) is nonextractable, and V(V), except in the absence of much Mo, is only slightly extracted at pH 1 or below. The extractability of V(V) increases sharply in the pH range of 1.8–2.5. A change in the chemical form of V apparently occurs after its extraction so that if the extract is aged, stripping becomes difficult.

Extraction of Fe(III) by high molecular weight amines depends markedly on amine structure,[5,6] whereas Fe(II) extraction is weak to negligible with all amines tested. Thus, primary amines extract Fe(III) very strongly, the secondary amines extract small but significant fractions of Fe(III), and Fe(III) extraction by tertiary amines is insignificant. Secondary amines in which alkyl chain branching occurs in close proximity to the nitrogen will extract much less Fe(III) than others of their type. Extraction of Fe(III) increases with increasing pH with all amines, but with the more selective (for U) amines, e.g., trioctylamine, the magnitude of the effect is not significant. Small amounts of Ti are extracted, but extraction of such elements as Al, Na, Mg, Ca, Zn, Ni, Co, Cu, Mn, and Cr(III) is negligible.

The amines appear to be colloidally dispersed (see Chapter 1) so that the amine activity is fairly constant over a considerable range of concentration. As might be expected, the distribution ratios for U from sulfate solutions are almost directly proportional to the free reagent (free amine salt) concentration in the organic phase.[5] If there is a tendency for emulsion formation, this is generally aggravated by increasing amine concentration. About 0.1 M amine solutions in kerosene (or kerosene containing a few per cent of capryl alcohol) seem to be reasonably effective, if not always quite optimal.

The extent of U extraction will decrease slowly with increasing sulfate concentration. Although the interference of fluoride and phosphate is removed by the presence of Al and Fe(III)—at least up to 0.3 M anion—chloride and especially nitrate markedly lower D values (1 tenfold less at about 0.025 M nitrate and about 0.1 M chloride). Hence U may be effectively stripped from the organic phase by using either nitrates or chlorides. The use of a nitrate to strip will leave small amounts of nitrate with the amine; the nitrate must be carefully removed by contacting the organic phase with a base (regenerates free amine) if re-use of the amine solution is planned. Chlorides or HCl (1 M chloride) are effective stripping agents for U, particularly since Mo would tend to remain behind in the organic phase. The metal-bearing organic extract may be completely stripped by the use of alkali ($NaOH$ or Na_2CO_3), which converts the extractant to the free amine. Use of Na_2CO_3 results in soluble U, V, and Mo salts, whereas Fe precipitates as hydrous ferric oxide.

Increasing the temperature at which extraction is carried out results in an appreciable decrease of efficiency, although even at 50°C the extraction is still quite high for U.[5]

The rate of extraction of U is extremely high with equilibration requiring a few seconds using either free amine or amine sulfate as extractant. Iron(III) extraction is also rapid, although not quite as rapid as that of U, whereas with V(V) appreciable extraction occurs rapidly (at a high pH), but complete equilibration is not achieved even after 10 minutes of vigorous shaking.

Although most of the work thus far with these compounds has been centered about only a relatively few metals, the reasonable analogy with anion exchange resins leads to the hope that amine extraction systems can be much more widely exploited.

REFERENCES: High Molecular Weight Amines

1. E. L. Smith and E. J. Page, *J. Soc. Chem. Ind.* (*London*), **67,** 48 (1948).
2. G. W. Leddicote and F. L. Moore, *J. Am. Chem. Soc.,* **74,** 1618 (1952).
3. J. Y. Ellenburg, G. W. Leddicote, and F. L. Moore, *Anal. Chem.,* **26,** 1045 (1954).
4. H. A. Mahlman, G. W. Leddicote, and F. L. Moore, *Anal. Chem.,* **26,** 1939 (1954).
5. K. B. Brown, C. F. Coleman, D. J. Crouse, J. O. Denis, and J. G. Moore, U.S. Atomic Energy Commission Report, ORNL-1734.
6. J. G. Moore, K. B. Brown, and C. F. Coleman, U.S. Atomic Energy Commission Report, ORNL-1922.
7. D. J. Crouse and K. B. Brown, U.S. Atomic Energy Commission Report, ORNL-1959.
8. D. J. Crouse and J. O. Denis, U.S. Atomic Energy Commission Report, ORNL-1855.

13. TETRAPHENYLARSONIUM AND TETRAPHENYL-PHOSPHONIUM CHLORIDES

Tetraphenylarsonium chloride [$(C_6H_5)_4AsCl$] is a white crystalline solid melting at 258–260°C. It is freely soluble in water, forming a dihydrate (which loses its water at 100°C), and is also soluble in alcohol. In aqueous solution the reagent, which ionizes to give $(C_6H_5)_4As^+$ and Cl^- ions, forms insoluble salts with a number of anions such as ReO_4^-, MnO_4^-, IO_4^-, $HgCl_4^{2-}$, $SnCl_6^{2-}$, $CdCl_4^{2-}$, and $ZnCl_4^{2-}$, which have been used as the bases for gravimetric and volumetric methods of determining these elements.[1] Some of these salts have been found to be extractable into chloroform. This fact has been applied to the separation of Re from Mo,[2,3] the Re(VII) being quantitatively extracted into chloroform from basic medium (pH 8–9).[2] Technetium (6-hour half life) has been isolated from both neutron-irradiated MoO_3 and U_3O_8 by the same method.[4] Manganese(VII) may also be extracted as a $(C_6H_5)_4As^+$ salt.[4]

Metal ions which form anionic thiocyanate complexes such as Fe(III), Co(II), Mo(V), and even Cu(II) have been shown to form salts with triphenylmethylarsonium chloride that are extractable into o-dichlorobenzene.[5,6]

Both tetraphenylphosphonium chloride [7] and triphenylbenzylphosphonium chloride [8] have also been shown to form chloroform-extractable salts with ReO_4^-.

Microgram quantities of boron may be extracted as $[(C_6H_5)_4As^+, BF_4^-]$ by chloroform.[9] This method is not very convenient, for at least 18 hours of equilibration is said to be required.

Fluoride is quantitatively extracted as $[(C_6H_5)_4Sb^+, F^-]$ by chloroform.[10]

REFERENCES: Tetraphenylarsonium and Tetraphenylphosphonium Chlorides

1. F. J. Welcher, *Organic Analytical Reagents,* Vol. IV, D. Van Nostrand Co., Inc., New York, 1948.
2. S. Tribalat, *Anal. Chim. Acta,* **3,** 113 (1949).
3. J. M. Beeston and J. R. Lewis, *Anal. Chem.,* **25,** 651 (1953).
4. S. Tribalat and J. Beydon, *Anal. Chim. Acta,* **6,** 96 (1952); **8,** 22 (1953).
5. F. P. Dwyer and N. A. Gibson, *Analyst,* **76,** 548 (1951).
6. K. W. Ellis and N. A. Gibson, *Anal. Chim. Acta,* **9,** 369 (1953).
7. S. Tribalat, *Anal. Chim. Acta,* **4,** 228 (1950).
8. S. Tribalat, *Anal. Chim. Acta,* **5,** 115 (1951).
9. J. Coursier, J. Hure, and R. Platzer, *Anal. Chim. Acta,* **13,** 379 (1955).
10. K. D. Moffett, J. R. Simmler, and H. A. Potratz, *Anal. Chem.,* **28,** 1356 (1956).

14. RHODAMINE B AND OTHER DYES

$$Et_2N-\!=\!N(Et)_2{}^+,\ Cl^-$$

$$CO_2H$$

Rhodamine B, a xanthone dye, consists of green crystals or a reddish-violet powder which is very soluble in water, giving bluish-red solutions. It forms a violet compound with Sb(V) [1,2] and Ga [3] that can be extracted into benzene or ethyl acetate.[2] Milligram quantities of Pb and at least 100 μg of Se, Te, Bi, Cu, Zn, Fe, Ni, Sn, and As can be present, but Au, Tl, Hg, and Ag are extracted in appreciable quantity. The extractability of Sb at constant HCl concentration has been shown to increase linearly with rhodamine B concentration and to fall off markedly as the HCl molarity increases beyond 5.[4] Trace amounts of As, Bi, and Mo are extracted into ethyl acetate.[5] A method for Au extraction into isopropyl ether has been developed.[6]

Methyl violet. Antimony(V) in 6 N HCl forms a violet-blue complex with methyl violet that is extractable into benzene.[7]

Malachite green. This dye, like methyl violet, forms a yellow-green compound with Sb(V) in HCl that extracts into benzene.[8]

Azo dyes. A saturated ethanolic solution of any of the following azo compounds will give a compound with Sb(V) in strong HCl (from 2–12 N) that is extractable into benzene.[9] The reactions are sensitive (1–8 μg/ml of Sb) and specific in that Hg, Ag, or Mo do not interfere. The compounds are: p-dimethyl- and p-diethylamino-azobenzene, p-aminoazobenzene, dimethyl- and diethylaminophenyl-azodiphenyl, and phenylaminophenylazoazobenzene.

REFERENCES: Rhodamine B and Other Dyes

1. T. M. Maren, *Anal. Chem.,* **19,** 487 (1947).
2. C. L. Luke, *Anal. Chem.,* **25,** 674 (1953).
3. H. Onishi and E. B. Sandell, *Anal. Chim. Acta,* **13,** 159 (1955).
4. R. W. Ramette and E. B. Sandell, *Anal. Chim. Acta,* **13,** 455 (1955).
5. C. E. White, *Anal. Chem.,* **25,** 351 (1953).
6. B. J. MacNulty and L. D. Woollard, *Anal. Chim. Acta,* **13,** 154 (1955).
7. M. Jean, *Anal. Chim. Acta,* **11,** 82 (1954).
8. P. Bevillard, *Compt. rend.,* **236,** 711 (1953).
9. P. Bevillard, *Compt. rend.,* **238,** 2087 (1954).

15. HETEROCYCLIC POLYAMINES

Dipyridyl   Terpyridyl   1,10-Phenanthroline

The reactions of dipyridyl, phenanthroline, and their derivatives with Fe(II) and Cu(I) have been extensively applied to the colorimetric determination of these metals.[1]

Tris-phenanthroline iron(II) perchlorate has been found to be moderately extractable into chloroform and other solvents, but most satisfactorily into nitrobenzene.[2]

2,2′,2″-Terpyridyl forms a cobalt complex readily extracted into nitrobenzene, with which only Cu, Fe, and larger amounts of Ni interfere.[3] The use of alkylated or arylated phenanthrolines in these reactions has resulted in the formation of Fe and Cu(I) complexes that can be easily extracted with the higher alcohols such as amyl and hexyl alcohols. Two such compounds are 4,7-diphenyl-1,10-phenanthroline;[4] and 2,9-dimethyl-1,10-phenanthroline (neocuproine).[5] The latter, because of the presence of the substituents in sterically sensitive positions, does not react with Fe(II) and, hence, is fairly specific for Cu. Indeed, a procedure has been devised which permits the specific extraction of Cu in the presence of 56 metals.[6,7] 2-(2-Pyridyl)-benzimidazole, structurally similar to dipyridyl, also gives an Fe(II) complex that is extractable into isoamyl alcohol.[8]

REFERENCES: Heterocyclic Polyamines

1. G. F. Smith and F. P. Richter, *Phenanthroline and Substituted Phenanthroline Indicators,* G. F. Smith Chemical Co., Columbus, Ohio, 1941.
2. D. W. Margerum and C. V. Banks, *Anal. Chem.,* **26,** 200 (1954).
3. R. R. Miller and W. W. Brandt, *Anal. Chem.,* **26,** 1968 (1954).
4. G. F. Smith, W. H. McCurdy, Jr., and H. Diehl, *Analyst,* **77,** 418 (1952).
5. G. F. Smith and W. H. McCurdy, Jr., *Anal. Chem.,* **24,** 371 (1952).
6. C. L. Luke and M. E. Campbell, *Anal. Chem.,* **25,** 1588 (1953).
7. A. R. Gahler, *Anal. Chem.,* **26,** 577 (1954).
8. J. L. Walter and H. Freiser, *Anal. Chem.,* **26,** 217 (1954).

16. MISCELLANEOUS EXTRACTIONS

It has been found that CH_3COOH can be extracted from aqueous solutions into tributyl phosphate.[1] Over the concentration range 0.1

to 3.8 N the per cent extraction (about 50%) is essentially independent of the acid concentration. Sulfuric acid is 1.0% extracted over the concentration range 0.1 to 2.0 N. Hydrochloric acid, however, shows a marked increase with increased concentration. For example, with 0.10, 0.49, 1.0, and 1.9 N acid, the per cent extracted is 0.8, 0.8, 1.8, and 4.2, respectively. Nitric acid shows pronounced extraction, ranging from 14.4% with 0.10 N to 31.6% with 2.0 N acid. Acetic acid can be separated from HCl, using tributyl phosphate, if the HCl in the mixture is partially neutralized to a pH approximately the same as that of comparable concentration of CH_3COOH alone, prior to extraction.[2]

There is very little information on the extraction of metals from sulfate solutions. Sometimes a dry residue obtained by evaporation with H_2SO_4 can be extracted with an organic solvent to effect a separation. For example, from $MgSO_4$ containing traces of $CaSO_4$ the $MgSO_4$ is dissolved by a mixture of methyl alcohol and ethyl ether, leaving the $CaSO_4$ contaminated with a little $MgSO_4$.

Solubility of H_3PO_4 and H_2SO_4 in ether in the absence of water can be used for the separation of phosphate, as well as in the analysis of phosphatic materials containing various cations.[3] Phosphate is converted to H_3PO_4 by the addition of concentrated H_2SO_4 and is extracted with excess H_2SO_4 into ethyl ether. Two such treatments with H_2SO_4 and extractions with ether reduce the phosphate content to less than 0.02% of the amount originally present.

An interesting example of the increase in the extractability of a substance by another is afforded by the effect of ferric iron on H_3PO_4. The latter is hardly extracted at all from an HCl solution by isopropyl ether when present alone, but if ferric iron is also present, more than one-half the H_3PO_4 may be extracted under certain conditions, presumably because of the formation of a complex ferric phosphate.

REFERENCES: Miscellaneous Extraction

1. H. A. Pagel and F. W. McLafferty, *Anal. Chem.*, **21**, 272 (1949).
2. H. A. Pagel, P. E. Toren, and F. W. McLafferty, *Anal. Chem.*, **22**, 1150 (1950).
3. F. H. Cripps, British Atomic Energy Research Establishment Report, CRL/AE-49.

Chapter 12

Chelate Systems

1. ACETYLACETONE

$$CH_3-\overset{\overset{\displaystyle \|}{O}}{C}-CH_2-\overset{\overset{\displaystyle \|}{O}}{C}-CH_3$$

Acetylacetone (mol. wt 100.11) is a colorless, mobile liquid that boils at 135–137°C at 745 mm Hg and has a density of 0.976 at 25°C. It is miscible with alcohol, ether, chloroform, benzene, and other organic solvents. Acetylacetone is soluble in water to the extent of 0.17 g/ml at 25°C.[1] Commercial acetylacetone, which may contain several per cent of CH_3COOH, is purified by shaking the liquid with one-tenth its volume of dilute (1:10) ammonia followed by two successive tenth-volume portions of distilled water. The acetylacetone (which may be dried over anhydrous Na_2SO_4) is distilled. Following a water–acetylacetone azeotrope forerun, the pure compound distills. It is stable and can be stored almost indefinitely.

Acetylacetone, a β-diketone, forms well-defined chelates with over 60 metals. Many of these chelates are soluble in organic solvents. The solubility of acetylacetonates in organic solvents is of a much higher order of magnitude than the solubilities of most analytically used chelates; their solubilities are of the order of grams per liter rather than milligrams per liter, so that macro- as well as microscale separations are feasible.

As an illustration of the effectiveness of acetylacetone for trace quantities of metals might be cited the quantitative extraction of

Fe^{59} produced (in less than spectrographic limits) in neutron-irradiated Co to give carrier-free Fe^{59}.[7]

Extractions have been carried out with acetylacetone dissolved in such solvents as carbon tetrachloride,[3,4,8] chloroform,[5] benzene,[6] and xylene,[7] as well as with the pure liquid acting as both extracting agent and solvent.[1,2,9] Use of EDTA as masking agent provides the basis for a selective extraction of Be[5] and of U(VI).[9]

The use of the acetylacetone as both solvent and extractant offers several advantages over the use of acetylacetone solutions in carbon tetrachloride, etc. Foremost of these is the fact that extraction may be carried out from more acidic solutions than otherwise feasible because of the higher reagent concentration. Again, in some instances, acetylacetonates are more soluble in acetylacetone than in solvents such as carbon tetrachloride. Sometimes, however, the optimum value of the distribution ratio for the chelate is not as high as the optimum value obtained using another solvent so that it becomes advisable to use a mixture of acetylacetone and carbon tetrachloride. In this way, quantitative extractions from solutions of relatively high acidity

Table 12.1. Acetylacetone Extractions

Metal	pH of Extraction	Solvent	Reference
Al	4	Acetylacetone	1
Be	2	Acetylacetone	2
Be	5–10	Benzene	5, 10
Ce	>4	Acetylacetone	9
Cr(III)	0.0–2	Acetylacetone-chloroform	8
Co(III)	−0.3–2	Acetylacetone	13
Cu	2.0	Acetylacetone	2
Ga	2.5	Acetylacetone	1
In	2.8	Acetylacetone	1
Fe	1.5	Acetylacetone	13
Mn	∼4	Acetylacetone	13
Mo(VI)	−0.8–0.0	Acetylacetone-chloroform	8
Pu(IV)	2–10	Benzene	11, 15
Th	>5.8	Benzene	14
Ti	1.6	Acetylacetone-chloroform (76% extracted)	8
U(VI)	4–6	Acetylacetone	9
V(III)	2.0	Acetylacetone-chloroform (93% extracted)	16
V(IV)	2.5	Acetylacetone (73% extracted)	8, 13
Zn	5.5–7	Acetylacetone (70% extracted)	13
Zr	2–3	Acetylacetone (73% extracted)	13

are obtained.[8] A further convenience of the acetylacetone–carbon tetrachloride mixture is the fact that the organic layer is then denser than the aqueous layer.

Neither Co(II) nor Ni(II) forms extractable chelates but, since the Co(III) chelate is extractable, a useful separation of these metals can be achieved by extraction following oxidation.

The slow rate of formation of the Cr(III) chelate at low pH values permits the separation of Cr(III) from such metals as Fe(III), Cu(II), Mo(VI), etc.; once formed, however, the Cr(III) acetylacetonate remains in the organic phase even at very high acidities.[8]

Dibenzoylmethane [$C_6H_5CO)_2CH_2$], a crystalline solid melting at 76–78°C, is readily soluble in alcohol, ether, chloroform, and benzene but is insoluble in water. Its reactions with metals parallel those of acetylacetone. The reagent has been applied to a very selective extraction of U(VI) with the help of EDTA.[12] An extractable complex with Pu(IV) has been described.[11]

REFERENCES: Acetylacetone

1. J. F. Steinbach and H. Freiser, *Anal. Chem.,* **26,** 375 (1954).
2. J. F. Steinbach and H. Freiser, *Anal. Chem.,* **25,** 881 (1953).
3. E. Abrahamczik, *Angew. Chem.,* **61,** 89, 96 (1949).
4. E. Abrahamczik, *Angew. Chem.,* **129,** 247 (1949).
5. J. A. Adams, E. Booth, and J. D. H. Strickland, *Anal. Chim. Acta,* **6,** 462 (1952).
6. A. G. Maddock and G. L. Miles, *J. Chem. Soc.,* **1949,** S 248.
7. A. W. Kenny, W. R. E. Maton, and W. T. Spragg, *Nature,* **165,** 483 (1950).
8. J. P. McKaveney and H. Freiser, *Anal. Chem.,* **29,** 290 (1957).
9. A. Krishen and H. Freiser, *Anal. Chem.,* **29,** 288 (1957).
10. R. A. Bolomey and A. Broido, U.S. Atomic Energy Commission Report, ORNL-196.
11. B. G. Harvey, H. G. Heal, A. G. Maddock, and E. L. Rowley, *J. Chem. Soc.,* **1947,** 1010.
12. R. Přibil and M. Jelinek, *Chem. Listy,* **47,** 1326 (1953).
13. J. F. Steinbach, Ph.D. Thesis, University of Pittsburgh, 1953.
14. J. Rydberg, *Acta Chem. Scand.,* **4,** 1503 (1950).
15. J. Rydberg, *Arkiv Kemi,* **9,** 190 (1955); *Svensk Kem. Tidskr.,* **87,** 499 (1955).
16. J. P. McKaveney and H. Freiser, Pittsburgh Conference on Analytical Chemistry and Applied Spectroscopy, March 1957.

2. THENOYLTRIFLUOROACETONE (TTA)

$$\text{C—CH}_2\text{—C—CF}_3$$

Thenoyltrifluoroacetone (TTA) (mol. wt 222), a crystalline solid melting at 42.5–43.2°C, is one of the best of a group of fluorinated

β-diketones, $X—COCH_2—CO—CF_3$.[1] The trifluoromethyl group was introduced to increase the acidity of the enol form so that extractions from solutions of very low pH would be feasible. Although the reactivity of TTA with metal ions is as general as that of acetylacetone and other β-diketones, it has found its greatest use in separations of the actinide metals. See Table 12.2. Thenoyltrifluoroacetone is generally used as a 0.1–0.5 M solution in benzene or toluene. Bolomey and Wish,[2] working with a much more dilute solution (0.01 M), found the rates of extraction to be very slow ($\sim$2–3 hours) in some cases [e.g., Be and Fe(III)]. This difficulty is minimized by the use of the more concentrated TTA solution and higher pH values.

Other fluorinated diketones. Trifluoroacetylacetone [$(CF_3CO)_2$ CH_2] [13] has been used for the extraction of Zr and Hf. A 0.075 M

Table 12.2. Thenoyltrifluoroacetone Extractions

Metal	pH of Extraction	TTA Concentration in Benzene Solution	Reference
Be	Optimum 6–7	0.02 M	2
Al	5.5	0.02 M	2
Ca	8.2	0.5 M	2, 3
Sc(III)	1.5	0.5 M	3
Fe(III)	2–3	0.02 M	2
Cu	3.4	0.02 M	2
Sr	>10	0.02 M	2
Y	>6	0.02 M	2
Zr	2 M HClO$_4$	0.02 M (or 0.5 M in xylene)	4, 5, 16
Eu	>3.4	0.2 M in toluene	6
Yb	>3.4	0.2 M in toluene	6
Hf	2 M HClO$_4$	0.02 M	4, 5
Tl(I)	>6.5	0.25 M	7
Tl(III)	>3.5	0.25 M	7
Pb	>4	0.25 M	7
Bi	>2	0.25 M	7
Po	>1.5	0.25 M	7
Ac	>7	0.25 M	7
Th	>0.8	0.25 M	7, 12, 15
Pa	Strong mineral acid	0.4 M	8
U(VI)	>3.0	0.2 M	8
Np(IV)	0.5 M H$^+$	0.15 M	9
Pu(IV)	0.5 M H$^+$	0.15 M	9, 10, 11, 17
Am(III)	>3.5	0.2 M	6
Cm	>3.5	0.2 M	6
Bk	$\sim$2.5	0.2 M	6
Cf	$\sim$3.0	0.2 M	6
E	$\sim$3.0	0.2 M	6
Fm	$\sim$3.0	0.2 M	6
La	>4.5	0.2 M	8

solution in benzene gave distribution ratios of 0.625 and 0.134 for Zr and Hf, respectively, from a 0.07 N HCl solution. More recently a mixture of isomeric dichloro derivatives of 1-phenyl-4,4,5,5,6,6,6-heptafluoro-1,3-hexanedione has been applied to the extraction of Th and Np.[14] The principal advantage of these compounds is the much greater solubility of the metal chelates than those of TTA. For example, the solubility of the thorium-TTA complex in carbon tetrachloride is about 3 g/l, whereas the corresponding dichlorophenylheptafluorohexanedione complex is sixty times greater. The compound does have a drawback in its strong tendencies toward emulsion formation in the presence of NH_4^+.[8]

REFERENCES: Thenoyltrifluoroacetone

1. J. C. Reid and M. Calvin, *J. Am. Chem. Soc.*, **72**, 2948 (1950).
2. R. A. Bolomey and L. Wish, *J. Am. Chem. Soc.*, **72**, 4483 (1950).
3. A. Broido, U.S. Atomic Energy Commission Report, AECD-2616.
4. R. E. Connick and W. H. McVey, *J. Am. Chem. Soc.*, **71**, 3182 (1949).
5. E. H. Huffman and L. J. Beaufait, *J. Am. Chem. Soc.*, **71**, 3179 (1949).
6. L. B. Magnusson and M. L. Anderson, *J. Am. Chem. Soc.*, **76**, 6207 (1954).
7. F. Hagemann, *J. Am. Chem. Soc.*, **72**, 768 (1950).
8. E. K. Hyde, *Proceedings of the International Conference on the Peaceful Uses of Atomic Energy*, Vol. 7, United Nations, New York, 1956, p. 281.
9. L. B. Magnusson, J. C. Hindman, and T. J. Chappelle, U.S. Atomic Energy Commission Report, ANL-4066.
10. D. F. Peppard, M. H. Studier, M. V. Gergel, G. W. Mason, J. C. Sullivan, and J. F. Mech, *J. Am. Chem. Soc.*, **73**, 2529 (1951).
11. J. C. Sullivan and J. C. Hindman, *J. Am. Chem. Soc.*, **76**, 5931 (1954).
12. R. A. Day, Jr., and R. W. Stoughton, *J. Am. Chem. Soc.*, **72**, 5662 (1950).
13. B. G. Schultz and E. M. Larsen, *J. Am. Chem. Soc.*, **72**, 3610 (1950).
14. U.S. Atomic Energy Commission Reports, UCRL-4377 and UCRL-4480.
15. R. W. Perkins and D. R. Kalkwarf, *Anal. Chem.*, **28**, 1989 (1956).
16. F. L. Moore, *Anal. Chem.*, **28**, 997 (1956).
17. J. G. Cuninghame and G. L. Miles, *J. Inorg. Nuclear Chem.*, **3**, 54 (1956).

3. QUINALIZARIN

Quinalizarin (1,2,5,8-tetrahydroxyanthraquinone), a red crystalline solid with a green metallic luster, is insoluble in water but readily soluble in alkalies and in H_2SO_4. It is slightly soluble in alcohol and may be used as a 0.1% ethanolic solution. It forms complexes with a large number of metals including Be, Mg, rare earths, Fe(III), Sc, Al, Ti, Zr, and Th. Of these only Fe(III), Sc, Al, Ti, Zr, and Th form complexes that are extractable by ethyl acetate or isoamyl alcohol. The reagent has been utilized for the separation of Sc.[1]

REFERENCE: Quinalizarin

1. G. Beck, *Mikrochim. Acta,* **34,** 282 (1949).

4. MORIN

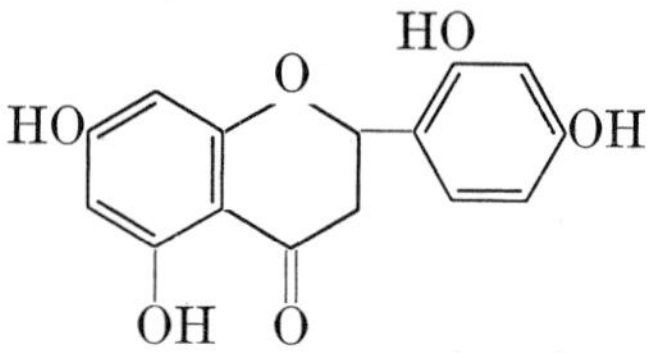

Morin (3,5,7,2,4-pentahydroxyflavone), a pale-yellow crystalline solid melting at 285°C, is insoluble in water but soluble in alcohol, acetone, and alkalies. In acidic medium this reagent reacts with a number of metals including Al, Be, Ce(III), Ga, In, Sb(III), Sc, Sn, Th, Ti, and Zr to form complexes that are extractable by butyl, amyl, and cyclohexyl alcohols.[1]

REFERENCE: Morin

1. E. B. Sandell, *Colorimetric Determination of Traces of Metals,* second edition, Interscience Publishers, Inc., New York, 1950, p. 127.

5. 8-QUINOLINOL (OXINE)

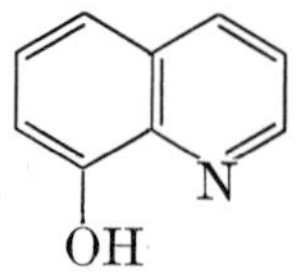

8-Quinolinol (oxine) (mol. wt 145), a white crystalline compound melting at 74–76°C, is almost insoluble in water and ether but freely soluble in alcohol, chloroform, benzene, and aqueous solutions of mineral acids. It is generally used in extraction as a 1% (0.07 M) solution in chloroform. The reagent is somewhat sensitive to light; the solutions should be stored in brown bottles and, if convenient, in a refrigerator. If U.S.P. chloroform is used, this should be first purified [4] by shaking with one-third its volume of a solution which contains 2.5% NH_4Cl, and 5 volume % concentrated NH_3, followed by three water washings. The chloroform is kept over anhydrous K_2CO_3 for several hours before transfer to a dry storage bottle.

Oxine, one of the most popular and versatile organic reagents, is known to react with at least 43 metals.[1] Generally, these are the same metals that precipitate with aqueous ammonia. The divalent and trivalent metal chelates have the general formula $M(C_9H_6ON)_2$ or $M(C_9H_6ON)_3$; the known composition of the higher-valent metal chelates may differ somewhat, e.g., $Ce(C_9H_6ON)_4$,[2] $Th(C_9H_6ON)_4 \cdot (C_9H_7ON)$,[1] $MoO_2(C_9H_6ON)_2$,[3] $WO_2(C_9H_6ON)_2$,[3] $U_3O_6(C_9H_6ON)_6 \cdot C_9H_7ON$.[2] Oxine, having both a basic nitrogen and a phenolic hydroxyl group, is an amphoteric substance in aqueous medium. The distribution of the neutral compound between chloroform and water is 720 at 18°C,[4] although its distribution ratio achieves this value only when the pH of the aqueous phase has a value between 5 and 9. Because of its amphoteric nature, oxine is incompletely extracted under pH 5 or over pH 9.[4] See page 10.

Oxine extraction has been studied in detail for almost twenty metals. The pertinent data is summarized in Table 12.3. The absence of any metal from the table should not be taken to imply that it is not extractable, but rather that the study has not yet been made. For example, until recently the alkaline earths could not be extracted with oxine. Magnesium was found to extract by Luke and Campbell [7] by the modification of the organic solvent to butyl cellosolve–chloroform mixture. Dyrssen [23] has made an interesting advance in oxine extractions. By the use of relatively high concentrations of oxine (up to 1.0 M) in chloroform, he was able to extract Sr as $SrOx_2 \cdot 2HOx$, the oxine replacing the usual water coordinated by the Sr. Preliminary experiments [8] indicate that the other alkaline earths are also extractable with the more concentrated oxine solutions.

In early extraction work [6] with oxine, chloroform solutions of a relatively low concentration (0.01%) of reagent were employed. This practice resulted in the need for multiple extractions and a restricted pH range of extraction. As the role of reagent concentration became better understood, this was accompanied by a trend toward use of 1%,[10] 3%,[7] and even 10% [23] oxine solutions.

As the data in Table 12.3 indicate, even with proper pH control, oxine is not a very selective extraction agent. The usefulness of this reagent has been greatly extended by the use of masking agents. Thus, interference from elements such as Fe, Cu, Mo, and Ni may be re-

Table 12.3. Extraction of Metals with 8-Quinolinol

Metal	Optimum Extraction, pH Range	Comments	Reference
Al	4.8–6.7, 8.2–11.5		4, 5
Bi	4.0–5.2		6
Cd	8	Incomplete extraction	8
Ca	13	Butyl cellosolve and chloroform	7, 8
Ce(III)	9.9–10.5		9
Co	>6.8		6
Cu(II)	2.8–14	Tartrate used in higher pH range	6, 10
Er	>8.5		17
Fe(III)	1.9–12.5	Tartrate used in higher pH range	6, 10
Ga	3.0–6.2		4, 11
In	>3.0		4, 6
Mg	10.2	Butyl cellosolve and chloroform	7
Mn	7.2–12.5	Tartrate and ferrocyanide present	10
Mo	1.6–5.6	Also in presence of EDTA	10, 14
Nd	>8.5		17
Ni	4.5–9.5		10
Nb	1 N NH$_4$OH	Citrate medium	29
Pa	Saturated (NH$_4$)$_2$CO$_3$	Incomplete extraction	20
Pb	8.4–12.3		19
Pd	Dilute HCl		19
Pu(IV) and Pu(VI)	4–8	Amyl acetate	21
Ru(III)	Acetate medium		19
Sc	6.5–8.5		19, 22
Sr	11.28	1 M 8-quinolinol in chloroform	23
Sn(IV)	2.5–5.5		10
Th	4.9	Chloroform or methyl isobutyl ketone	24, 25
Ti	3.8–5.0	H$_2$O$_2$ present	12
Tl(III)	6.5–7.0	85–89% extracted	11
U(VI)	4.7–8.0		14, 16
V(V)	3.3–4.5		13
W(VI)	2.4–4.3	EDTA present	14
Zn	4.6–13.4	Incomplete extraction	19
Zr	Acetic acid–acetate		19

moved by the use of cyanide, either by forming the cyanide complex prior to extraction,[9,16] or by washing the chloroform layer with aqueous cyanide solution.[15] The extraction of Fe may also be prevented by reduction to Fe(II) and masking with 1,10-phenanthroline.[15] Masking of Th may be accomplished by the use of either 4-sulfobenzene arsonic acid or concentrated (6 M) ammonium acetate.[15] It might be possible to mask Zr by using 2-sulfoethane arsonic acid.[15]

A most interesting systematic study of the application of EDTA as masking agent in oxine extractions was recently carried out by Taylor.[14] In the presence of EDTA, relatively little or no effect is observed for the extraction of U(VI), W(VI), and Mo(VI), whereas the range for complete extraction of Ti is raised to pH values between 7.9 and 9.0. The extraction of Cu begins at pH 2.5, but quantitative extraction is not achieved until pH 9.0. Complete inhibition of the extraction of Al, Co, Fe(III), Mn, and Ni is obtained to pH values slightly above 8. When calcium ethylenediaminetetraacetate is used in place of the sodium salt, the masking action is less pronounced. Thus, Cu could be quantitatively extracted in the pH region of 6.0–9.1 and V(III) between 4.1–5.6, and complete inhibition of the extraction of Al, Co, and Mn is possible only at pH values below 6.0. Iron(III) and Ni will be masked by this means in solutions whose maximum pH value is 7.5.

Substituted 8-quinolinols. Dyrssen[27] found 5,7-dihalo-8-quinolinols to extract Th, La, and UO_2^{2+} at lower pH values than did oxine. 5,7-Dichloro-8-quinolinol has been applied to the extraction of some of the rare earth ions; it is said to extract these metals more quantitatively than does the parent compound.[17] Erbium(III) and Nd(III) are quantitatively extracted at pH values of 8.5 or over.

Palladium has been extracted with 5-methyl-8-quinolinol into chloroform.[18]

2-Methyl-8-quinolinol, which was found by Merritt and Walker[26] to be non-reactive toward Al but otherwise like 8-quinolinol in behavior, offers advantages in extractions from aluminum-containing solutions. It has been applied to the removal of interfering metal ions before the oxine extraction of Al in both ferrous and non-ferrous alloys.[28]

REFERENCES: 8-Quinolinol (Oxine)

1. F. J. Welcher, *Organic Analytical Reagents,* Vol. I, D. Van Nostrand Co., Inc., Princeton, N. J., 1947, pp. 264 ff.
2. C. Duval, *Inorganic Thermogravimetric Analysis,* Elsevier Publishing Co., New York, 1953.
3. H. Goto, *J. Chem. Soc. Japan,* **55,** 201 (1934).
4. S. Lacroix, *Anal. Chim. Acta,* **1,** 260 (1947).
5. C. H. R. Gentry and L. G. Sherrington, *Analyst,* **71,** 432 (1946).
6. T. Moeller, *Ind. Eng. Chem., Anal. Ed.,* **15,** 271, 346 (1943).
7. C. L. Luke and M. E. Campbell, *Anal. Chem.,* **26,** 1778 (1954); C. L. Luke, *Anal. Chem.,* **28,** 1443 (1956).
8. S. Jankowski and H. Freiser, private communication.

9. W. Westwood and A. Mayer, *Analyst*, **73**, 275 (1948).
10. C. H. R. Gentry and L. G. Sherrington, *Analyst*, **75**, 17 (1950).
11. T. Moeller, *Anal. Chem.*, **22**, 686 (1950).
12. K. Gardner, *Analyst*, **76**, 485 (1951).
13. N. A. Talvitie, *Anal. Chem.*, **25**, 604 (1953).
14. R. P. Taylor, Ph.D. Thesis, Princeton University, 1954.
15. D. W. Margerum, W. Sprain, and C. V. Banks, *Anal. Chem.*, **25**, 249 (1953).
16. L. Silverman, L. Moudy, and D. W. Hawley, *Anal. Chem.*, **25**, 1369 (1953).
17. T. Moeller and D. E. Jackson, *Anal. Chem.*, **22**, 1393 (1950).
18. A. Sa, *Rev. asoc. bioquím. argentina*, **16**, 7 (1949).
19. E. B. Sandell, *Colorimetric Determination of Traces of Metals*, second edition, Interscience Publishers, Inc., New York, 1950.
20. A. G. Maddock and G. L. Miles, *J. Chem. Soc.*, **1949**, S 248, 253.
21. G. B. Harvey, H. G. Heal, A. G. Maddock, and E. L. Rowley, *J. Chem. Soc.*, **1947**, 1010.
22. L. Pokras and P. M. Bernays, *J. Am. Chem. Soc.*, **73**, 7 (1951); *Anal. Chem.*, **23**, 757 (1951).
23. D. Dyrssen, *Svensk Kem. Tidskr.*, **67**, 311 (1955).
24. D. Dyrssen, *Svensk Kem. Tidskr.*, **65**, 43 (1953).
25. T. Moeller and M. V. Ramaniah, *J. Am. Chem. Soc.*, **75**, 3946 (1953).
26. L. L. Merritt and J. K. Walker, *Ind. Eng. Chem., Anal. Ed.*, **16**, 387 (1944).
27. D. Dyrssen, M. Dyrssen, and E. Johansson, *Acta Chem. Scand.*, **10**, 341 (1956).
28. R. J. Hynek and L. J. Wrangell, *Anal. Chem.*, **28**, 1520 (1956).
29. J. L. Kassner, A. Garcia-Porrata, and E. L. Grove, *Anal. Chem.*, **27**, 492 (1955).

6. DIMETHYLGLYOXIME

$$CH_3—C—C—CH_3$$
$$HON \quad NOH$$

Dimethylglyoxime (mol. wt 116) is a white crystalline solid melting at 238–240°C with decomposition; it is fairly insoluble in water but soluble in alcohol. Dimethylglyoxime, one of the earliest and most specific of the organic analytical reagents, gives a scarlet-red precipitate with Ni in alkaline medium and a yellow precipitate with Pd in acid medium. These dimethylglyoxime complexes may be formed in the aqueous phase and are then subsequently extracted into chloroform.[1,2] The optimum pH range for extraction of the Ni complex is 4–12 in the presence of tartrate and 7–12 in the presence of citrate.[11] The solubility of the Ni complex in chloroform at room temperature corresponds to approximately 35–50 μg Ni per ml.[1,7] Some extraction of Co out of alkaline solutions may be expected if large amounts (>5 mg) are present.[2] This may be prevented by the formation of $Co(NH_3)_6{}^{3+}$. Palladium(II) may be extracted out of approximately 1 M H_2SO_4.[3] Rhenium(VII) partially reduced with $SnCl_2$ gives a yellow dimethylglyoxime complex in acid solution that is soluble in benzyl alcohol.[4] In the presence of pyridine, Fe(II) forms an extractable complex with dimethylglyoxime.[8] Up to 50 μg Fe can be extracted into chloroform in the presence of small amounts of Cu, Co, Mn, Ti, Al, and Zn. Nickel and Pb must be absent.

Other α-dioximes

Cyclohexanedionedioxime   Furildioxime   Benzildioxime

Extraction of Ni complexes of cyclohexanedionedioxime[5] and furildioxime[6,9] have been found to be similar to that of dimethylglyoxime. Chloroform, o-dichlorobenzene, ethyl ether, or ethyl acetate can be used to extract the nickel furildioxime complex, but o-dichlorobenzene is preferred because of its low volatility and high density. The nickel furildioxime complex is more soluble than any of the nickel dioxime complexes in chloroform or o-dichlorobenzene.[6] The optimum pH range for extraction of the nickel furildioxime complex is 7.5–8.3. The reagent is of limited usefulness, both because of the narrow pH extraction range and the partial solubility of its other metal (notably Cu) complexes.

α-Benzildioxime forms a complex with partially reduced Re(VII) salts that is extractable with benzyl alcohol[4] from 9 M H_2SO_4. As few as 5 μg of Re can be separated from 5 mg Mo in this way. Iron and Ni do not interfere, but nitrates must be absent. Benzildioxime has also been used for Ni extraction over a wide pH range.[10]

REFERENCES: Dimethylglyoxime

1. E. B. Sandell and R. W. Perlich, *Ind. Eng. Chem., Anal Ed.,* **11,** 309 (1939).
2. A. J. Hall and R. S. Young, *Analyst,* **71,** 479 (1946).
3. R. S. Young, *Analyst,* **76,** 49 (1951).
4. S. Tribalat, *Compt. rend.,* **224,** 469 (1947).
5. P. G. Butts, A. R. Gahler, and M. G. Mellon, *Metal Finishing,* **49,** 50 (1951).
6. A. R. Gahler, A. M. Mitchell, and M. G. Mellon, *Anal. Chem.,* **23,** 500 (1951).
7. W. Nielsch, *Z. Anal. Chem.,* **143,** 272 (1954).
8. N. Oi, *J. Chem. Soc. Japan, Pure Chem. Sect.,* **75,** 1069 (1954).
9. C. G. Taylor, *Analyst,* **81,** 369 (1956).
10. Y. Uzumasa and S. Washizuka, *Bull. Chem. Soc. Japan,* **29,** 403 (1956).
11. A. Claassen and L. Bastings, *Rec. trav. chim.,* **73,** 783 (1954).

7. SALICYLALDOXIME

Salicylaldoxime, a white crystalline solid melting at 57°C, is only slightly soluble in water but dissolves readily in various organic solvents. Complete extraction of Cu(II) in the pH range 3.5–9.5 can be obtained by using a 0.02 M solution of salicylaldoxime in n-amyl acetate.[1] The method has been used in the analysis of Cu in aluminum- and zinc-base alloys. None of the metals commonly occurring in these alloys interferes. Nickel will also extract quantitatively, but at a pH below 5.0 it does not interfere with the extraction.

α-Benzoinoxime

α-Benzoinoxime can be used to separate Mo and W from all other common metal ions in an acid solution, using chloroform to extract their benzoinoxime complexes.[2]

REFERENCES: Salicylaldoxime

1. S. H. Simonsen and H. M. Burnett, *Anal. Chem.,* **27,** 1336 (1955).
2. P. G. Jeffery, *Analyst,* **81,** 104 (1956).

8. 1-NITROSO-2-NAPHTHOL AND RELATED COMPOUNDS

1-Nitroso-2-naphthol, an orange-brown crystalline solid, melting at 108–110°C, is slightly soluble in water and cold alcohol but freely soluble in hot alcohol, benzene, ether, and glacial acetic acid. The reagent forms extractable complexes with Co(III) in acid medium and Fe(II) in basic medium.[1,2]

2-Nitroso-1-naphthol forms a violet complex with Pd that can be extracted into benzene or toluene.[5]   Interference by Fe, Co, Cu, Ni, Cr, and other metals is removed by use of EDTA.

o-Nitrosophenol, quite analogous to the nitrosonaphthol, reacts with Cu(II), Hg(II), Ni(II), and Fe(II) in weakly acid solution to form complexes which may be extracted into ethyl ether but which are not soluble in petroleum ether.[3]   This reagent has found but little application because of its instability.   Since the reagent is stable only in solution, it must be prepared in the laboratory.

Isonitrosoacetophenone $(C_6H_5COCH{=}NOH)$, a white crystalline solid melting at 126–128°C is slightly soluble in water but readily soluble in chloroform.   It forms chloroform-extractable complexes with traces of Fe(II), Co, Ni, Cu, Mn, Zn, Cd, Pb, and Hg.[4]   Cobalt will extract from an acid solution but Ni requires an alkaline medium.[4]

REFERENCES: 1-Nitroso-2-Naphthol and Related Compounds

1. R. Vanossi, *Anales soc. cient. argentina,* **131,** 226 (1941); *Chem. Abstracts,* **35,** 5412 (1941).
2. L. Waldbauer and N. M. Ward, *Ind. Eng. Chem., Anal. Ed.,* **14,** 727 (1942).
3. G. Cronheim, *Ind. Eng. Chem., Anal. Ed.,* **14,** 445 (1942).
4. F. Krohnke, *Ber. deut. chem. Ges.,* **60,** 527 (1927).
5. K. L. Cheng, *Anal. Chem.,* **26,** 1895 (1954).

9. AMMONIUM SALT *N*-NITROSOPHENYLHYDROXYLAMINE (CUPFERRON)

Cupferron, a white crystalline powder melting at 163–164°C, soluble in water and in alcohol, was first introduced by Baudisch [1] in 1909 as a specific precipitant for Cu and Fe, but later many other metals were found to react.   Since metal cupferrates are soluble in ether and chloroform, the reagent is now widely used in solvent extraction separation schemes.

Cupferron is generally used in aqueous solution (about 6%).   Since both the reagent and its chelates may decompose upon heating to form nitrosobenzene, for best results cupferron solutions are refrigerated and extractions carried out in the cold.   Decomposition of the reagent solution may be detected by a cloudy appearance.   The addition of 50 mg acetophenetide to each 150 ml of reagent solution has been suggested as a stabilizer.[2]

One of the earliest applications of cupferron to the extraction of metals was performed by Meunier,[3] who quantitatively extracted Fe(III), Ti, and Cu from a 1.2 M HCl solution into chloroform, using an excess of cupferron. Furman, Mason, and Pekola [4] made a careful systematic study of cupferron separations and consider extraction far superior to precipitation for removal of microgram to milligram quantities of metals. Table 12.4 summarizes the extraction behavior of metals as cupferrates. The distribution coefficient of hydrogen cupferrate between acidified aqueous solutions and chloroform was found to be 211.[4] Cupferron has been used to separate Am and Cm.[5,6]

Neocupferron

Neocupferron

The ammonium salt of N-nitrosonaphthylhydroxylamine, called neocupferron, has been prepared and shown to behave similarly to cupferron.[16] It has not been extensively applied to extraction studies. A point of interest is the extractability of Nd with this reagent, re-

Table 12.4. Cupferron Extractions

Metal	Extraction Range	Solvent	Reference
Al	pH 2–5	Chloroform	3, 7
Sb(III)	$(1 + 9)H_2SO_4$	Chloroform	4, 8
Bi	HCl, H_2SO_4	Toluene, methyl ethyl ketone	8
Cd	Neutral solution	Boiling ether	8
Ce(IV)	pH 2	Butyl acetate	8, 14, 15
Co	Dilute acetic acid	Ethyl acetate or ether	8
Cu	$(1 + 9)$HCl	Chloroform	3, 7, 10
In	Dilute acid	Benzene, chloroform	8
Fe(III)	$(1 + 9)H_2SO_4$	Chloroform, ether, ethyl acetate	3, 4, 9, 11, 12
Mn(II)	Neutral solution	Ether	7
Hg(II)	Neutral solution	Benzene and chloroform	8
Mo(VI)	$(2 + 9)$HCl	Ethyl acetate, chloroform	4, 10, 11
Ni	Neutral solution	Organic solvents	7
Nb	Acidic solution	Chloroform	4
Pa	pH 1–4 N acid	Benzene, ethyl ether, chloroform	13
Th	$(1 + 9)$HCl	Ethyl or butyl acetate	11, 14, 15
Sn(IV)	$(1 + 9)$HCl	Ethyl acetate	11
Sn(II)	1.5 N acid	Benzene and chloroform	8
Ti(II)	$(1 + 9)$HCl	Chloroform, ether, ethyl acetate	3, 4, 11
W	$(1 + 9)$HCl	Partial extraction by ethyl acetate	11
U(IV)	$(1 + 9)H_2SO_4$	Ether	4
V(V)	$(1 + 9)$HCl or H_2SO_4	Ethyl acetate or ether	4, 11
Zn	Neutral	Ether (incompletely extracted)	7
Zr	$(1 + 9)H_2SO_4$	Ethyl acetate	11

flecting the effect of structure on solubility.[7] Another homolog of cupferron at least as sensitive as neocupferron is the fluorene homolog,[17] whose behavior also parallels that of cupferron.

REFERENCES: Cupferron

1. O. Baudisch, *Chem.-Ztg.*, **33**, 1298 (1909).
2. F. G. Germuth, *Chemist-Analyst*, **17**, No. 3, 3 (1928).
3. P. Meunier, *Compt. rend.*, **199**, 1250 (1934).
4. N. H. Furman, W. B. Mason, and J. S. Pekola, *Anal. Chem.*, **21**, 1325 (1949).
5. J. P. Nigon and T. A. Penneman, Abstracts National A.C.S. Meeting, Chicago, Fall 1950.
6. J. P. Nigon and R. A. Penneman, U.S. Atomic Energy Commission Report, AECU-1006.
7. O. Baudisch and R. Furst, *Ber. deut. chem. Ges.*, **50**, 324 (1917).
8. V. Auger, L. Lafontaine, and C. Caspar, *Compt. rend.*, **180**, 376 (1925).
9. R. Paulais, *Compt. rend.*, **206**, 783 (1938).
10. D. Bertrand, *Bull. soc. chim.*, **6**, 1676 (1939).
11. M. D. Foster, F. S. Grimaldi, and R. E. Stevens, *U.S. Geol. Survey*, Rept. 2 (1944).
12. O. Baudisch, *Arch. Kemi Mineral Geol.*, **12B**, No. 8 (1938).
13. A. G. Maddock and G. L. Miles, *J. Chem. Soc.* (Supplement No. 2), S 253 (1949).
14. Z. Hagiwara, *Technol. Repts. Tôhoku Univ.*, **18**, 16 (1953).
15. Z. Hagiwara, *Technol. Repts. Tôhoku Univ.*, **19**, 73 (1954).
16. F. J. Welcher, *Organic Analytical Reagents*, Vol. III, D. Van Nostrand Co., Inc., Princeton, N. J., 1947, p. 400.
17. R. E. Oesper and R. E. Fulmer, *Anal. Chem.*, **25**, 908 (1953).

10. CUPFERRON ANALOGS

N-Benzoylphenylhydroxylamine

A colorless crystalline compound melting at 121–122°C, *N*-benzoylphenylhydroxylamine is slightly soluble in water but reasonably soluble in aqueous ammonia, alcohol, benzene, and ether. The compound, unlike cupferron which it resembles in analytical reactions, is quite stable toward heat, light, and air. It forms water insoluble complexes with Sn, Ti, Zr, V(V), Mo(VI), and W(VI) in acid solution, Cu, Fe, and Al at a *p*H of about 4.0, but Co, Cd, Pb, Hg, Mn, U(VI), and Zn do not react at all at *p*H 4.0.[1,2] The V(V) complex is soluble in benzene.[3]   A 0.1 M solution of the reagent in chloroform will extract Th at a pH of 2, U(VI) at a pH of 3.5, and La at pH 7.[4]

Benzohydroxamic acid

$$\text{C}_6\text{H}_5-\text{C}=\text{O}$$
$$\text{HN}-\text{OH}$$

This acid [5,6] forms a colored complex with V(V) which is extractable by oxonium solvents such as 1-hexanol.

3-Hydroxyl-1,3-diphenyltriazine

$$\text{C}_6\text{H}_5-\text{N}=\text{N}$$
$$\text{HO}-\text{N}-\text{C}_6\text{H}_5$$

This compound [7] forms complexes with Cu(II), Pd(II), Fe(II), Fe(III), V(III), V(V), Ti(IV), and Mo(VI) at a pH below 3.   All but those of Cu(II) and Pd(II) are decomposed by heating in acid solution.   Nickel forms a complex in the pH range of 4.4–7.0.   The Cu(II), Pd(II), and Ni(II) complexes are quite soluble in benzene and chloroform.

REFERENCES: Cupferron Analogs

1. S. C. Shome, *Analyst,* **75,** 27 (1950).
2. D. E. Ryan and G. D. Lutwick, *Can. J. Chem.,* **31,** 9 (1953).
3. S. C. Shome, *Anal. Chem.,* **23,** 1187 (1951).
4. D. Dyrssen, *Acta Chem. Scand.,* **10,** 353 (1956).
5. A. S. Bhaduri and P. Ray, *Science and Culture (India),* **18,** 97 (1952).
6. W. M. Wise and W. W. Brandt, *Anal. Chem.,* **27,** 1392 (1955).
7. N. C. Sogani and S. C. Bhattacharya, *Anal. Chem.,* **28,** 81, 1616 (1956).

11. 1-(2-PYRIDYLAZO)-2-NAPHTHOL

$$\text{pyridyl}-\text{N}=\text{N}-\text{naphthol}$$
$$\text{HO}$$

1-(2-Pyridylazo)-2-naphthol is an orange-red amorphous solid, nearly insoluble in water but soluble in a variety of organic solvents to which it imparts a yellow color.   The reagent forms complexes with Bi, Cd, Cu, Pd, Pt, Sn(II), U(VI), Hg, Th, Co, Pb, Fe(III), Ni, Zn, La, Ce(IV), In, Sc, and Eu.[1] Most of these complexes are soluble in amyl alcohol, and the complexes of Ni, Co, Cd, and Zn are also soluble in carbon tetrachloride. Further study with this reagent, particularly of the effect of pH upon extraction, might be quite fruitful.

Erio OS(I)

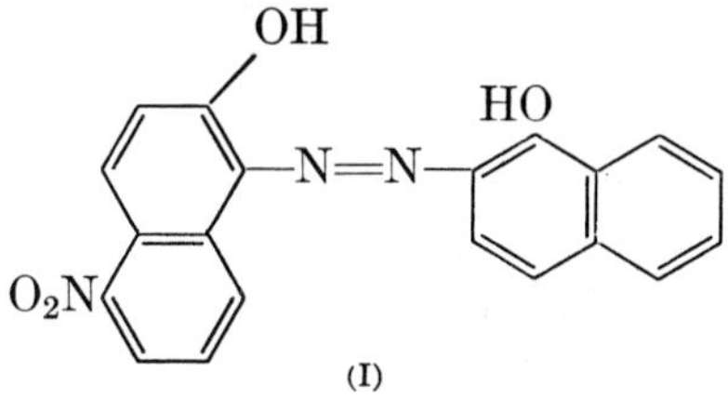

(I)

Another orthohydroxyazo compound, Erio OS(I) has been suggested as an extraction agent. It forms red extractable complexes with several divalent metals and with In and Ga.[2]

REFERENCES: 1-(2-Pyridylazo)-2-naphthol

1. K. L. Cheng and R. H. Bray, *Anal. Chem.*, **27**, 782 (1955).
2. H. Flaschka, *Mikrochim. Acta*, **416**, 784 (1956).

12. DIPHENYLTHIOCARBAZONE (DITHIZONE)

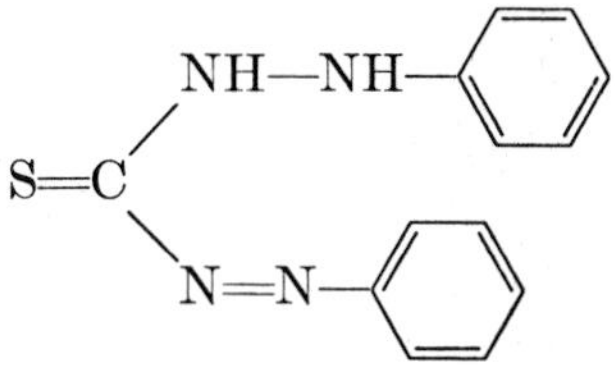

Diphenylthiocarbazone, or dithizone (mol. wt 256), is a purplish-black crystalline compound, decomposing sharply at a temperature between 165–169°C and soluble in many organic solvents. It is insoluble in water and dilute mineral acids but is readily soluble in dilute aqueous ammonia. In most of its analytical applications, dithizone is used in chloroform or carbon tetrachloride solution. It is quite sensitive to oxidation, forming diphenylthiocarbodiazone, and the commercial product must almost always be purified before use. If a 0.01% solution in carbon tetrachloride is shaken with dilute (1:100) metal-free ammonia and only a faint yellow color remains in the carbon tetrachloride layer, the product may be used without further purification.[1] It may be purified by dissolving about 1 g of commercial product in 100 ml of chloroform and filtering away from any insoluble residue. The chloroform solution is extracted with several 100-ml portions of metal-free, redistilled 0.2 M aqueous ammonia. The dithizone dissolves in the aqueous phase to give an orange solution, and the diphenylthiocarbodiazone lacking acid hydrogen atoms remains behind in the chloroform. (Probably a higher yield of dithizone would be obtained if hydroxylamine were added to the ammonia used for extraction in order to reduce the carbodiazone oxidation product.) The ammonia extracts are slightly acidified with dilute HCl, and the precipitated dithizone is extracted with several 20-ml portions of chloroform. These extracts are washed several times with water and evaporated in a beaker on a steam bath at a low heat to remove the chloroform. The last traces of moisture are removed by heating for an hour at a maximum temperature of 50°C in vacuo. The reagent should be stored in a dark, tightly stoppered bottle.[2]

An alternative purification procedure is based on recrystallization from chloroform.[1] An almost saturated solution of dithizone is filtered and evaporated in a stream of filtered air at 40°C until about a third or a half of the dithizone has crystallized. The precipitate is collected in a sintered-glass crucible, washed several times with small portions of carbon tetrachloride, and air-dried.

Pure dithizone solutions of known concentrations may be obtained by extraction, so that highly purified solid dithizone may not be necessary.[3] A chloroform solution of dithizone is stripped twice with 10 volumes of (1:100) NH_4OH. The aqueous phase is removed, filtered, and carefully neutralized with 1:1 HCl to precipitate the dithizone. This, in turn, is re-extracted into chloroform. The dithizone concentration may be obtained by dividing the observed absorbance in a 1.00-cm cell at 606 mμ by 40.6 $\times$ 10³, the molar absorbance at this wavelength.

Dithizone was first extensively applied to the analysis of metals by H. Fischer.[4] Sandell,[1] who has done considerable researches with dithizone, presents a most comprehensive review of the field. The compound exhibits a tautomerism

$$C_6H_5NHN \diagdown$$
$$C\text{—}SH$$
$$C_6H_5N\text{==}N \diagup$$
(enol) I

$$C_6H_5NHNH \diagdown$$
$$C\text{==}S$$
$$C_6H_5N\text{==}N \diagup$$
(keto) II

and is a monobasic acid ($pK_a = 4.7$) up to a pH of 12. The acid proton is that of the mercapto group in structure I, since, when this proton is replaced by a methyl group, the resulting compound is no longer soluble in alkali.[5] The mercapto group is involved in metal complex formation, proved by the fact that the sulfur-methylated derivative does not react with metals.[5] Metal dithizonates are formed according to the reaction

$$M^{n+} + nH_2Dz \rightleftharpoons M(HDz)_n + nH^+$$

Some metals, notably $Cu(I)$, $Cu(II)$, Ag, $Au(I)$, $Hg(II)$, Bi, and Pd, form a second complex at a higher pH range or in a deficiency of reagent in which another proton is replaced, thus:

$$2M(HDz)_n \rightleftharpoons M_2Dz_n + nH_2Dz$$
(enol form)

The names keto and enol forms for the two types of dithizone complexes, assigned by Fischer, who mistakenly believed that only the dibasic complex involved the mercapto group, have become accepted nomenclature. The probable structure for the keto complex is

and that for the enol form would probably involve dithizone as a tridentate chelating agent. The enol form of dithizonates of trivalent hexacoordinated metals would probably be more stable than those of other metals, unless, of course, polymerization (complexes containing more than one metal atom) occurred to stabilize the coordination sphere of the metal. The equilibrium constants for the extraction of a number of metal dithizonates are given in Table 12.5.

In general, the keto dithizonates are of far greater analytical utility than the enol counterparts, which are less stable and less soluble in organic solvents.[6] As can be seen from Table 12.7, page 178, the order of extractability of metal dithizonates is $Pd > Ag > Hg(II) > Cu(II) > Bi \gtrsim Pt(II) > Tl(III) > Fe(II) > Sn(II) \gtrless Co \gtrsim Ni > Zn \gtrsim Pb > Mn > Cd$; therefore Hg may be extracted out of dilute acid solution, but Cd extraction requires a strongly alkaline solution with the other metals requiring intermediate pH values for extraction. Thus extraction from dilute acid solution $(0.1–0.5\ N)$ would permit separation of Ag, Hg, Cu, and Pd from the other metals.

Table 12.5.   Extraction Constants of Metal Dithizonates [7, 16]

$$NiDz_2 \quad 1.7 \times 10^{-17}$$
$$BiDz_3 \quad 1.1 \times 10^{-37}$$
$$HgDz_2 \quad 0.7 \times 10^{-44}$$
$$SnDz_2 \quad 4.5 \times 10^{-16}$$
$$CoDz_2 \quad 5 \ \ \times 10^{-18}$$
$$CuDz_2 \quad 1.1 \times 10^{-27} \ (2.5 \times 10^{-28})$$
$$AgDz \quad 2.3 \times 10^{-18}$$

$$K = \frac{[M^{n+}][HDz]_{CCl_4}^n K_i^n}{[MDz_n]_{CCl_4}[H^+]^n}$$

where $K_i = \dfrac{[H^+][Dz^-]}{[HDz]} = 2 \times 10^{-9}$

Bismuth can be extracted from a weakly acid medium, but Pb and Zn require a neutral or mildly alkaline solution for their extraction. A number of metals such as Pb, Zn, and Bi are less easily extracted as the pH is increased in the alkaline range. From a strongly basic solution ($1 N$ NaOH) to which citrate or tartrate has been added to prevent hydroxide precipitation, Cd may be quantitatively extracted by a carbon tetrachloride solution of dithizone; Pb and Zn, however, do not extract under these conditions.

In order to obtain higher selectivity in dithizone reactions which cannot be achieved with pH regulation alone, extensive use of masking agents such as cyanide, thiocyanate, and thiosulfate has been made. As may be seen from Table 12.6, dithizone reacts with far fewer metals in the presence of masking agents. In some instances combinations of two masking agents have been effectively employed. Thus, thiosulfate will inhibit the extraction of all metals with the exception

Table 12.6.   Masking Agents in Dithizone Reactions

Conditions	Metals Reacting
Basic solution containing cyanide	Pb, Sn(II), Tl(I), Bi
Slightly acid solution containing cyanide	Pd, Hg, Ag, Cu
Dilute acid solution containing thiocyanate	Hg, Au, Cu
Dilute acid solution containing thiocyanate plus cyanide	Hg, Cu
Dilute acid solution containing bromide or iodide	Pd, Au, Cu
Dilute acid solution containing EDTA	Ag, Hg
Slightly acid solution (pH 5) containing thiosulfate (carbon tetrachloride solution of dithizone)	Pd, Sn(II), Zn (Cd, Co, Ni)
Slightly acid solution (pH 4–5) containing thiosulfate plus cyanide	Sn(II), Zn
Citrate and tartrate in basic medium	Usually do not interfere with extraction of reacting metals

of Zn, Sn(II), Pd, and, if present in higher concentrations, Cd, Co, and Ni.[8] By the addition of cyanide to the mixture, only Zn and Sn(II) are now extractable. Thiosulfate in dilute H_2SO_4 [2 volume % (approximately $0.5 M$)] will prevent Hg but not Cu from reacting.[8] Sodium diethyldithiocarbamate has also been used as a masking agent after Cu removal in the determination of Zn.[9] More recently, sodium bis(2-hydroxyethyl)-dithiocarbamate has been proposed as a superior substitute for the diethyldithiocarbamate to complex Cd more effectively.[10] Ethylenediaminetetraacetic acid prevents the extraction of Cu from dilute acid solution but not that of Ag and Hg. If the Cu concentration is too high it will extract very slowly.[11] If the Ca salt of EDTA is used, Cu may be extracted at pH 9. Ethylenediaminetetraacetic acid also prevents the extraction of Pb, Zn, Bi, Cd, Ni, Co, and Tl at any pH.[11] Silver may be separated from Hg by extracting it back into the aqueous phase with a solution containing 10% NaCl and $0.015 N$ HCl. The Ag in this aqueous phase when diluted by ten volumes of water may now be re-extracted by dithizone.[11]

Not all metal-dithizone reactions are simply reversible.[1] Thus, although neither Co nor Ni may be extracted out of dilute acid medium (e.g., pH 2), once formed (in basic solution) their dithizonates are not readily decomposed by dilute acids. This may be attributable to kinetic factors rather than equilibrium; the dithizonates of Co and Ni may decompose at a slow rate. Another example of the influence of kinetic factors in dithizone extractions is found in the rapid extraction of mercury dithizonate into chloroform at pH 1.4, whereas the extraction of Cu under these conditions is sufficiently slow to permit the separation of the pair.[12, 13]

In contrast to the behavior of chloroform, extraction of copper dithizonate into carbon tetrachloride is rapidly equilibrated. Most dithizonates, like dithizone itself, are more soluble in chloroform than in carbon tetrachloride and usually require a somewhat higher pH when extracted into the former solvent.

Di-β-naphthylthiocarbazone [14]

Table 12.7.   Extraction of Dithizonates [1]

K = keto E = enol S = soluble I = insoluble

Based on data of H. Fischer and others. K and E in table are used in sense of monobasic and dibasic (1 : 2 and 1 : 1 divalent metal salts).

Metal	Com-plex	Color (CCl$_4$)	Solubility in CCl$_4$ or CHCl$_3$	pH for Extraction	Remarks
Bismuth	K	Orange-yellow	S	>2(CCl$_4$)	
	E	Orange-red	S	Basic solution	See Reith and van Dijk, *Chem. Weekblad*, **36**, 343 (1939). Also reacts in presence of KCN (pH 7–8).
Cadmium	K	Red	S	Basic solution	Stable when shaken with 1 N NaOH.
Cobalt	K	Violet	S	7–9 (optimum in CCl$_4$)	Organic solution of dithizonate quite stable to dilute mineral acids.
	E?	Brownish	S	Strongly basic solution	May be decomposition product.
Copper(I)	K	Violet	S	Dilute mineral acid solution (*ca.* 0.1 N)	
(I)	E	Red-brown	S	Basic solution	Only slightly soluble in CCl$_4$.
(II)	K	Violet-red	S	Dilute mineral acid solution	
(II)	E	Yellow-brown	S	Basic solution	Can also be formed in slightly acid solution when Cu is in excess of Dz.
Gold		Yellow	S(CHCl$_3$)	Dilute mineral acid solution	Red color first appears on shaking; this quickly changes to orange and then to yellow. Flocs in CCl$_4$. Au(III) probably reduced to Au(I).
Indium		Red	S	$\begin{cases} 5\text{–}6\ (CCl_4) \\ 8.3\text{–}9.6(CHCl_3) \end{cases}$	Also reacts in presence of cyanide.
Iron(II)		Violet-red	S	6–7 (CCl$_4$)	Fe(III) does not form a complex but oxidizes Dz in basic medium, especially in presence of cyanide.
Lead	K	Cinnabar red	S	8.5–11 (optimum in CHCl$_3$)	Cyanide does not prevent reaction.
Manganese		Violet-brown (CHCl$_3$)	S(CHCl$_3$)	*ca.* 11	Solution very unstable. Brown flocs in CCl$_4$.
Mercury(I)	K	Orange	S	Dilute mineral acid solution	
(I)	E	Purplish red	S	Basic medium	
(II)	K	Orange-yellow	S	Dilute mineral acid solution	Can also be formed in weakly alkaline solution with an excess of Dz. Light sensitive.
(II)	E	Purplish red	S	Basic medium	Can also be formed in slightly acid solution with a deficiency of Dz.
Nickel		Brownish	S	Weakly basic medium	CCl$_4$ solution not easily decomposed by dilute mineral acids. From a strongly basic solution, CCl$_4$ extract is gray.
Palladium	E?	Brown-red (CHCl$_3$)	S(CHCl$_3$)	Dilute mineral acid solution	Partly soluble in CCl$_4$ (dark violet). Reaction is slow.
	K	Brownish green (CHCl$_3$)	S(CHCl$_3$)		By addition of Dz to solution of enol compound. Stable toward 6 N NaOH and 6 N H$_2$SO$_4$.
Platinum(II)		Violet or violet-red aqueous layer; green CCl$_4$		Weakly acid solution	Probably a colloidal solution; sometimes violet flocs are obtained (insoluble in CHCl$_3$). Pt(IV) does not react; neither do other Pt metals in quadrivalent or trivalent state.
Silver	K	Yellow	S	Dilute mineral acid solution	
	E	Red-violet	I	Basic solution	Slightly soluble in CHCl$_3$ (red solution).
Thallium(I)	K?	Red	S	9–12 (CCl$_4$)	Also formed in presence of cyanide.
(III)	K?	Yellowish red	S	3–4 (CCl$_4$)	Reaction not complete. Tl(III) also oxidizes Dz.
Tin(II)	K	Red	S	>4 (optimum 6–9 in CCl$_4$)	Not stable.
Zinc	K	Purplish red	S	Neutral or weakly basic solution (optimum 8.3 in citrate buffer with CHCl$_3$).	With an excess of Dz, extraction can be made complete in weakly acid medium. Thiosulfate does not prevent reaction.

The naphthyl analog of dithizone is quite similar in its action to dithizone. The compound is so soluble in chloroform that it cannot be transferred from this solvent into an aqueous ammonia solution; it can be transferred from carbon tetrachloride solution in which its solubility is lower. Certain metals, such as Zn, can be readily extracted with this reagent in chloroform from solutions as alkaline as pH 11,[1] possibly reflecting higher K_{D_R} values (see page 54). Other than in the determination for Zn, this reagent does not seem to possess any real advantage over dithizone.

o-Ditolylthiocarbazone

This compound has been claimed by Suprunovich and Shamshin[15] to be more resistant to oxidation than is dithizone.

REFERENCES: Diphenylthiocarbazone

1. E. B. Sandell, *Colorimetric Determination of Traces of Metals*, second edition, Interscience Publishers, Inc., New York, 1950.
2. Assoc. Official Agr. Chem., *Official and Tentative Methods of Analysis*, 1935, p. 378.
3. A. S. Landry and S. F. Redondo, *Anal. Chem.*, **26**, 732 (1954).
4. H. Fischer, *Angew. Chem.*, **50**, 919 (1937).
5. H. Irving and C. F. Bell, *J. Chem. Soc.*, **1954**, 4253.
6. H. Fischer, *Angew. Chem.*, **47**, 685 (1934).
7. R. W. Geiger and E. B. Sandell, *Anal. Chim. Acta*, **8**, 197 (1953).
8. H. Fischer and G. Leopoldi, *Z. anal. Chem.*, **107**, 241 (1936).
9. R. L. Shirley, D. R. Waldron, E. D. Jones, and E. J. Beune, *J. Assoc. Offic. Agr. Chemists*, **31**, 285 (1948).
10. E. J. Serfass and W. S. Levine, *Chemist-Analyst*, **36**, 55 (1947).
11. H. Friedeberg, *Anal. Chem.*, **27**, 305 (1955).
12. H. Barnes, *J. Marine Biol. Assoc. United Kingdom*, **26**, 305 (1946).
13. H. Irving, G. Andrew, and E. J. Risdon, *J. Chem. Soc.*, **1949**, 541.
14. I. B. Suprunovich, *J. Gen. Chem. (U.S.S.R.)*, **8**, 839 (1938).
15. I. B. Suprunovich and D. L. Shamshin, *Zhur. Anal. Khim.*, **1**, 198 (1946); *Chem. Abstracts*, **41**, 4116 (1947).
16. A. T. Pilipenko, *J. Anal. Chem. (U.S.S.R.)*, **8**, 286 (1953).

13. TOLUENE-3,4-DITHIOL

$$CH_3 \overset{\displaystyle\bigcirc}{} \overset{\text{—SH}}{\underset{\text{—SH}}{}}$$

Toluene-3,4-dithiol is a low melting (31°C) solid which forms complexes in acid solution with $Mo(VI)$, $W(VI)$, and $Re(VII)$ that are extractable by amyl acetate or chloroform.[1,2,3] Molybdenum may be selectively extracted from W by preventing the formation of the W complex either by the use of citric acid[4] or by pH control.[5] The latter method seems preferable since W may then be easily extracted following the removal of Mo.[6] Since the dithiol is readily oxidized, a solution of the reagent should be prepared within hours of its use.

REFERENCES: Toluene-3,4-dithiol

1. J. H. Hamence, *Analyst,* **65,** 152 (1940).
2. C. C. Miller, *J. Chem. Soc.,* **1941,** 792.
3. C. C. Miller, *Analyst,* **69,** 109 (1944).
4. C. F. Bickford, W. S. Jones, and J. S. Krene, *J. Am. Pharm. Assoc., Sci. Ed.,* **37,** 255 (1948); *Chem. Abstracts,* **42,** 8703 (1948).
5. J. E. Wells and R. Pemberton, *Analyst,* **72,** 185 (1947).
6. B. Bogshawe and R. J. Truman, *Analyst,* **72,** 189 (1947).

14. SODIUM DIETHYLDITHIOCARBAMATE

$$(C_2H_5)_2N \overset{\displaystyle S}{\underset{\displaystyle S^-}{-C\diagdown}} \quad Na^+$$

Sodium diethyldithiocarbamate (mol. wt 171), a white, crystalline compound, is readily soluble in water but less so in alcohol. It is generally used as a 2% aqueous solution. First applied to the analysis of Cu and Fe in 1908,[1] its reactions have been studied with a large number of metals.[2] The reagent has proved an effective extraction reagent for almost two dozen metals (see Table 12.8). The selectivity of the reagent has been improved by the use of sodium ethylenediaminetetraacetate alone as masking agent in the extraction of Cu in steel,[7] and together with cyanide in the extraction of Bi.[8,9] A systematic study of extractions with this reagent, including effects of masking agents, has been carried out by Bode.[9] Pohl[11] reports that Bi does not extract from those basic solutions containing citrate ion in which Pb is present. The reagent decomposes rapidly in solutions of low pH.[12] Although this is not usually important since most procedures call for $pH > 6$, Chernikov *et al.*[6] indicate that Bi, Pb, and Ni may be extracted from very acid solutions. Extractions carried out at low pH should be performed without delay and with an excess of reagent to offset decomposition.

Table 12.8. Extractions with Sodium Diethyldithiocarbamate

Metal	pH of Extraction	Solvent	Reference
Cu(II)	1–3.5	Chloroform	3, 13
Fe(II)	4–11	Carbon tetrachloride	9
Fe(III)	0–10	Chloroform	3
Co	6–8	Chloroform	3
Bi	1–10	Chloroform, ethyl ether	3, 5
Ni	0–10	Chloroform	3
U(VI)	6.5–8.5	Chloroform, amyl acetate, ether	3, 9
Cr(VI)	0–6	Chloroform	3
Te(IV)	5 N H$^+$–pH 3.3, 8.5–8.7	Chloroform, benzene, carbon tetrachloride	4, 6, 9
Se	3	Ethyl acetate	4, 6
Ag	3	Ethyl acetate	6
Ag	4–11	Carbon tetrachloride	9
Hg	3	Ethyl acetate	5, 6
As(III)	4–5.8	Carbon tetrachloride	9
Sb(III)	4–9.5	Carbon tetrachloride	9
Sn(IV)	5–6	Carbon tetrachloride	9
Pb	"Very acid"	Ethyl ether, ethyl acetate	5, 6
Cd	3	Ethyl acetate	6
Mo(VI)	3	Ethyl acetate	6
Mn	6.5	Ethyl acetate (excess reagent needed)	6, 10
V	3	Ethyl acetate	6
Zn	3	Ethyl acetate	6
In	3	Ethyl acetate	6
Ga	3	Ethyl acetate (excess reagent needed)	6
Tl	3	Ethyl acetate (excess reagent needed)	6
W	1–1.5	Ethyl acetate	6
Re	Concentrated HCl	Ethyl acetate	6
Os	7–9 (incomplete and slow)	Carbon tetrachloride	9
Nb(V)	Weakly acid	Carbon tetrachloride	9

REFERENCES: Sodium Diethyldithiocarbamate

1. M. Delepine, *Compt. rend.*, **146**, 981 (1908).
2. T. Callan and J. Henderson, *Analyst*, **54**, 650 (1929).
3. R. J. Lacoste, M. H. Earing, and S. E. Wiberly, *Anal. Chem.*, **23**, 871 (1951).
4. H. Goto and Y. Kakita, *Sci. Repts. Research Insts. Tôhoku Univ.*, **7A**, 365 (1955).
5. S. L. Thompsett, *Analyst*, **61**, 591 (1936); **63**, 250 (1938).

6. Y. A. Chernikov and B. M. Dobkina, *Zavodskaya Lab.*, **15,** 1143 (1949) ; *Chem. Abstracts,* **44,** 1358 (1950).

7. J. L. Hague, E. D. Brown, and H. A. Bright, *J. Research Natl. Bur. Standards,* **47,** 380 (1951).

8. K. L. Cheng, R. H. Bray, and S. W. Melsted, *Anal. Chem.,* **27,** 24 (1955).

9. H. Bode, *Z. anal. Chem.,* **142,** 414 (1954) ; **143,** 182 (1954) ; **144,** 90, 165 (1955).

10. H. Specker, H. Hartkamp, and M. Kuchtner, *Z. anal. Chem.,* **143,** 425 (1954).

11. H. Pohl, *Anal. Chim. Acta,* **12,** 54 (1955).

12. A. E. Martin, *Anal. Chem.,* **25,** 1260 (1953).

13. A. Claassen and L. Bastings, *Z. anal. Chem.,* **153,** 30 (1956).

15. POTASSIUM XANTHATE

$$C_2H_5O—C\begin{smallmatrix} \\ \diagup\!\!\!\diagup\,S \\ \\ \diagdown\,S^- \end{smallmatrix}\ \ K^+$$

Alcohols react with carbon disulfide in alkaline solutions to give xanthates; for example

$$C_2H_5OH + KOH + CS_2 \rightarrow C_2H_5O\overset{\overset{\textstyle S}{\|}}{—C}—S^-,\ K^+ + H_2O$$

These xanthates give extractable complexes with metals such as Cu, Co, Fe, Mn, Ni, As, and Mo.

Potassium xanthate is a pale-yellow crystalline solid, soluble in both water and alcohol. The aqueous solution is highly alkaline. The solid or its solution should be stored in a stoppered bottle protected from the light. The reagent is commonly used as a 0.1% aqueous solution and should be prepared fresh every few days.

Table 12.9. Extractions with Xanthate

Metal	Extraction Medium	Solvent	Reference
Cu	pH 7–8.5 or ammoniacal	Ethyl ether	1
Mo(VI)	Weakly acid to neutral	Petroleum ether and ethyl ether or chloroform	2, 3
Fe	Weakly acid to neutral	Chloroform	3, 5
Ni	Weakly acid to neutral	Chloroform	3, 5
V	Weakly acid to neutral	Chloroform	3
U	Weakly acid to neutral	Chloroform	3
Co	Ammoniacal	Ether	4, 5
Te	Thiourea	Ether	6
As	Acid	Carbon tetrachloride	7
Sb	Acid	Carbon tetrachloride	7

REFERENCES: Xanthates

1. I. M. Korenman and A. I. Aufilow, *J. Applied Chem.* (*U.S.S.R.*), **13**, 1262 (1940).
2. E. Pavelka and A. Laghi, *Mikrochemie ver. Mikrochim. Acta*, **31**, 138 (1943).
3. D. Hall, *J. Am. Chem. Soc.*, **44**, 1462 (1922).
4. L. Compin, *Ann. chem. anal. et chim. appl.*, **2**, II, 218 (1920).
5. A. Kutzelin, *Z. anorg. Chem.*, **256**, 46 (1948).
6. P. Falciola, *Ann. chim. appl.*, **17**, 357 (1927).
7. A. K. Klein and F. A. Vorhes, *J. Assoc. Offic. Agr. Chemists*, **22**, 121 (1939).

16. MISCELLANEOUS REAGENTS

2-Mercaptobenzothiazole

A white crystalline compound melting at 179°C, 2-mercaptobenzo-thiazole is insoluble in water but soluble in alkalis, alkali carbonates, alcohol, and ether and forms precipitates with Bi, Cd, Co, Cu, Au, Pb, Hg, Ni, Tl, and Zn.[1] The Cu precipitate formed at a pH of 2.6 to 4.2 may be quantitatively extracted into amyl acetate without the interference of Pb, Cd, Zn, or Ni.[2] Following the removal of Cu and Fe, the Cd precipitate formed in ammoniacal solution may be extracted away from Ni with chloroform.[3]

Thiocarbanilide

A colorless crystalline compound melting at 154°C, thiocarbanilide is only slightly soluble in water but readily soluble in alcohol and ether. Colored, ether-extractable complexes are formed with Ru and Os salts in HCl that has been briefly heated with thiocarbanilide.[4] The sensitivity of the color test is (blue-green) 0.3 μg Ru/ml and (red) 10 μg Os/ml.

Thiosemicarbazide ($H_2NNHSCNH_2$), a white crystalline solid melting at 182–184°C, is soluble in water and alcohol. This reagent gives an indigo-blue-colored compound with Pt(IV) in weakly basic solution that can be extracted into either ethyl or amyl acetate. It is a sensitive reaction, free from the interference of Au, Pd, and Ru.[5]

Thiosalicylideneethylenediimine

$$SH$$

$$HS$$

$$CH \qquad\qquad CH$$

$$N—CH_2CH_2—N$$

Formed by the action of NaHS on the condensation product of
o-chlorobenzaldehyde and ethylenediamine, thiosalicylideneethylenediimine has been shown to form highly colored chloroform-extractable
complexes with a number of metals.[6] This reagent is promising and
seems worthy of further development. The metal complexes are
discernible even at microgram concentration levels. Mercury forms
the most stable complex and can displace other metals. The behavior
of the chloroform solutions of the complexes toward acid and base
reagents is given in Table 12.10.

**Table 12.10. Behavior of Chloroform Solutions of Complexes of Thio-
salicylideneethylenediimine toward Acids and Bases** [6]

Stable in HCl or NH₃	Stable in HCl	Unstable in HCl and NH₃	Unreactive
Co (brown-red)	Ni (purple-red)	Zn (yellow)	Al
Tl(I) (orange-brown, slightly soluble in chloroform)	In (golden yellow)		Fe(II) and Fe(III)
	Te(IV) (leather brown)		Mn
Bi (red-brown)	Sn(II) (yellow)		Ga
Cu (dark orange)	Sb(III) (orange-		
Ag (brown)	brown, insoluble		
Hg (yellow)	in chloroform)		
Pd(II) (red-brown)	Cd (orange-yellow)		
	Pb (brown)		
	Au(III) (yellow-brown)		
	Pt(II) (reddish yellow)		
	Pt(IV) (brownish yellow)		

Phenylthiourea

$$NHC_6H_5$$

$$C=S$$

$$NH_2$$

This white crystalline solid melting at 154°C is slightly soluble in water and readily soluble in alcohol. It forms a complex with Pd(II) in dilute HCl solutions which is quantitatively extracted into either ethyl or amyl acetate.[7] Other mineral acids, e.g., H_2SO_4, reduce the efficiency of extraction. Of the other metals tested, 40% Pt(IV) and 16% Cu were extracted, and under 1% of Ir(IV), Rh(III), Ru(III), Os(IV), Au(III), Fe(III), Co, Ni, and Cr(VI) extracted.

Dithio-β-isoindigo

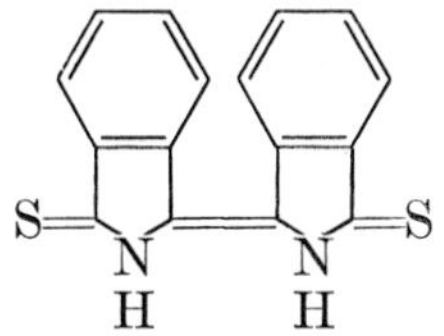

S=⟨⟨⟩⟩=S
    N   N
    H   H

This dark-red solid has been used for the extraction of Ag in the presence of Pb. The reagent in butanol reacts with Ag to give a dark-red complex that extracts into the butanol layer while Pb remains behind.[8]

Ephedrine

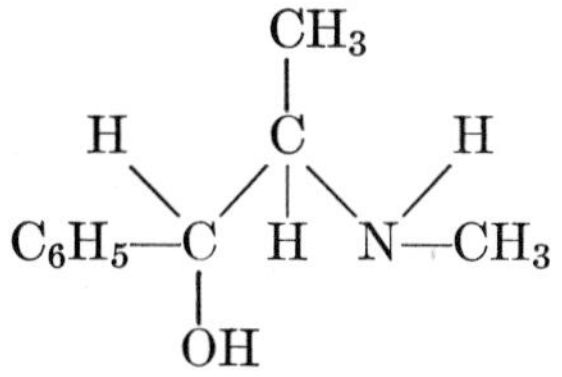

$$CH_3$$
H   C   H
C_6H_5—C H N—CH_3
    OH

Ephedrine hydrochloride (1-phenyl-2-methylaminopropanol hydrochloride) is a water-soluble, white crystalline solid melting at 216–220°C. In alkaline solution it forms a yellow complex with Os(VIII) that can be extracted into carbon tetrachloride.[9] Platinum and Rh produce no color reaction, but in higher concentration Pd and Au give a faint yellow color and Ir produces a very faint green.

Antipyrine

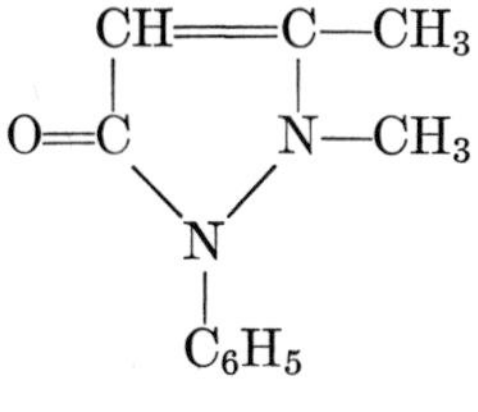

CH====C—CH_3
O=C   N—CH_3
     N
     C_6H_5

Antipyrine, or phenazone, a white crystalline solid melting at 111–113°C, is very soluble in water, alcohol, and chloroform. It has been applied to the separation of Sb and Bi from each other and both from Hg, Sn(IV), As(III), Zn, Co, Ni, and Cr.[10]

REFERENCES: Miscellaneous Reagents

1. F. J. Welcher, *Organic Analytical Reagents,* Vol. IV, D. Van Nostrand Co., Inc., Princeton, N. J., 1948.
2. E. J. Serfass and W. S. Levine, *Monthly Rev. Am. Electroplaters' Soc.,* **34,** 454 (1947); *Chem. Abstracts,* **41,** 4406a (1947).
3. E. J. Serfass, W. S. Levine, G. F. Smith, and F. Duke, *Plating,* **35,** 458 (1948); *Chem. Abstracts,* **42,** 5748i (1948).
4. W. Singleton, *Ind. Chemist,* **3,** 121 (1927); *Chem. Abstracts,* **21,** 1605 (1927).
5. V. Arreguine, *Rev. asoc. bioquím. argentina,* **14,** 196 (1947); *Chem. Abstracts,* **42,** 5374c (1948).
6. G. Beck, *Mikrochemie ver. Mikrochim. Acta,* **33,** 188 (1947).
7. G. H. Ayres and B. L. Tuffly, *Anal. Chem.,* **24,** 949 (1952).
8. E. Gagliardi, M. Theis, and W. Klementschitz, *Mikrochim. Acta,* **1954,** 653.
9. S. O. Thompson, F. E. Beamish, and M. Scott, *Ind. Eng. Chem., Anal. Ed.,* **9,** 420 (1937).
10. E. Sudo, *J. Chem. Soc. Japan, Pure Chem. Sect.,* **75,** 1291 (1954).

Part 4

Separations

Chapter 13

Selected Procedures

for the Extraction

of the Elements

In the following pages are presented a representative selection of extraction methods for the elements. The choice of an extraction method involves the following considerations. An effective extraction method must be (*a*) selective (ideally, only the element of interest should extract quantitatively and the other elements present should not extract at all); (*b*) applicable to both macro and micro concentration levels of the element of interest; and (*c*) convenient. The reagents used should be stable, readily accessible, and inexpensive. The extracted element should be in a form that readily permits analytical measurement.

The choice of a particular method for an individual element has been left to the reader since the nature of such a choice will vary with the particular separation problem confronting the analyst. It is beyond the scope of any book to anticipate all situations that may arise in analytical separation problems. However, by perusal of the selections listed for the element of interest, a reasonable choice should be possible for most situations.

It is strongly recommended that this section be used in conjunction with the previous section on extraction systems. Once a tentative selection of a method has been made, examination of the section on the extraction system involved will give the reader a proper orientation to the general overall characteristics of the extraction.

ACTINIUM

Thenoyltrifluoroacetone (TTA) method.[1]   Adjust the pH of the solution to 5.5 and extract with an equal volume of 0.25 M TTA in benzene for 15 minutes. In the presence of metals that form extractable TTA complexes at lower pH values, draw off and discard the aqueous phase and replace it with a dilute HNO_3 solution adjusted to pH 4.0 to strip the Ac from the benzene. This will leave the other metals, e.g., Pb, Tl(III), Bi, Po, and Th in the organic layer. Isolate the aqueous layer, readjust its pH to 5.5, and extract again with the 0.25 M TTA in benzene.

REFERENCE: Actinium

1. F. Hagemann, *J. Am. Chem. Soc.*, **72**, 768 (1950).

ALUMINUM

Acetylacetone method.[1]   Adjust the pH of the solution to a value between 4 and 6, and extract with a 50 volume % solution of acetylacetone in chloroform. A single extraction will give at least 90% Al in the organic phase. Fluoride ion interferes. Only 50% Al extraction is obtained at a pH of 7 in the presence of a 4:1 F:Al mole ratio.

Benzoate method.[2]   Bring the sample solution containing microgram quantities of Al to approximate neutrality. Add 2 ml of a solution containing 50 g ammonium acetate per 100 ml water, 1 ml of a solution containing 25 g sodium benzoate per 100 ml water, and 4 ml ethyl acetate, and shake vigorously to extract. Phosphate and F^- hinder or prevent the extraction of Al. Beryllium, Fe(III), Ga, In, and Sc are also extracted.

8-Quinolinol method.[3]   Buffer the sample solution (10–50 μg Al) to a pH of 9, dilute to 50 ml, and shake for 3 minutes in a separatory funnel with 10 ml 1% oxine in chloroform. Tungsten and Mo do not interfere. In the presence of up to 100 mg Cu, Ni, Co, Zn, or Cd, 1 g KCN is added to the alkaline solution. (Alternatively, these metals can be extracted with 2-methyl-8-quinolinol.[4]) In the presence of Fe (up to 25 mg), add 2 g KCN, heat to 50°C for 3 minutes, and add 10 ml of 10% Na_2S. Transfer the cooled solution to a separatory funnel, dilute to 50 ml, add 2 g NH_4NO_3, and extract as before. The Al complex has an absorption peak at 395 mμ and also fluoresces.

REFERENCES: Aluminum

1. J. Steinbach and H. Freiser, *Anal. Chem.*, **26**, 375 (1954).
2. S. E. J. Johnson, in E. B. Sandell, *Colorimetric Determination of Traces of Metals*, second edition, Interscience Publishers, Inc., New York, 1950, p. 537.

3. C. H. R. Gentry and L. G. Sherrington, *Analyst,* **71,** 432 (1946).
4. R. J. Hynek and L. J. Wrangell, *Anal. Chem.,* **28,** 1520 (1956).

AMERICIUM

Nitrate method.[1] Extract an HNO_3 solution saturated with NH_4NO_3 with an equal volume of ethyl ether. Americium(VI) is completely extracted. When methyl isobutyl ketone is used as solvent, the extraction is less complete, apparently because of reduction by the solvent.

Thenoyltrifluoroacetone (TTA) method.[2] A solution that has been previously extracted with 0.2 M TTA-benzene solution to remove contaminants such as Pu(IV), Pa(V), Th(IV), Fe(III), and Zr(IV) is adjusted to a pH of 3.25 or higher and extracted three times with successive portions of equal volumes of 0.2 M TTA-benzene solutions to obtain 97% Am(III) extraction. At pH 3.25, from 3 to 8% La accompanies the Am.

REFERENCES: Americium

1. L. B. Asprey, S. E. Stephanou, and R. A. Penneman, *J. Am. Chem. Soc.,* **72,** 1425 (1950).
2. L. B. Magnusson and M. L. Anderson, *J. Am. Chem. Soc.,* **76,** 6207 (1954).

ANTIMONY

Chloride method.[1] Transfer a sample solution which contains 30–40 μg Sb in HCl to a separatory funnel and then add, drop by drop, a 0.1 N $Ce(SO_4)_2$ solution in 2 N H_2SO_4 until the yellow color persists. Remove the excess $Ce(SO_4)_2$ by adding a 0.1% hydroxylamine hydrochloride solution. Add 10 mg of oxalic acid and then add 10 mg of citric acid. Upon dilution to 25 ml volume, the solution should be 1–2 N in HCl. Extract for 3 minutes with 25 ml of ethyl acetate. Extract the aqueous phase twice more with fresh solvent. Combine the organic extracts and evaporate to a small volume on a steam bath, followed by the addition of 5 ml of concentrated HCl to prevent hydrolysis of the Sb. Estimate Sb colorimetrically, using the rhodamine B or other convenient method. Iron, Sn, Cu, Cd, Pb, Ge, and Te are not extracted. Silver and Hg are extracted in moderate quantities, and Au is almost completely extracted. In all extractions the ions are at their highest states of oxidation.

Cupferron method.[2] Add 2 ml H_2SO_4 to a solution containing up to 3 μg Sb and evaporate off the water. Add about 30 mg pure powdered S and then boil down on a Meeker-type flame to a volume of 1 ml. Cool, add 10 ml water, and heat to dissolve any salts. Cool and transfer to a small separatory funnel. Dilute to 20 ml, add 2 ml of freshly prepared 1% aqueous cupferron solution, and mix. Add 10 ml redistilled chloroform, stopper, and shake vigorously for 30 seconds. In this way Sb reduced by S to Sb(III) may be separated from Tl(I) and most of any Ir. Antimony(V) will not extract with cupferron so that oxidation with HNO_3 and $HClO_4$, followed by a second cupferron extraction, will remove Fe, if present, and leave Sb behind in the aqueous phase.

Diethyldithiocarbamate method.[3] To a solution containing up to 300 μg Sb(III), add 10 ml of 5% EDTA, adjust the pH of the solution to 9.0, add 5 ml of 10% NaCN, and readjust the pH to 9.2–9.5. Add 1 ml 0.2% sodium diethyldithiocarbamate and 10 ml carbon tetrachloride. Shake the mixture for 1 minute. The Sb complex absorbs strongly at 350 mμ. Only Bi, Tl(III), Te, and larger amounts of Hg, As, Se, and Cu interfere.

Iodide method as a spot test.[4] To 1 drop of the solution to be tested add 5 drops of 9 N H_2SO_4, followed by 1 drop of 10% KI. Extract the solution with 1 ml benzene, using an extraction pipette. Remove the benzene layer and test with 1 drop of a 0.2% solution of rhodamine B. A violet color indicates the presence of Sb. If nitrites are not known to be absent, add a few milligrams of solid urea to the test solution before adding the KI. If oxidizing agents are present, add Na_2SO_3 just prior to the extraction until the color from free iodine is discharged. The Sb is quantitatively and exclusively extracted into the benzene layer, and the limit of identification of the method is 0.2 μg.

Rhodamine B method.[5,6] A solution containing approximately 0.5–2.5 μg Sb is made 3–6 N with respect to HCl and transferred to a separatory funnel. Add 3 ml of 85% H_3PO_4 and 1 ml 0.1 N Ce$(SO_4)_2$, stopper, and invert. Add 5 ml 0.1% aqueous rhodamine B solution, 1 ml butyl cellosolve solution (1 volume butyl cellosolve and 2 volumes water), and 15 ml benzene. Shake vigorously for 1 minute to extract rhodamine B chloroantimoniate. The complex absorbs strongly at 565 mμ.

The method may be applied to the separation of Sb from W, V, and Fe(III), by prior precipitation of Sb_2S_3 from a sulfuric acid–tartaric acid solution containing about 1 mg Cu to provide CuS as collector.[6] Alternately Sb may be separated from Tl and Ir by a cupferron extraction.[2] Gallium(III) interference may be eliminated by extraction out of 7 N HCl into isopropyl ether.[6] Gold(III) is removed by precipitation with SO_2 using Se as carrier.[2] The small amounts of Fe remaining are complexed with H_3PO_4 in the procedure above. Amounts of Tl(III) up to 20 μg may be tolerated in the final solution. With prior collection of Sb on a MnO_2 precipitate, only Tl or large amounts of Pt or V interfere with the method.[7]

REFERENCES: Antimony

1. C. E. White and H. J. Rose, *Anal. Chem.*, **25**, 351 (1953).
2. C. L. Luke and M. E. Campbell, *Anal. Chem.*, **25**, 1588 (1953).
3. H. Bode, *Z. anal. Chem.*, **144**, 165 (1955).
4. P. W. West and W. C. Hamilton, *Anal. Chem.*, **24**, 1025 (1952).
5. S. H. Webster and L. T. Fairhall, *J. Ind. Hyg. Toxicol.*, **27**, 184 (1945).
6. H. Onishi and E. B. Sandell, *Anal. Chim. Acta*, **11**, 444 (1954).
7. D. J. MacNulty and L. D. Woollard, *Anal. Chim. Acta*, **13**, 64 (1955).

ARSENIC

Chloride method for traces of As in Ge.[1] Wash 1 ml of Ge solution (0.02 to 1 μg) in 6 M HCl into a semimicro separatory funnel with 2 ml of concentrated HCl and add 1 drop 1% (volume/volume) H_2O_2. Add 4 ml of reagent grade (thiophene-free) benzene and extract for 3 minutes. Remove the benzene layer containing all the Ge initially present in the sample with a medicine dropper and discard. Add to the aqueous phase containing the As as As(V) 2 ml of concentrated HCl along with 2 drops (approximately 0.08 ml) of reagent grade 48% (weight/volume) HBr. Add 5 ml of benzene and extract for 3 minutes. Withdraw the aqueous phase into another separatory funnel and extract with an additional 5 ml of benzene. Combine the two benzene extracts in a separatory funnel and add 1 ml of water with a few milligrams of hydrazine hydrochloride. Shake the mixture for a few minutes and remove the water. Repeat the washing with another 1 ml of water. The combined water extracts contain all the As. The hydrazine hydrochloride serves to remove the free bromine formed by oxidation of hydrogen bromide.

Diethyldithiocarbamate method.[2] To 20 ml of a solution containing up to 25 μg As and 5–6 N in HCl, add 2 ml of 20% KI solution and heat to 40°C. Then add 0.5 ml of 5% $NaHSO_3$ solution and, following transfer of the mixture to a separatory funnel, dilute to 35 ml. Five ml of 1% diethylammonium diethyldithiocarbamate in chloroform (prepared fresh daily) is added and the mixture shaken vigorously for 40 seconds. The aqueous phase is re-extracted with another (2 ml) portion of the reagent solution. The extraction of As is said to be complete over the range of 1 to 10 N H_2SO_4. Lead will not be extracted if HCl is at least 2 N. Zinc, Cd, Ni, and Fe are not extracted, but Cu, Hg, and Bi accompany the As.

Heteropoly acid method.[3] Adjust a sample solution containing up to 1 mg of As(V) to pH 5–9 using M HCl or M NaOH and dilute to a volume of 20 ml. Add 10 ml of sodium molybdate–hydrochloric acid solution (dissolve 5 g of sodium molybdate dihydrate in 200 ml of water, add 84 ml of concentrated HCl, and dilute to 500 ml; store out of contact with glass). Transfer to a separatory funnel. Pour 20 ml of 1-butanol into the beaker that held the sample and then pour the alcohol into the funnel. Gently shake the solutions together for 30 seconds and allow the phases to separate. Extract the aqueous phase again with 20 ml of 1-butanol. Combine the organic phases and dilute to 50 ml with fresh solvent. Absorption of 12-molybdoarsenic acid may be measured at 370 mμ. Interference by soluble silica can be prevented by making sure that the two extractions are completed within 6 minutes after the addition of sodium molybdate reagent. Interference by orthophosphates (less than 2 mg P) can be obviated by selectively extracting 12-molybdophosphoric acid into a 3:1 mixture by volume of chloroform and 1-butanol as follows: after adjusting the pH and diluting to a volume of 20 ml as described above, add 10 ml of sodium molybdate–hydrochloric acid solution (dissolve 15 g of sodium molybdate dihydrate in 200 ml of water and add 84 ml of concentrated HCl; dilute to 500 ml). Extract the aqueous phase for 30 seconds with 20 ml of a 3:1 mixture of chloroform and 1-butanol. Discard the lower layer and repeat the extraction with mixed chloroform and 1-butanol twice more. Treat with 1-butanol and measure the absorption as previously described. Interference of up to 10 mg of Fe can be eliminated by prior extraction of the sample solution of pH 1.5 ± 0.5 after adding 10 ml of a solution containing 1 g of cupferron per 100 ml with chloroform as solvent.[4]

REFERENCES: Arsenic

1. M. Green and J. A. Kafalas, *J. Chem. Phys.*, **22**, 760 (1954).
2. N. Strafford, P. F. Wyatt, and F. G. Kershaw, *Analyst*, **70**, 232 (1945).
3. C. Wadelin and M. G. Mellon, *Analyst*, **77**, 708 (1952).
4. P. G. Butts, A. R. Gahler, and M. G. Mellon, *Sewage & Ind. Wastes*, **22**, 1543 (1950).

BERKELIUM

Thenoyltrifluoroacetone (TTA) method.[1] Berkelium can be extracted with a 0.2 M TTA-benzene solution if the pH is adjusted to a value of at least 2.5.

REFERENCE: Berkelium

1. L. B. Magnusson and M. L. Anderson, *J. Am. Chem. Soc.*, **76**, 6207 (1954).

BERYLLIUM

Acetylacetone method.[1] To 50 ml of solution containing up to 10 μg Be (not limit of extraction) at a pH 0.5–1.5, add 2.0 ml of 10% EDTA and adjust the pH to about 7–8 by the addition of 0.1 N NaOH (greenish-blue tint of bromthymol blue). Add 5 ml of 5% aqueous acetylacetone and readjust pH to 7–8. Allow the solution to stand 5 minutes and then extract it with three 10-ml portions of chloroform. The Be complex has an absorption maximum at 295 mμ. Beryllium is separated from milligram quantities of Fe, Al, Cr, Zn, Cu, Mn, Pb, Ag, Ce, and U.

Butyric acid method.[2] To a solution containing up to 25 mg Be add 10–15 ml butyric acid and 3 g KCl. Adjust the pH of the solution with NH_4OH to a value of 9.3–9.5. The aqueous phase, which should be about 50 ml in volume, is extracted with 50 ml chloroform. Over 94% Be extracts, and four successive extractions can raise this to 99%. Copper(II), Al(III), and Fe(III) will not interfere if the extraction is carried out in the presence of an excess of EDTA.[3]

REFERENCES: Beryllium

1. J. A. Adam, E. Booth, and J. D. H. Strickland, *Anal. Chim. Acta,* **6,** 462 (1952).
2. A. K. Sundaram and S. Banerjee, *Anal. Chim. Acta,* **8,** 526 (1953).
3. S. Banerjee, A. K. Sundaram, and H. D. Sharma, *Anal. Chim. Acta,* **10,** 256 (1954).

BISMUTH

Diethyldithiocarbamate method.[1] Transfer a solution containing 50–300 μg Bi to a separatory funnel, add 10 ml of complexing mixture, 1 ml 0.2% aqueous sodium diethyldithiocarbamate, then 10 ml of carbon tetrachloride. Stopper and shake for 30 seconds. The complex absorbs strongly at 370 and 400 mμ.

The complexing mixture is prepared by dissolving 50 g disodium salt of EDTA and 50 g NaCN in 1 l of 1.5 M NH_4OH. With large amounts of interfering metals, more complexing mixture may be used. An excess of 10–20 ml complexing mixture may be present.

Dithizone method.[2] Bring 0.5–1 g sample of metal (Bi 0.01%) into solution by appropriate treatment with acid. Boil out oxides of N if HNO_3 is used. Add 1 to 2 g ammonium citrate to the solution (about 25 ml), neutralize with ammonia, and add at least 2 g KCN (up to 10 g may be used if much Cu, Ag, and other similar metals are present) and 5 ml of 10% ammonia. Extract in a separatory funnel with four 15-ml portions of dithizone solution (0.1 g/100 ml) in chloroform. The complex absorbs well at 500 mμ.

8-Quinolinol method.[3] Adjust the sample solution (up to 10 mg Bi) to a pH of 4.0 and extract with 1% quinolinol in chloroform. Interferences of Fe and Cu may be removed by KCN treatment. The Bi complex absorbs well at 395 mμ.

REFERENCES: Bismuth

1. K. L. Cheng, R. H. Bray, and S. W. Melsted, *Anal. Chem.,* **27,** 24 (1955).
2. L. A. Haddock, *Analyst,* **59,** 163 (1934).
3. T. Moeller, *Ind. Eng. Chem., Anal. Ed.,* **15,** 346 (1943).

BORON

Borate method.[1] It is possible to separate small amounts of B from various materials by extracting solid residues with various alcohols. Thus, a rapid method for the determination of microgram amounts of B in sodium metal involves the separation of B from an acidified residue of NaCl by extracting with ethyl alcohol, followed by colorimetric estimation. This method is much more rapid than the classical methyl borate distillation.

Tetraphenylarsonium chloride method.[2] Five ml of a sample solution containing between 0.05 and 1 μg B, to which enough NH$_4$F or HF has been added to give a total fluoride concentration of 0.8 M, is allowed to stand for at least 18 hours. Then add 5 ml of 0.02 M (C$_6$H$_5$)$_4$AsCl in chloroform and shake mixture for 30 minutes. Withdraw the aqueous layer with a polythene pipette and wash the chloroform layer with 5 ml of distilled water. This is repeated twice. The chloroform layer is transferred to a platinum crucible, 15 drops of 0.1 N NaOH are added, and the solvent is evaporated to obtain the B.

REFERENCES: Boron

1. J. Rynasiewicz, M. P. Sleeper, and J. W. Ryan, *Anal. Chem.,* **26,** 935 (1954).
2. J. Coursier, J. Hure, and R. Platzer, *Anal. Chim. Acta,* **13,** 379 (1955).

CADMIUM

Diethyldithiocarbamate method.[1] Transfer a solution containing up to 300 μg Cd to a separatory funnel. After adding 5 ml of 20% sodium potassium tartrate, add sufficient ammonia to bring the pH to 11, 2 g KCN, 1 ml of 0.2% aqueous sodium diethyldithiocarbamate, and 10 ml of carbon tetrachloride. Stopper and shake for 1 minute. Only Bi, Pb, and Tl are extracted with Cd. The Cd complex absorbs in the ultraviolet region.

Dithizone method.[2] Add 5 ml of 20% sodium potassium tartrate solution and 1 ml of 20% hydroxylamine hydrochloride solution to the sample solution, which has a volume near 50 ml and contains up to 50 μg Cd. Make the solution basic with KOH and add an excess of 5 ml 25% KOH solution. Shake for 1 minute with 5 ml dithizone solution (20 mg/l chloroform). Separate the phases. If the aqueous layer is brown to light brown, add a 10-ml portion of dithizone to the aqueous phase, shake for a minute, and combine the organic phases. Continue adding 5-ml portions of dithizone until the aqueous layer remains brown. Up to 30 ml of dithizone solution will be required in the range of 50–75 μg Cd.

Add 5 ml of 200 mg/l dithizone solution to the combined chloroform extracts and wash with a 50-ml portion of water to remove entrained base. Shake the chloroform solution with 50 ml of pH 2 buffer (Clark and Lubs, double strength) for at least 2 minutes. All the Cd will now be in the aqueous phase and should probably be shaken with a little dithizone solution to remove traces of metals such as Cu and Hg.

This method serves to separate Cd from Pb and Zn, which do not extract from the highly alkaline solution, and from Ag, Hg, Ni, Co, and Cu, whose dithizonates are stable at pH 2.

Pyridine-thiocyanate method in the presence of Ag, Hg, and Cu.[3] When Ag and Hg are present, add to the slightly acid solution containing 3–30 μg of Cd sufficient ammonium thiocyanate (25% solution) to redissolve the silver thiocyanate first precipitated. Use a greater excess of thiocyanate in the presence of Hg (5 ml NH$_4$SCN per 10 mg of Hg). Add a 5% sodium acetate solution until blue Congo paper just turns red (pH 5). Extract with small portions of pyridine-chloroform (5 ml of pyridine and 100 ml of chloroform) totaling 15 ml. Wash the combined extracts once with an equal volume of 2% NH$_4$SCN solution.

Evaporate the chloroform extract to dryness on a water bath, add 3 ml of concentrated HNO$_3$, and again evaporate to dryness. Take up the residue in 2 or 3 ml of 1% H$_2$SO$_4$, transfer to a separatory funnel, and rinse with a little water. Extract with small portions of dithizone to remove traces of Ag and Hg.

When Cu is present, add Na$_2$CO$_3$ solution to the acid sample solution until a turbidity appears; then clear the solution with a few drops of H$_2$SO$_3$. Heat nearly to boiling, add 5–6 ml H$_2$SO$_3$ (for 30 mg Cu), boil briefly, and cool to room temperature. Most of the Cu is reduced to Cu(I). Reduce the acidity of the solution by the addition of sodium acetate, as described above, and add sufficient ammonium thiocyanate to dissolve the precipitated cuprous thiocyanate. Extract with chloroform-pyridine as above. Some Cu is extracted and can be removed by shaking with dithizone in acid solution.

REFERENCES: Cadmium

1. H. Bode, *Z. anal. Chem.*, **144**, 165 (1955).
2. F. W. Church, *J. Ind. Hyg. Toxicol.*, **29**, 34 (1947).
3. H. Fischer and G. Leopoldi, *Mikrochim. Acta*, **1**, 30 (1937).

CALCIUM

Nitrate method for separation of Ca from small amounts of Sr or Ba or both.[1] Convert the sample to the nitrate by evaporation to dryness in the presence of HNO_3. The final temperature should be 150 to 160°C. When cool, pour upon the dry mass ten times its weight of absolute alcohol, swirl gently, and let stand for 1 to 2 hours. Collect the insoluble nitrates of Ba and Sr on a perforated filter with thin asbestos pad, or a platinum felt, and under gentle suction. The wash fluid is a mixture of absolute alcohol and absolute ether in equal volumes. If there is much insoluble matter, dissolve the washed and dried contents of the filter in hot water and evaporate as before, and repeat treatment with alcohol and ether. In the combined filtrates and washings, after evaporation at a low temperature, determine the Ca by one of the usual methods.

Nitrate method for separation of Ca from large amounts of Sr or Ba ˚or both.[2] Dry the nitrates in a casserole at 130°C, crush them, and extract with five 5-ml portions of a mixture of equal volumes of absolute alcohol and absolute ether. Stir the solution after each addition and decant into a small flask as soon as the residue settles. Stopper the flask and set it aside. Dissolve the residue in water, evaporate to dryness, and again dry at 130°C. Crush the residue, transfer it to the flask, and sluice as much of any adhering nitrates as possible from the casserole to the flask by means of three 5-ml portions of the solvent. Stopper the flask, shake occasionally, and let stand for 24 hours, filter through a small filter, and wash by decantation with twelve 5-ml portions of the solvent. The combined filtrates and washings may then be used for the determination of Ca by one of the usual methods.

Nitrate method for separation of Ca from Sr.[3] Evaporate a 1 ml solution of the nitrates to incipient dryness with the burner flame. (Do not evaporate to complete dryness—i.e., avoid overheating the calcium and strontium nitrates.) To this practically dry residue, add 10 drops of monobutyl ether of ethylene glycol (butyl cellosolve), and again evaporate to incipient dryness. To the residue add 1 ml of solvent and bring to boiling. Filter the hot solution through a dry filter medium, glass or cotton. Add to the test tube another milliliter of solvent; heat to boiling and filter through the filter which was just used. Calcium nitrate is completely separated from strontium nitrate. The hydrated nitrates and the reagent are rendered anhydrous by boiling the nitrates in the reagent (boiling point 170.6°C). The solubility of anhydrous calcium nitrate in the reagent is 2.43×10^{-1} g/ml, and the solubility of the anhydrous barium and strontium nitrates in anhydrous solvent is not more than 2.3×10^{-6} and 1.1×10^{-5} g/ml, respectively.

8-Quinolinol method.[4] Adjust the pH of a solution containing up to 80 μg Ca to a value of 13, using 3 N NaOH. Add to this 5.0 ml butyl cellosolve. Transfer this solution, which should now be approximately 40–50 ml, to a separatory funnel and extract with 20 ml of a 3% 8-quinolinol solution in chloroform.

REFERENCES: Calcium

1. W. F. Hillebrand, G. E. F. Lundell, H. A. Bright, and J. I. Hoffman, *Applied Inorganic Analysis,* second edition, John Wiley & Sons, Inc., New York, 1953, p. 615.
2. W. F. Hillebrand, G. E. F. Lundell, H. A. Bright, and J. I. Hoffman, *Applied Inorganic Analysis,* second edition, John Wiley & Sons, Inc., New York, 1953, p. 616.
3. H. H. Barber, *Ind. Eng. Chem., Anal. Ed.,* **13,** 572 (1941).
4. C. Jankowski and H. Freiser, private communication.

CERIUM

Cupferron method.[1] Adjust the pH of a solution containing up to 100 mg Ce(IV) to a value of 2 or greater after adding 1.5 g of cupferron; then dilute to 50 ml. Extract with 65 ml of butyl acetate by shaking for 3–5 minutes. Smaller amounts of Ce require proportionally less cupferron.

Nitrate method for separation of Ce from fission products.[2] To the aliquot (1–5 ml) taken for analysis, add 1 ml (10 mg) of standardized Ce carrier, 2 ml of 2 M sodium bromate, and sufficient concentrated HNO_3 to make the solution 8–10 M in HNO_3. Transfer to a separatory funnel containing 50 ml of methyl isobutyl ketone (which has been equilibrated with 50 ml of 9 M HNO_3 containing 2 ml of 2 M sodium bromate) and shake for 30 seconds. Withdraw the aqueous phase and wash the methyl isobutyl ketone phase twice with 10 ml of 9 M HNO_3 containing a few drops of 2 M sodium bromate. Strip the Ce from the organic phase by shaking with 5 ml of water containing two drops of 30% H_2O_2. Next, neutralize this aqueous solution by adding concentrated ammonium hydroxide (3–5 ml) until a precipitate just appears, and acidify with 1.5 ml of 6 M HNO_3. Perform a cerium oxalate precipitation for gravimetric determination of yield and activity measurements. The method can be used for both trace and macro concentrations of Ce. Separation from Zr, Nb, and Ru is entirely adequate for fission product mixtures generally encountered. Separation from trivalent rare earths is also good, not more than 0.1% of trivalent Ce being extracted.

8-Quinolinol method: cerium in ferrous materials.[3] To a suitable aliquot (containing up to about 0.2 mg Ce) of a cast iron dissolved in HCl, add 2 ml citric acid solution (500 g/l) and NH_4OH (sp gr 0.88) drop by drop until alkaline. During the addition of NH_4OH the solution assumes a deep yellow color, and the first drop in excess produces a light green color. Add 5–6 drops in excess and then 4.0 ml KCN solution (400 g KCN and 15 g NaOH per liter). Heat to boiling, add 15 drops of freshly prepared sodium dithionate solution (2.5 g $Na_2S_2O_4$ in 25 ml water containing 4–5 drops NH_4OH), add 3 drops of dilute (1+4)H_2SO_4, boil for 15 seconds, and wash down the sides of the beaker with hot water. Cool to room temperature and add 2–3 drops of 0.5% phenolphthalein. Add citric acid drop by drop until the pink color is discharged and then NH_4OH until a faint pink reappears. Add 5.0 ml excess NH_4OH and transfer to a separatory funnel. Adjust the volume of the solution to 50 ml and add 11 ml 3% 8-quinolinol in chloroform containing 10% acetone. Shake vigorously for 3 minutes. The Ce complex exhibits an absorption maximum at 505 $m\mu$. Quantities of Mn in excess of 1.2 mg interfere. Borate, chloride, nitrate, and up to 2% P as phosphate, Al, Sb, As, Cr, Co, Cu, Pb, Hg, Mo, Ni, Se, Zr do not interfere at all, although Bi, Te, Sn, Ti, and W do to a very minor extent. Vanadium present in amounts greater than 0.3% interferes. Fluoride ion must be absent.

REFERENCES: Cerium

1. Z. Hagiwara, *Technol. Repts. Tôhoku Univ.,* **19,** 73 (1954).
2. L. E. Glendenin, K. F. Flynn, R. F. Buchanan, and E. P. Steinberg, *Anal. Chem.,* **27,** 59 (1955).
3. W. Westwood and A. Mayer, *Analyst,* **73,** 275 (1948).

CESIUM

Carrier-free cesium can be quantitatively extracted from 0.001 M sodium tetraphenylboride solution (freshly prepared) at a pH of about

6.6 into nitrobenzene.[1]   Rubidium is also extracted.   Cesium may also be extracted (78%) from a 0.4 M solution of potassium hexafluorophosphate (KPF_6) into nitromethane.[2]

REFERENCES: Cesium

1. R. C. Fix and J. W. Irvine, Jr., *Mass. Inst. Technol., Lab. Nuclear Science, Progr. Rept.,* Nov. 30, 1955.
2. R. C. Fix and J. W. Irvine, Jr., *Mass. Inst. Technol., Lab. Nuclear Science, Ann. Progr. Rept.,* May 31, 1955.

CHROMIUM

Acetylacetone method.[1]   Extract a solution containing Cr(III) with a 50 volume % acetylacetone in chloroform solution at a pH 3–4 to remove other metals.   Separate the aqueous phase which still contains the Cr(III), adjust its pH to 6, add 10 ml acetylacetone and heat under reflux for an hour to permit the formation of the chromium acetylacetonate to proceed to completion.   The solution is cooled, acidified to between 1 and 3 N in H^+, and extracted with the acetylacetone in chloroform.   The complex absorbs strongly at 560 mμ.

Diphenylcarbazide method.[2]   To about 10–15 ml of a solution containing microgram quantities of Cr(VI) and sufficient H_2SO_4 to make the solution 0.4 N, add 1 ml 0.25% diphenylcarbazide solution (reagent in 1:1 acetone-water).   Add 15 ml of a saturated NaCl solution and extract with isoamyl alcohol.   The complex absorbs at the same wavelength as it does in aqueous solution (543 mμ).   Oxidation of Cr is accomplished by boiling briefly with a small amount of $KMnO_4$ solution, the excess being destroyed in the cold solution by the addition of a little sodium azide.

Peracid method for separation of Cr from V.[3]   After removing small amounts of Fe by precipitation from alkaline solution, neutralize the filtrate containing Cr(VI) and V(V) with H_2SO_4 and evaporate the solution to 15–20 ml.   If much Fe is present, acidify the sample solution with H_2SO_4 and oxidize Cr with ammonium persulfate, if necessary.   This will prevent loss of Cr during the precipitation of Fe. Cool the solution and carefully buffer to a pH of 1.7.   Transfer this buffered solution to a separatory funnel, dilute to 50 ml, and add 75 ml of ethyl acetate.   Cool the mixture and then add 1 ml of 1 M (3.8%) H_2O_2.   After shaking the funnel vigorously for 30 seconds, allow the layers to separate and then draw off the aqueous solution.   Repeat the extraction of the aqueous layer at least twice, using 15 ml of ethyl acetate each time.   Combine the organic fractions.   Add 1 ml of 10% KOH solution to the blue solution of perchromic acid and shake until the blue color is replaced by yellow. Extract the yellow chromate with water, and boil the solution for 10 minutes. Dilute to 50 ml and determine the Cr with diphenylcarbazide. Alternatively, a photometric determination of the blue perchromic acid can be made directly on the organic phase at 565 mμ.[4] There is no interference in the extraction from the following elements: Fe, Hg, V, Ti, Ni, and Mo.

REFERENCES: Chromium

1. J. P. McKaveney, Ph.D. Thesis, University of Pittsburgh, 1957.
2. J. E. Delaney, *Sanitalk,* **1,** 9 (1953).
3. R. K. Brookshier and H. Freund, *Anal. Chem.,* **23,** 1110 (1951).
4. A. Glassner and M. Steinberg, *Anal. Chem.,* **27,** 2008 (1955).

COBALT

Acetylacetone method.[1] Adjust the pH of the solution to a pH of about 6–7 and extract with either acetylacetone or 50 volume % of acetylacetone in chloroform to remove metals which form extractable complexes with the reagent. The aqueous phase is separated, and several milliliters of acetylacetone and 5 ml 3% H_2O_2 are added to form the extractable Co(III) complex. The solution is adjusted to a pH of 8–9, heated to incipient boiling for 10 minutes, cooled, and reacidified to pH 1. The Co is now quantitatively extracted with 50 volume % acetylacetone in chloroform. The complex is an intense green in color.

Dithizone method.[2,3] To a sample containing 1–50 μg Co in about 10 ml, add 5 ml 10% sodium citrate, neutralize with NH_4OH, and adjust to a pH 8 (0.2–0.25 ml concentrated NH_4OH in excess). Add 5 ml of a solution containing 10 mg dithizone per 100 ml of carbon tetrachloride, shake vigorously for 30 seconds, and draw off the carbon tetrachloride extract. Repeat with 2–3-ml portions of dithizone until the last portion does not become red after shaking for 1 minute. This will separate Co from Fe(III), Ti, Cr, V, and other metals not forming dithizonates.

Copper and other metals forming dithizonates in acid solution may be removed with a solution containing 0.2 g dithizone per 100 ml of chloroform from a citrate solution at pH 3–4 without simultaneous extraction of any Co.[3] Nickel will ordinarily accompany Co in the dithizone extraction. It might be possible to prevent this by adding dimethylglyoxime prior to the extraction.

1-Nitroso-2-naphthol method.[4] Separation of microgram quantities of Co in biological samples such as bone or other high ash samples can be accomplished.

The sample is treated with 1:1 HNO_3 and ashed at 400°C. The ash is dissolved in 25 ml of 1:49 H_3PO_4, cooled, and transferred to a separatory funnel. One drop of methyl orange is added, and the material is titrated to an orange end point (pH 3–4) with sodium citrate (500 g/l).* Five ml of 1% 1-nitroso-2-naphthol (dissolve 1 g in 50 ml glacial acetic acid and dilute to 100 ml with distilled water) are added and the solution is allowed to stand for 1 hour with occasional shaking. The Co complex is then extracted by shaking vigorously for 3 minutes with three successive 10-ml portions of chloroform. Impurities are removed from the combined extracts by shaking for 2 minutes with 25 ml of 1:99 HCl.

8-Quinolinol method.[5] Up to 10 mg of Co may be extracted from an aqueous solution whose pH is 7 or greater by 1% 8-quinolinol in chloroform. The complex exhibits an absorption maximum of 420 mμ. Since no Co is extracted below pH 3.5, metals such as Fe, Cu, and Bi may be extracted with 8-quinolinol at this pH prior to the removal of Co; Al and Ni interfere by extracting in the same pH region as does Co.

Tetraphenylarsonium chloride method.[6] A sample containing 10–200 μg Co in approximately 200 ml of solution is treated in a large separatory funnel with 8 ml 50% KSCN solution and 5 g NH_4F to mask $Fe(III)$ and $U(VI)$. Two ml of 0.05 M tetraphenylarsonium chloride solution and 8 ml chloroform are added, and the mixture is shaken vigorously. The organic layer is drawn off into a small separatory funnel. This extraction is repeated three times with 4 ml of $(C_6H_5)_4AsCl$ solution before each extraction. The combined chloroform extracts are shaken with 10 ml water to which has been added approximately 0.1 g NH_4F, 2 ml 50% KSCN, and 1 ml 0.05 M $(C_6H_5)_4$ AsCl. A yellow-green color in the chloroform layer indicates the presence of Cu. To reduce the Cu to $Cu(I)$, add 1 ml 10% KI and shake the mixture vigorously. Remove the liberated iodine by shaking with 1 ml 10% $Na_2S_2O_3$. The blue chloroform layer (colorless in the absence of Co) absorbs strongly at 615 mμ. None of the other metals will interfere. About 95% recovery can be obtained.

Thiocyanate method.[7] Dissolve the sample (containing, for convenience, 10 to 20 μg of Co) in HCl so that the resulting solution contains an excess of about 5 ml of 6 M HCl. Add 20 ml of 60% NH_4SCN (420 g of salt in 280 ml of water). Add ammonium citrate solution

---

* The sodium citrate solution may be purified by extracting metallic impurities with successive portions of strong dithizone in chloroform until a green extract is obtained. The excess dithizone may be removed by extracting at pH 7 with chloroform.

(210 g of citric acid neutralized to phenolphthalein with ammonia and diluted to 1 l) until the red color of the ferric thiocyanate complex first disappears. Dilute with water to 50 ml and add 4 ml of ethyl ether to saturate the solution. Extract with three successive 20-ml portions of a mixture of 35% amyl alcohol and 65% ether (by volume). Strip the Co from the combined organic phases by shaking with two 20-ml portions of 2 M NH$_4$OH. Evaporate this aqueous solution to dryness and destroy thiocyanate by adding 20 ml of 6 M HNO$_3$ and evaporating to dryness. Neutralize the resulting NH$_4$HSO$_4$ with ammonia, and again evaporate to dryness. Cobalt can then be determined in the residue by any of the usual methods.

Under these conditions 86% of the Co is removed in a single batch extraction; three extractions removes 99.7% of the Co. The addition of citrate to the disappearance of the red iron thiocyanate color adjusts the pH to about 3.5, which is claimed to be close to the optimum.

The method provides a means of separating Co from many elements. Iron, Ni, Cu, and Zn also form thiocyanates that are at least partially extracted. Extraction of Fe can be prevented by the addition of citrate or by reduction to Fe(II). Nickel, Cu, and Zn do not interfere with the final estimation of Co as the nitroso R salt complex.

REFERENCES: Cobalt

1. *a.* J. Steinbach, Ph.D. Thesis, University of Pittsburgh, 1953. *b.* J. P. McKaveney, Ph.D. Thesis, University of Pittsburgh, 1957.
2. E. B. Sandell and R. W. Perlich, *Ind. Eng. Chem., Anal. Ed.,* **11,** 309 (1939).
3. H. R. Marston and D. W. Dewey, *Australian J. Exptl. Biol. Med. Sci.,* **18,** 343 (1940).
4. B. E. Saltzman, *Anal. Chem.,* **27,** 284 (1955).
5. T. Moeller, *Ind. Eng. Chem., Anal. Ed.,* **15,** 346 (1943).
6. H. A. Potratz, U.S. Atomic Energy Commission Report, CC-464.
7. N. S. Bayliss and R. W. Pickering, *Ind. Eng. Chem., Anal. Ed.,* **18,** 446 (1946).

COPPER

Carboxylic acid method.[1] Adjust the pH of the sample solution to between 6.3 and 10.3. Extract for 2 minutes with an equal volume of a 5% solution of n-capric acid in ethyl acetate. Maximum extraction is assured by providing a 2:1 ratio of acid to Cu(II). Chromium(III), Rh, and ferrocyanide prevent the extraction of Cu. Manganese, Fe, Ni, Pd, Co, and Ru give positive interference. Precipitates of Co and Ni settle at the interface. Using butyric acid in benzene as the extraction agent, only Mn and Fe are extracted along with Cu.

Cupferron method.[2] Add sufficient HCl to the sample solution to make the solution $1.2\,N$ in HCl (the acidity must be lower in the presence of sulfates). Add an excess of cupferron, either as solid or aqueous solution, and extract by shaking for 1 minute with 25 ml chloroform.

Diethyldithiocarbamate method.[3] For alloys, dissolve a 0.1 g sample in suitable acid solvent, fume off excess, dilute, add 10 ml 25% citric acid solution; neutralize with an excess of NH_4OH. Add 15 ml of EDTA solution (40 g of the disodium salt per liter) to the warm test solution and cool to room temperature or lower. Transfer to a separatory funnel, add 10 ml of sodium diethyldithiocarbamate solution, and shake for 30–60 seconds. Pipette 20 ml of butyl acetate into the funnel, shake for 30 seconds, and cool in running water for about 2–3 minutes. Repeat the shaking for 15 seconds; cool and allow layers to separate. Drain off the lower aqueous layer and discard it. Add 25 ml dilute $(5+95)\,H_2SO_4$, shake for 15 seconds, cool in running water, and allow layers to separate; then drain off aqueous layer and discard it. The copper complex absorbs at 560–600 mμ.

Dithizone method.[4] Adjust the pH of the sample solution to 1.5–2.0 (in the presence of Ag add an excess of NaCl; the precipitate may be ignored) and extract with successive portions of 13 parts per million dithizone in carbon tetrachloride (made by diluting a stock solution of 100 parts per million), shaking for 1 minute each time until a portion of the dithizone solution remains green. The copper dithizonate may be conveniently decomposed by shaking the carbon tetrachloride extracts twice with 3 ml $6\,N$ HCl. The Cu transfers quantitatively to the aqueous acid layer.

Since Hg interferes, it must be removed prior to the Cu extraction. This may be accomplished by dithizone extraction in the presence of EDTA as described under mercury. Copper may be determined in the presence of EDTA at a pH of 9 if Ca^{2+} is added to the solution. Under these conditions Pb, Zn, Bi, Cd, Ni, Co, and Tl do not extract.

To the mercury-free solution containing 1 ml $0.01\,N$ EDTA for each 50 μg Cu present, add 1 ml of $0.1\,N$ $CaCl_2$ solution, 3 ml of ammonium citrate (250 g/l, purified by dithizone extraction), and sufficient NH_4OH to produce a pH of 9. Extract with successive portions of 13 ppm dithizone solution until a portion no longer shows a purplish color.

Neocuproine (2,9-dimethyl-1,10-phenanthroline) method.[5] To a solution containing up to 0.2 mg Cu in a separatory funnel, add 5 ml of hydroxylamine hydrochloride solution (10 g/100 ml H_2O) to reduce the Cu to Cu(I) and 10 ml of sodium citrate solution (30 g/100 ml H_2O) to complex the metals present. Add NH_4OH until the pH is 4–6. Add 10 ml of a neocuproine solution (0.1% reagent in absolute ethanol) and 10 ml of chloroform. Shake for about 30 seconds and allow the layers to separate. Repeat the extraction with an additional 5 ml of chloroform. The complex absorbs at 457 mμ. This method has been found reliable with cast iron, high alloy steels, manganese and tungsten ores, in aluminum, germanium, titanium, and silicon metals as well as in lead-tin solder.

8-Quinolinol method.[6] To a sample containing up to about 300 μg Cu, add 5 ml of masking solution * and adjust to pH 6.45. (If Sn is present it must be removed at this point by heating at 95°C for 20 minutes to coagulate metastannic acid, which is then filtered. Unless removed, metastannic acid would cause emulsion formation.) Dilute the solution to 100 ml and extract by shaking for 2 minutes with 2 successive 10-ml portions of 1.0% 8-quinolinol in chloroform. The Cu complex absorbs strongly at 400 mμ. Copper may be determined in the presence of Fe, Al, Co, Ni, and Mn. Uranium, V, Mo, and Ti interfere. It is probable that Cu may be determined in the presence of V and Mo by changing the pH of extraction to 8.3–8.5 (Fe might extract at this higher pH).

REFERENCES: Copper

1. P. W. West, T. G. Lyons, and J. K. Carlton, *Anal. Chim. Acta,* **6**, 400 (1952).
2. N. H. Furman, W. B. Mason, and J. S. Pekola, *Anal. Chem.,* **21**, 1325 (1949).
3. J. L. Hague, E. D. Brown, and H. A. Bright, *J. Research Natl. Bur. Standards,* **47**, 380 (1951); A. Claassen and L. Bastings, *Z. anal. Chem.,* **153**, 30 (1956).
4. H. Friedeberg, *Anal. Chem.,* **27**, 305 (1955).
5. A. R. Gahler, *Anal. Chem.,* **26**, 577 (1954).
6. R. P. Taylor, Ph.D. Thesis, Princeton University, 1954.

CURIUM

Thenoyltrifluoroacetone method.[1] Curium is extracted with a 0.2 M TTA-benzene solution if the pH is adjusted to a value of at least 3.5.

REFERENCE: Curium

1. L. B. Magnusson and M. L. Anderson, *J. Am. Chem. Soc.,* **76**, 6207 (1954).

* *Masking solution:* Dissolve 2.00 millimoles of disodium ethylenediaminetetra-acetate and 3.00 millimoles of calcium acetate in sufficient 0.4 M ammonium acetate to make the final volume of solution 100 ml.

ERBIUM

5,7-Dichloro-8-quinolinol method.[1] Erbium is quantitatively extracted from a solution of pH 8.3 or higher by extraction with 0.02 M 5,7-dichloro-8-quinolinol in chloroform. Neodymium and probably other rare earths are also extracted. The Er complex absorbs strongly at 520 mμ.

REFERENCE: Erbium

1. T. Moeller and D. E. Jackson, *Anal. Chem.*, **22**, 1393 (1950).

FLUORINE

Tetraphenylstibonium sulfate method.[1] To a solution containing up to 5 mg of fluoride, add a few drops of dilute H_2SO_4 and 0.125 millimole of tetraphenylstibonium sulfate and adjust to a volume of 19 ml. Shake with three successive 5-ml portions of carbon tetrachloride. Evaporate the combined extracts. The residue is weighed and gives 97–98% recovery. Up to 1 g Na_2SO_4 does not interfere. Iron(III) and Al(III) when present in excessive amounts inhibit the extraction. Chloride and bromide, which also extract to some extent, give high results. If they are first removed with excess Ag, excellent recoveries of F are made.

REFERENCE: Fluorine

1. K. D. Moffett, J. R. Simmler, and H. A. Potratz, *Anal. Chem.*, **28**, 1356 (1956).

GALLIUM

Acetylacetone method.[1] Adjust the pH of the solution to 3 and extract with either pure acetylacetone or a 50 volume % chloroform solution of the reagent. About 95% extraction occurs with a single-stage extraction. At a pH of 1.2 a single extraction results in 50% removal of Ga with only 4% of In and 22% of Al accompanying it. Hence, repeated extractions and back washings at pH 1.2 or even somewhat lower might be useful in obtaining a good separation of Ga from In. Addition of fluoride would be effective in removing Al interference.

Benzoate method.[2] Bring to approximate neutrality the sample solution containing microgram quantities of Ga. Add 2 ml of ammonium acetate solution (50 g/100 ml H_2O), 1 ml of sodium benzoate solution (25 g/100 ml H_2O), and 4 ml ethyl acetate and mix. Shake well and allow layers to separate. Aluminum, Be, Fe(III), In, and Sc are also extracted.

Chloride method for separation of Ga from silicate rocks.[3] To 0.25 g of 100-mesh rock powder in a platinum dish add 2 ml of 6 N H_2SO_4 and 3 ml of HF. Evaporate to dryness and fume off the excess H_2SO_4, avoiding decomposition of $Fe_2(SO_4)_3$. Take up the residue in 0.5 ml of 6 N H_2SO_4 and 1 or 2 ml of water, evaporate to dryness, and again fume off the H_2SO_4. Treat the residue with 10 ml of 6 M HCl, warm the covered dish gently, and stir at intervals to bring all soluble material into solution. Filter off any $CaSO_4$ or other insoluble matter and wash the precipitate with 5 ml of water containing a few drops of HCl. Catch the filtrate and washings in a 25-ml volumetric flask.

Add 0.5 g of silver powder to the flask and swirl the solution until most of the ferric iron has been reduced (almost complete disappearance of the yellow color). Add 8 ml of concentrated HCl and dilute with water to 25 ml. Mix and run the solution through a funnel containing dry silver powder in its stem and collect a little more than 10 ml. Without delay transfer 10.0 ml of the solution to a separatory funnel which has been rinsed with 6 M HCl. Add 8 ml of ethyl ether and shake for 30 seconds. Allow the layers to separate, drain off the aqueous phase into another separatory funnel (rinsed with 6 M HCl), and shake with 5 ml of ether. Draw off and discard the acid layer and combine the two organic layers. Separate any small amounts of aqueous solution present and shake the ether for 10 seconds with 1 ml of 6 M HCl. Drain off the aqueous layer and repeat with another 1-ml portion of acid. Discard the HCl washings. Germanium, Mo, Re, As, Sb, and Sn are extracted with the Ga. Iron(III), Au(III), and Tl(III) are reduced to a lower valence state or metal and do not extract.

8-Quinolinol method.[4,5] Adjust the pH of the sample solution (25 ml) to 3.5 and extract with two 10-ml portions of 1% 8-quinolinol in chloroform.

REFERENCES: Gallium

1. J. F. Steinbach and H. Freiser, *Anal. Chem.*, **26**, 375 (1954).
2. S. E. J. Johnson in E. B. Sandell, *Colorimetric Determination of Traces of Metals*, second edition, Interscience Publishers, Inc., New York, 1950, p. 537.
3. E. B. Sandell, *Anal. Chem.*, **19**, 63 (1947).
4. T. Moeller, *Anal. Chem.*, **22**, 686 (1950).
5. S. Lacroix, *Anal. Chim. Acta*, **1**, 260 (1947).

GERMANIUM

Chloride method.[1] Dissolve a 0.25–0.5-g ore sample by heating with 5 ml of orthophosphoric acid and 5 ml of concentrated HNO_3. Cool, and to the viscous semiglassy mass add 25 ml of concentrated HCl. Stir gently until dissolved and, with the aid of small portions of concentrated HCl, transfer to a separatory funnel. Extract twice with 15-ml portions of carbon tetrachloride, shaking with each extraction for 2 minutes. Transfer the organic layers to another separatory funnel and again extract twice, for 2 minutes, with 10-ml portions of an ammonium oxalate–oxalic acid solution (dissolve 5.0 g of ammonium oxalate and 5.0 g of oxalic acid in 1 l of water, the pH of the solution being adjusted to 5). Transfer the oxalate extracts to a 250-ml beaker and add 20 ml of concentrated HNO_3. Cautiously evaporate to dryness but do not bake. Cool, and then determine the Ge colorimetrically with quinalizarin acetate or phenylfluorone. The method is applicable to microgram quantities of Ge and is virtually free from interferences; however, chloride must be absent while the sample is being dissolved to prevent loss by volatilization.

Chloride method for removal of impurities.[2] Methods for the removal of trace amounts of impurities from Ge are important for the purification of this element for use in electronic devices. An attractive method of purification is based on the fact that when liquid $GeCl_4$ is equilibrated with concentrated HCl, many elements are distributed in favor of the HCl. Thus Sb, Sn, Ti, B, and Cu can be completely removed. If an oxidizing agent such as H_2O_2 or chlorine is added, As(V) can be completely extracted. This extraction method can be used in the trace analysis of impurities in Ge.

REFERENCES: Germanium

1. E. H. Strickland, *Analyst,* **80,** 548 (1955).
2. G. H. Morrison, E. G. Dorfman, and J. F. Cosgrove, *J. Am. Chem. Soc.,* **76,** 4236 (1954).

GOLD

Bromide method.[1] Adjust the volume of the sample solution containing 0.1 mg of Au to 10–12 ml and add 5 ml of concentrated HBr. Extract twice with 15-ml portions of isopropyl ether (free from alcohols). Combine the ether extracts and wash with 5 ml of $4 M$ HBr. Strip the Au from the ether phase by shaking with one 20-ml and two 10-ml portions of water. Add 1 ml of concentrated HBr to this combined aqueous solution containing the Au and heat on a water bath to remove ether. Dilute the solution to volume and find the transmittancy at 380 mμ. With the exception of Os as the tetroxide, the platinum metals are not extracted. Iron(III) is extracted approximately 1%. If Fe may be present, add 0.5 ml of concentrated phosphoric acid.

p-Dimethylaminobenzalrhodanine method.[2] The sample solution is acidified with a few drops of 1 N HNO$_3$ and treated with 0.5–1.0 ml of reagent (1 ml of 0.03% ethanolic p-dimethylaminobenzalrhodanine, 13 ml of benzene, and 36 ml of chloroform). The mixture is shaken vigorously to extract a pink-violet Au complex. As little as 0.1–0.2 μg Au in 5 ml can be detected. Silver does not interfere if separated as chloride.

REFERENCES: Gold

1. W. A. McBryde and J. H. Yoe, *Anal. Chem.*, **20**, 1094 (1948).
2. N. S. Poluektov, *Trudy Vsesoyus Konferentsii Anal. Khim.*, **2**, 393 (1943); *Chem. Abstracts*, **39**, 3494 (1945).

HAFNIUM

Thenoyltrifluoroacetone (TTA) method.[1] Milligram quantities of Hf can be quantitatively extracted from a solution that is 2 M in HClO$_4$ by extraction with 0.1 M TTA-benzene.

Thiocyanate method.[2,3] Solvent extraction of acidified thiocyanate solutions using ethyl ether has been used as a method for separating Hf from Zr. Both are extracted; however, by employing a fractional extraction procedure it is possible to obtain a pure Hf fraction. The method has not yet been applied for analytical purposes.

REFERENCES: Hafnium

1. E. H. Huffman and L. J. Beaufait, *J. Am. Chem. Soc.*, **71**, 3179 (1949).
2. W. Fischer and W. Chalybaeus, *Z. anorg. Chem.*, **254**, 79 (1947).
3. W. Fischer, W. Chalybaeus, and C. Zumbusch, *Z. anorg. Chem.*, **255**, 277 (1948).

HOLMIUM

Butylphosphoric acid method.[1] Milligram quantities of Ho can be quantitatively extracted from an aqueous solution that is 1 M in H$_2$SO$_4$, 2.5 M in (NH$_4$)$_2$SO$_4$, 0.004 M in oxalic acid, and 6% in H$_2$O$_2$ by shaking for 5 minutes with an equal volume of 0.6 M dibutylphosphoric acid (containing some monobutylphosphoric acid) in butyl ether. Metals of the La group of rare earths are not extracted under these conditions.

REFERENCE: Holmium

1. E. M. Scadden and N. E. Ballou, *Anal. Chem.*, **25**, 1602 (1953).

INDIUM

Acetylacetone method.[1] Adjust the solution to a pH of 3 and add either pure acetylacetone or its 50 volume % solution in chloroform to obtain a quantitative extraction. A number of other metals also extract under these conditions.

Benzoate method.[2] Add NaOH to the sample solution containing microgram quantities of In until it is approximately neutral. Add 2.0 ml of ammonium acetate solution (50 g/100 ml H_2O) and 1.0 ml of sodium benzoate solution (25 g/100 ml H_2O); mix and add 4 ml ethyl acetate. Shake well and allow layers to separate. Gallium, Al, Be, Fe(III), and Sc are also extracted.

Bromide method.[3] Extract a solution 4.5 M in HBr with ethyl ether. Elements which also extract include Ga, Fe(III), Au(III), Tl(III), Mo(VI), Re, and small amounts of Zn and Te.

Butylphosphoric acid method.[4] Carrier-free concentrations of In can be quantitatively (>95%) removed from an aqueous solution made 1 M in HNO_3 and 3% in H_2O_2 by extracting for 5 minutes with an equal volume of 0.06 M dibutylphosphoric acid (containing some monobutylphosphoric acid) in butyl ether. Accompanying In will be Zr (>95%), Sn(IV) (50%), Mo (15%), and Y (15%); other elements tested will extract to less than 5%.

Diethyldithiocarbamate method.[5,6] To a solution containing up to 300 μg In add sufficient ammonia to bring the pH to 8.5 and 5 ml of 10% NaCN; readjust the pH to 9.0. Add 1 ml 0.2% sodium diethyldithiocarbamate and 10 ml carbon tetrachloride. Shake the mixture for 1 minute. The complex absorbs at 305 mμ. Manganese, Sb, Te, and small amounts of Fe also extract under these conditions.

Dithizone method.[7] To a solution of the sample (50 ml) add 5 ml of ammonia-cyanide solution (200 ml 10% KCN and 150 ml concentrated NH_4OH diluted to 1 l) and shake for 1 minute with 15 ml of dithizone solution (1 mg/100 ml chloroform).

In the presence of Pb and Zn a preliminary separation with 8-quinolinol is recommended.

Iodide method.[8] Extract a solution 1.5 M in HI with an equal volume of ethyl ether. Indium is completely extracted over the concentration range of 0.6 mg to 3 g/l. The presence of 0.5 M fluoride, chloride, bromide, cyanide, phosphate, or citrate ions does not interfere. Iron and Be do not extract, and Ga is only negligibly extracted.

REFERENCES: Indium

1. J. F. Steinbach and H. Freiser, *Anal. Chem.*, **26**, 375 (1954).
2. S. E. J. Johnson in E. B. Sandell, *Colorimetric Determination of Traces of Metals*, second edition, Interscience Publishers, Inc., New York, 1950, p. 537.
3. I. Wada and R. Ishii, *Sci. Papers Inst. Phys. Chem. Research (Tokyo)*, **34**, 787 (1937–1938).
4. E. M. Scadden and N. E. Ballou, *Anal. Chem.*, **25**, 1602 (1953).
5. A. Claassen, L. Bastings, and J. Visser, *Anal. Chim. Acta*, **10**, 373 (1954).
6. H. Bode, *Z. anal. Chem.*, **144**, 165 (1955).
7. I. May and J. I. Hoffman, *J. Washington Acad. Sci.*, **38**, 329 (1948).
8. H. M. Irving and F. J. C. Rossotti, *Analyst*, **77**, 801 (1952).

IRON

Acetylacetone method.[1] Adjust the pH of the solution containing up to a gram of Fe(III) to a value of 1.00 and shake for 3 minutes with a 50-ml portion of 50 volume % acetylacetone in chloroform. Approximately 96% extraction can be obtained in a single extraction. Repeated extractions which may be needed for the larger amounts of Fe result in complete ($>$99.5%) removal. The complex absorbs at 440 mμ. Beryllium, Mo, V, Cu, and Ga will extract to some extent under these conditions.

Benzoate method.[2] Bring the sample solution containing microgram quantities of Fe(III) to approximate neutrality; add 2 ml of ammonium acetate solution (50 g/100 ml H_2O) and 1 ml of sodium benzoate solution (25 g/100 ml H_2O). After mixing add 4 ml ethyl acetate and shake well to extract Fe. Aluminum, Be, Ga, In, and Sc are also extracted.

Chloride method.[3] Adjust a sample solution containing 125–250 mg of Fe(III) to 7.75–8 M in HCl in a volume of 25 ml. Extract for several minutes with an equal volume of isopropyl ether. With such large amounts of Fe, three phases appear. The two upper phases are used as the organic extract. Strip the Fe from the ether with water. Approximately 99.9% of the Fe is removed by this method. The extraction decreases with smaller amounts of Fe; however, as little as 1 mg of Fe can be quantitatively removed by shaking with three successive portions of isopropyl ether. Very satisfactory separation of Fe from Cu, Co, Mn, Ni, Al, Cr, Zn, V(IV), Ti, and sulfate is obtained. Large amounts of V(V), Sb(V), Ga(III), and Tl(III) are extracted, and phosphoric acid and Mo pass into the ether layer with Fe(III).

Cupferron method.[4] Both micro and macro amounts of Fe(III) are quantitatively extracted from (1+9)HCl or (1+9)H_2SO_4 with excess cupferron using ether, chloroform, or ethyl acetate, leaving not even a spectrographic trace.

4,7-Diphenylphenanthroline (bathophenanthroline) method.[5]
Add 2 ml of 10% hydroxylamine hydrochloride solution to a sample
containing from 1–10 μg Fe. Add 4 ml of 10% sodium acetate solution to bring the pH of the solution to approximately 4. Add 4 ml of
0.002 M bathophenanthroline in 50% ethanol. Add 10 ml of n-hexa-
nol, shake well, and set aside for 5 minutes. The Fe complex which is
in the alcohol layer absorbs strongly at 533 mμ. It is advisable to
purify all reagents used by prior extraction with bathophenanthroline.
Copper(I) also extracts but does not interfere in the colorimetric determination of Fe.

8-Quinolinol method.[6,7] A solution of 50 ml containing 50–200 μg
Fe can be shaken with 10 ml of 1% 8-quinolinol in chloroform in a
separatory funnel for 1 minute. Complete Fe extraction is obtained
when the pH of the aqueous phase is between 2.5 and 12.5. For solutions at the higher pH values, 10 ml of 10% sodium potassium tartrate
is used prior to pH adjustment. With a double or triple extraction, the
Fe could be completely extracted from an even more acid solution, say
at pH 2, to permit better separation from other heavy metals such as
Ni. Copper, Bi, Ga, In, Mo(VI), Sn(IV), and Ti interfere with low
pH extraction of Fe but Ni, Co, Mn, Ce(III), and Al do not. Molyb-
denum(VI) no longer extracts above pH 6.8, and Sn(IV) does not
above pH 10.0; Ga stops extracting above pH 10.2, Ce(III) above
pH 12.0, and Al above pH 12.3.

The presence of EDTA will keep Fe extraction below 5% up to a pH
of 9.5; its Ca salt might permit extraction at pH values above 9.[7]

Thiocyanate method.[8] Transfer a 25-ml aliquot of the sample solution to a separatory funnel and add 5 ml of concentrated HCl. Add
1 ml of 2% potassium persulfate and swirl the funnel to ensure complete
mixing. Add 10 ml of 20% potassium thiocyanate reagent (prepared
frequently and stored in a refrigerator). Add 25 ml of isobutyl alcohol
and extract for 2 minutes. Draw off and discard the aqueous layer.
Invert and slowly revolve the funnel to dislodge any water particles
clinging to the walls and allow to stand for 10 minutes. Draw off the
small amount of water which has separated from the alcohol and transfer the alcohol phase to a dry Erlenmeyer flask. Immediately before
reading the per cent transmission, add a small amount (about 0.1 g)
of anhydrous sodium sulfate and agitate to remove suspended particles
of water from the alcoholic extract. Read at 485 mμ.

REFERENCES: Iron

1. J. P. McKaveney and H. Freiser, *Anal. Chem.,* **29,** 290 (1957).
2. S. E. J. Johnson in E. B. Sandell, *Colorimetric Determination of Traces of
   Metals,* second edition, Interscience Publishers, Inc., New York, 1950, p. 537.

3. R. W. Dodson, G. J. Forney, and E. H. Swift, *J. Am. Chem. Soc.*, **58**, 2573 (1936).
4. N. H. Furman, W. B. Mason, and J. S. Pekola, *Anal. Chem.*, **21**, 1325 (1949).
5. G. F. Smith, W. H. McCurdy, Jr., and H. Diehl, *Analyst*, **77**, 418 (1952).
6. C. H. R. Gentry and L. G. Sherrington, *Analyst*, **75**, 17 (1950).
7. R. P. Taylor, Ph.D. Thesis, Princeton University, 1954.
8. J. B. Thompson, *Ind. Eng. Chem., Anal. Ed.*, **16**, 646 (1944).

LANTHANUM

Cinnamic acid method.[1] Lanthanum can be quantitatively extracted from a solution of pH 7 by 0.1 M cinnamic acid in hexane.

REFERENCE: Lanthanum

1. B. Hök-Bernström, *Svensk Kem. Tidskr.*, **68**, 1 (1956).

LEAD

Diethyldithiocarbamate method.[1,2] Transfer a solution containing up to 300 μg Pb to a separatory funnel, add 1 ml 50% ammonium
citrate, make slightly ammoniacal, add 10 ml 5% NaCN, and adjust
to pH 11. Now add 1 ml 0.2% aqueous sodium diethyldithiocarbamate
and 10 ml carbon tetrachloride. Stopper and shake for 1 minute. The
complex absorbs in the ultraviolet spectral region. Cadmium, Bi, and
Tl(III) are the only other metals extracting.

Dithizone method.[3,4] In a separatory funnel to a slightly acid solution containing up to 100 μg of Pb in a volume of 25 ml, add 75 ml of
ammonia-cyanide-sulfite mixture. (Prepare by diluting 350 ml of concentrated NH_4OH and 30 ml of 10% KCN to 1 l. Dissolve 1.5 g of
sodium sulfite in the solution.) Run in 7.5 ml 0.005% dithizone in
chloroform (1 ml 0.005% dithizone is equivalent to about 20 μg Pb)
and 17.5 ml chloroform. Shake for 1 minute and allow the phases
to separate. The complex absorbs strongly at 510 mμ. Only Bi and Tl
will accompany the Pb. As much as 5 mg phosphate can be tolerated.

Procedure in the presence of bismuth.[3,5] To a sample solution
containing up to 25 μg Pb and 5 mg Bi, add 1 ml 50% ammonium citrate
solution and then ammonia until slightly basic. For each 10 ml of solution add 10 ml of 10% KCN; shake 3–5 minutes with 2 ml 0.003%
dithizone in carbon tetrachloride. Since the extraction of Pb is slow
in the presence of Bi, mechanical shaking would be convenient. Separate the carbon tetrachloride and repeat the extraction with 2-ml portions of dithizone until the last portions are colored pure orange (bi-
dithizonate). To be certain that all the Pb has been extracted, shake
the last portion of carbon tetrachloride extract with 3 small portions of
1% KCN. The carbon tetrachloride layer should not show any pink
color. Shake the combined extracts, containing all the Pb and Bi, with

5 ml of 1:100 HNO_3, separate the lead-containing aqueous phase, adjust its pH to 2.8–3 (yellow color of thymol blue), and shake with small portions of 0.006% dithizone in carbon tetrachloride for 3–4 minutes until the last portion remains pure green. The Pb will be contained in the carbon tetrachloride extracts.

Procedure in presence of thallium. To the sample solution containing up to 500 μg Tl, add 1 ml 50% ammonium citrate, make slightly ammoniacal, and add 10 ml of 10% KCN. Extract with 2-ml portions of 0.004% dithizone in carbon tetrachloride. Shake each extract with twice its volume 0.5% KCN. The Tl complex but not the Pb complex is decomposed in this way. Wash the combined carbon tetrachloride extracts with 0.5% KCN.

Iodide method.[6] Add an excess of KI to a solution containing 0.1 mg of Pb and adjust the acidity to 5 volume % in HCl. Extract with an equal volume of methyl isopropyl ketone. Repeat the extraction with fresh solvent. Partial extraction of Zn, Cd, Cu, As, Sb, Sn, Rh, Ru, and Pt occurs. In the presence of Pb, Rh and Ru are extracted to a larger extent. Interference from Fe, Cu, Zn, Hg, Au, and Pd can be eliminated by a prior extraction with methyl isopropyl ketone of the acidic solution containing thiocyanate. Lead is not extracted; after the preliminary extraction, add KI and perform the extraction described above.

REFERENCES: Lead

1. H. H. Lockwood, *Anal. Chim. Acta,* **10,** 97 (1954).
2. H. Bode, *Z. anal. Chem.,* **144,** 165 (1955).
3. E. B. Sandell, *Colorimetric Determination of Traces of Metals,* second edition, Interscience Publishers, Inc., New York, 1950.
4. L. J. Snyder, *Anal. Chem.,* **19,** 684 (1947).
5. K. Bambach and R. E. Burkey, *Ind. Eng. Chem., Anal. Ed.,* **14,** 904 (1942).
6. P. W. West and J. K. Carlton, *Anal. Chim. Acta,* **6,** 406 (1952).

LITHIUM

Chloride method for separation of Li from Na and K.[1] The sample solution may conveniently contain from 20–100 μg of Li. The alkali metals must be present as the chlorides and other metals must be absent. Evaporate the solution to dryness, and dissolve the salts in a minimum volume of water (0.5–0.6 ml for 200 mg of the chlorides). Add 7 or 8 ml of absolute ethyl alcohol and 20 ml of anhydrous ether, stir the mixture well, and allow to stand for 5 minutes. Filter the solution through a small dry filter crucible and wash the salts with 5 ml of a 1:4 alcohol and ether mixture. Evaporate the combined filtrate and washings to dryness in a small beaker.

Chloride method for separating Li from Na and K.[2] Transfer an aliquot, not more than 20 ml, containing 5–25 mg of Li in the form of the chloride, and not more than 500 mg of total alkali metal chlorides, free from other cations, to a 50-ml Erlenmeyer flask and gently evaporate to dryness. Bake to ensure removal of excess HCl; dissolve salts in 3–5 ml of water. Add 10–15 ml of 2-ethyl-1-hexanol and one or two glass beads. Heat slowly on an electrically controlled heater until the temperature of the solution is about 135°C and the aqueous phase is completely volatilized. Continue heating at 135°C until the bulk of the salts that crystallize out of solution becomes free-flowing and no longer clings to the walls of the vessel; then heat for 3 additional minutes. Cool; then filter the solution through a sintered-glass crucible of medium porosity. Wash with 1–2-ml volumes of cold 2-ethyl-1-hexanol and catch the filtrate in a flask. Lithium chloride can be determined by titration of chloride by the Volhard method.

Dipivaloylmethane method.[3] Evaporate the sample which may contain milligram quantities of Li almost to dryness and take up in 1 ml of 1.0 N KOH. Shake this with 50 ml of a 0.1 M dipivaloylmethane [$(CH_3)_3C-COCH_2CO \cdot C(CH_3)_3$] solution in ether for 2 minutes. Repeat the extraction. This will separate Li from Na and K.

REFERENCES: Lithium

1. E. B. Sandell, *Colorimetric Determination of Traces of Metals,* second edition, Interscience Publishers, Inc., New York, 1950, p. 415.
2. J. C. White and G. Goldberg, *Anal. Chem.,* **27,** 1188 (1955).
3. G. A. Guter and G. S. Hammond, *J. Am. Chem. Soc.,* **78,** 5166 (1956).

MAGNESIUM

8-Quinolinol method.[1] To 10 ml of a solution containing up to 100 μg Mg, add 2 ml of HNO_3 (1:1) and dilute to 40 ml. Neutralize the solution with NH_4OH using Congo red paper as indicator. Add 5.0 ml butyl cellosolve solution (1 + 1 with water) and then 10 ml NH_4OH (this should give a pH of 10.0–10.2). Transfer to a separatory funnel, add 20.0 ml of 3% 8-quinolinol solution in chloroform, stopper, and shake vigorously for 1 minute. Allow the layers to separate. The complex absorbs at 400 mμ (shows a maximum at 380 mμ).

Sulfate method for separating Mg from Ca.[2] After precipitating Mg together with Ca as phosphate, dissolve the precipitate in a little dilute H_2SO_4, avoiding more than approximately 0.5 ml in excess. Should the precipitate dissolve with difficulty, boil it with HNO_3 and evaporate until fumes of H_2SO_4 appear. Add 100 ml of 75% ethyl alcohol (by volume) for every 0.3 g pyrophosphate originally present;

allow the solution to stand for several hours, or preferably overnight if the amount of Ca is very small. Filter; wash the residue of $CaSO_4$ with alcohol of 75% strength and combine the organic extracts. The solvent dissolves approximately 0.06 g of MgO as $MgSO_4$ and less than 0.1 mg of CaO per 100 ml. A mixture containing 90 parts of ethyl alcohol, 10 parts of methyl alcohol, and 1 part of H_2SO_4 dissolves 0.46 g of MgO as $MgSO_4$ per 100 ml.

REFERENCES: Magnesium

1. *a.* C. L. Luke and M. E. Campbell, *Anal. Chem.*, **26**, 1778 (1954). *b.* C. L. Luke, *Anal. Chem.*, **28**, 1443 (1956).
2. W. F. Hillebrand, G. E. F. Lundell, H. A. Bright, and J. I. Hoffman, *Applied Inorganic Analysis,* second edition, John Wiley & Sons, Inc., New York, 1953, p. 613.

MANGANESE

Pyridine method.[1] Pyridine is added to a solution containing Mn as permanganate in a centrifuge bottle; after being shaken for a few seconds, 4 N NaOH is poured into the bottle. The mixture is shaken again for a few seconds and then immediately centrifuged to hasten separation of the layers. Speed is essential to minimize the decomposition of the permanganate to form the green manganate. Rhenium(VII) and Tc(VII) also extract.

8-Quinolinol method.[2,3,4] To 50 ml of a solution in a separatory funnel containing up to 200 μg Mn and 10 ml of 10% sodium potassium tartrate, adjust the pH to a value between 7.5 and 12.5. Shake for 1 minute with 10 ml of 1% 8-quinolinol in chloroform. If the Mn is to be photometrically determined, 1 mg $K_4Fe(CN)_6$ should be added to the solution prior to the extraction. Extraction at pH 12.5 will permit separation from Ni and Al. Copper and Fe will extract over the entire pH range.

Tetraphenylarsonium chloride method.[3] The sample containing Mn is made alkaline with NaOH. Potassium persulfate is added to oxidize the Mn to MnO_4^-. Enough 1% $(C_6H_5)_4AsCl$ solution is added to make the test solution 5×10^{-5} M in reagent. The mixture is shaken for 5 minutes with an equal volume of chloroform. The Mn will be quantitatively extracted as the purple-colored $((C_6H_5)_4As^+, MnO_4^-)$.

REFERENCES: Manganese

1. W. Goishi and W. F. Libby, *J. Am. Chem. Soc.*, **74**, 6019 (1952).
2. C. H. R. Gentry and L. G. Sherrington, *Analyst*, **75**, 17 (1950).
3. S. Tribalat and J. Beydon, *Anal. Chim. Acta*, **6**, 96 (1952); **8**, 22 (1953).
4. H. Bode, *Z. anal. Chem.*, **143**, 182 (1954).

MERCURY

Diethyldithiocarbamate method.[1] To a solution containing 0.2–0.3 mg of Hg, add 10 ml of 5% disodium ethylenediaminetetraacetate and adjust the pH of the solution to 11. Add 1 ml 0.2% aqueous sodium diethyldithiocarbamate and 10 ml carbon tetrachloride. Shake the mixture for 1 minute. The Hg complex absorbs in the ultraviolet region of the spectra. Under these conditions Ag, Cu, Pd, Bi, and Tl(III) are the only other metals extracted.

Dithizone method.[2] *To determine Hg in the presence of Cu and Ag,* add an excess of 20% NaCl solution to the sample and, ignoring the AgCl precipitate, extract with successive portions of 13 ppm dithizone (made by diluting a stock solution of 100 ppm dithizone) in carbon tetrachloride until a portion remains green. Extract the combined carbon tetrachloride solution twice with 3 ml of 6 N HCl. Discard the organic phase. Neutralize the acid with 6 N NH₄OH and adjust to pH 1.5–2. Add 1 ml of 0.01 N EDTA (2 g of disodium salt in a liter of water) for each 50 μg Cu present. Extract Hg with 13 ppm dithizone solution, avoiding prolonged shaking. For large quantities of Cu, add 2 equivalents of EDTA [0.1 N solution (20 g disodium salt per liter)] per equivalent of Cu present and use 5 portions of dithizone in the initial extraction. The method allows quantitative separation of 1 part Hg in 10,000 parts Cu.

Iodide method.[3] The sample solution containing the Hg is made 6.9 N in HI in a volume of 5 ml and extracted with 20 ml of ethyl ether. The Hg(II) is completely extracted and thereby separated from K, Ca, Ba, Cs, Fe(II), Ni, Cr, Co, Mn, Ti, Zr, Pb, Th, Al, Ga, Be, U, V, Pt, Pd, Ir, Os, and Ru. Antimony(III), Cd, and Au(III) are also completely extracted, and As(III), Bi, In, Mo(VI), Te(IV), and Zn are extracted to a lesser extent.

REFERENCES: Mercury

1. H. Bode, *Z. anal. Chem.,* **144,** 165 (1955).
2. H. Friedeberg, *Anal. Chem.,* **27,** 305 (1955).
3. S. Kitahara, *Bull. Inst. Phys. Chem. Research (Tokyo),* **24,** 454 (1948).

MOLYBDENUM

Acetylacetone method.[1] Molybdenum(VI) in milligram quantities can be extracted out of 6 N H₂SO₄ by shaking for one-half hour with a 50 volume % chloroform solution of acetylacetone. Under these conditions about 3% extraction of Fe(III) also occurs. The method has been applied to a variety of ferrous materials including low- and high-alloy steels, as well as ferrovanadium and ferrotitanium.

8-Quinolinol method. This method is suitable for ferrous alloys.[2] To a sample containing up to 0.5 mg Mo(VI), add 5 ml 0.02 M disodium ethylenediaminetetraacetate and adjust the pH to 1.55 (complete extraction is obtained from solutions of pH between 1.4–5.0) and dilute to 100 ml. Extract by shaking for 2 minutes with two successive 10-ml portions of 1.0% 8-quinolinol in chloroform. Only W might interfere.[1] The complex has an absorption maxima at 370 mμ.

Thiocyanate method for separating Mo from W.[3] Add 6 drops of 50% thioglycolic acid to the solution followed by 1 ml of 20% potassium thiocyanate solution. Add 7 ml of H_2SO_4 for each 30 ml of solution. Cool the solution for 15 minutes and extract the thiocyanate complex with butyl acetate. Other elements that extract can be removed if an α-benzoinoxime precipitation of Mo and W is used before the extraction.

Toluenedithiol method.[4] This method is suitable for Mo in the presence of W and all other elements found in alloy steels. A solution of 4 mg of the steel, or an aliquot representing this quantity, in 0.5 ml of a mixture of 12.7 M H_2SO_4 and 2.5 M H_3PO_4 and 0.5 ml concentrated HNO_3, is evaporated to fumes and taken up in 3 ml 4 N HCl (sp gr 1.075) and cooled in a water bath. Add 3 ml of a 1% toluene-3,4-dithiol solution in amyl acetate (prepared just before use) and allow mixture to stand for 15 minutes with occasional shaking. Wash the mixture into a separatory funnel with a small amount of amyl acetate, shake, and allow layers to separate. After removing and, unless it is desired to determine W, rejecting the aqueous phase, wash the organic layer with 3 ml concentrated HCl to remove the light cloudiness. The Mo may now be spectrophotometrically determined at 607 mμ.

Trioctylamine method.[5] Molybdenum(VI) can be quantitatively extracted from a solution which contains milligram quantities of Mo and which has been brought to a pH of 0.85 by shaking the solution with half its volume of a 0.1 M solution of trioctylamine in kerosene containing 2% capryl alcohol for 1 minute. Uranium will also extract. Vanadium(V), probably combined with Mo as a heteropoly acid, extracts in a 1:2 ratio with Mo.

REFERENCES: Molybdenum

1. J. P. McKaveney and H. Freiser, *Anal. Chem.,* **29,** 290 (1957).
2. R. P. Taylor, Ph.D. Thesis, Princeton University, 1954.

3. C. J. Rodden, *Analytical Chemistry of the Manhattan Project*, McGraw-Hill Book Co., Inc., New York, 1950, p. 456.
4. J. E. Wells and R. Pemberton, *Analyst*, **72**, 185 (1947).
5. K. B. Brown, C. F. Coleman, D. J. Crouse, J. O. Denis, and J. G. Moore, U.S. Atomic Energy Commission Report, ORNL-1734.

NEODYMIUM

5,7-Dichloro-8-quinolinol method.[1] Neodymium is quantitatively extracted from a solution of pH 8.3 or higher by extraction with 0.02 M 5,7-dichloro-8-quinolinol in chloroform. Erbium and probably other rare earths are also extracted. The Nd complex absorbs strongly at 520 mμ.

REFERENCE: Neodymium

1. T. Moeller and D. E. Jackson, *Anal. Chem.*, **22**, 1393 (1950).

NEPTUNIUM

Nitrate method.[1] Neptunyl nitrate can be extracted from HNO_3 solutions saturated with NH_4NO_3 using ethyl ether as solvent. Uranium(VI) and Pu(VI) are similarly extracted.

Thenoyltrifluoroacetone (TTA) method.[2] Make the solution 0.5 M in H^+ and extract Np(IV) with 0.15 M TTA-benzene solution. Plutonium(IV) also extracts.

REFERENCES: Neptunium

1. E. Glueckauf and H. A. C. McKay, *Nature*, **165**, 594 (1950).
2. L. B. Magnusson and M. L. Anderson, U.S. Atomic Energy Commission Report, ANL-4066.

NICKEL

Dimethylglyoxime method.[1] A sample containing from 20–400 μg Ni in 100–200 ml of solution is treated with 10 ml 50% ammonium citrate solution and sufficient ammonia to make the solution just alkaline to litmus. Cool and transfer to a separatory funnel; add 20 ml of dimethylglyoxime solution (1 g dimethylglyoxime dissolved in 500 ml of NH_4OH and brought to a liter with water). Allow to stand for a minute or two and then add 12 ml chloroform. Shake well. Milligram amounts of Co do not interfere provided sufficient dimethylglyoxime is used. (For 5 mg Co use 40 ml of a 1% dimethylglyoxime solution.)

Nickel may be extracted in the presence of large quantities of Cu.[2] Dissolve 1 g of a copper salt in 10 ml water. Add 0.5 g sodium tartrate,

5 g $Na_2S_2O_3$, 5 ml of pH 6.5 buffer solution (prepared by adding 30% CH_3COOH to a 30% sodium acetate solution until the pH is 6.5), and 50 mg $NH_2OH \cdot HCl$, shaking vigorously after each addition. Add 2 ml of 1% ethanolic dimethylglyoxime and 6 ml chloroform, shake for 1 minute, and separate. The Ni complex absorbs at 366 mμ.

8-Quinolinol method.[3] To a solution containing up to 200 μg Ni add 10 ml of 10% sodium potassium tartrate solution, adjust the pH to any value between 4.5 and 9.5, transfer to a separatory funnel, and dilute to 50 ml. Add 10 ml 1% 8-quinolinol in chloroform and shake for 1 minute.

REFERENCES: Nickel

1. A. J. Hall and R. S. Young, *Analyst*, **71**, 479 (1946).
2. W. Nielsch, *Z. anal. Chem.*, **150**, 114 (1956).
3. C. H. R. Gentry and L. G. Sherrington, *Analyst*, **75**, 17 (1950).

NIOBIUM

Butylphosphoric acid method.[1] Niobium will be quantitatively removed (98%) from a solution which contains 1 mg Nb/ml and which has been made 1 M in H_2SO_4, 2.5 M in $(NH_4)_2SO_4$, and 0.004 M in oxalic acid by extracting for 5 minutes with an equal volume of 0.6 M dibutylphosphoric acid (containing some monobutylphosphoric acid) in n-butyl ether. Under these conditions Zr, Y, Ho, and In will be quantitatively extracted and Sn(IV) and Ta will be extracted in substantial amount (50% and 35%, respectively). Other elements will be extracted to negligible extents ($<5\%$). The Nb is best removed from the organic phase by stripping with 4 M HF.

Fluoride method for separating Nb from Pa.[2] Adjust the sample solution to be 6 M in HF and 6 M in H_2SO_4. Extract for 3 minutes with an equal volume of diisobutylcarbinol that has been pretreated for 3 minutes with an HF solution of the same concentration as that of the original aqueous phase. After extraction, separate the the original aqueous phase. One batch extraction results in the extraction of only 0.01% of the Pa. A second extraction completely removes the Nb from the aqueous phase. Strip the Nb from the solvent by shaking with small portions of water. Use polyethylene bottles for the extraction of the fluoride solutions.

8-Quinolinol method.[3] Fuse a sample of earth acid oxides containing from 0.5–6 mg Nb in 2.5 g $KHSO_4$ and dissolve the cooled melt in 40 ml of a citric acid solution containing 10.00 $\pm$ 0.02 g of the acid. Dilute this to 250 ml with water in a volumetric flask. Transfer a

15-ml aliquot to a 125-ml separatory funnel and add 15 ml of recently standardized $1 \pm 0.01 N$ NH$_4$OH. After mixing thoroughly, add 10 ml of a $1 \pm 0.01\%$ 8-quinolinol solution in chloroform. Shake for exactly 3 minutes to extract Nb. The complex absorbs at 385 mμ.

Thiocyanate method for samples soluble in concentrated HCl.[4] Transfer an aliquot containing between 1 and 65 μg of Nb in not over 4 ml to a separatory funnel. Add the reagents in the following order: first, 3 ml of 15% SnCl$_2$ in $4 M$ HCl; then HCl in amount and concentration suitable to bring the final concentration to $4 \pm 0.25 M$ hydrogen ion in a final volume of 14 ml; and then 5 ml of 20% KSCN. Add within 5 minutes a 7-ml portion of peroxide-free ethyl ether and extract the yellow color. Draw off the aqueous layer into a second separatory funnel and extract with another 7-ml portion of ether. With amounts of Nb greater than 25 μg, add more thiocyanate reagent along with sufficient HCl to maintain the acidity at $4.0 N$, and perform a third extraction. Extraction should be continued as long as more color is being separated. Transfer the combined ether layers to a 25-ml volumetric flask and dilute to the mark. The Nb may be determined spectrophotometrically at 385 mμ. Iron, U, Mo, V, and Ti cause positive interferences in amounts one thousand times greater than Nb. Nickel also interferes. The presence of W, Cu, Pt, and Hg(II) results in precipitates which collect in the ether phase and interfere in the extraction. Smaller amounts of W and Pt give interfering colors. Cobalt extracts but does not interfere in the colorimetric measurement except when present in very high concentrations.

Thiocyanate method for samples insoluble in concentrated HCl.[4] Fuse the solid sample with fifty times its weight of potassium bisulfate or potassium pyrosulfate, cool, and dissolve the melt in $1 M$ tartaric acid. Transfer a 1-ml aliquot of this solution containing 1–65 μg of Nb into a separatory funnel as before, and add the following reagents: 3 ml of 15% SnCl$_2$ in $4 M$ HCl, 5 ml of $9 M$ HCl which is also $1 M$ in tartaric acid, and 5 ml of 20% KSCN. Perform the extractions as before.

Tribenzylamine method.[5] Niobium can be quantitatively extracted out of an $11 M$ HCl solution by shaking the solution for 5 minutes with an 8% tribenzylamine solution in methylene chloride. Tantalum does not extract under these conditions.

REFERENCES: Niobium

1. E. M. Scadden and N. E. Ballou, *Anal. Chem.*, **25**, 1602 (1953).
2. F. L. Moore, *Anal. Chem.*, **27**, 70 (1955).

3. J. L. Kassner, A. Garcia-Porrata, and E. L. Grove, *Anal. Chem.*, **27**, 492 (1955).
4. A. B. H. Lauw-Zecha, S. S. Lord, Jr., and D. N. Hume, *Anal. Chem.*, **24**, 1169 (1952).
5. J. Y. Ellenburg, G. W. Leddicote, and F. L. Moore, *Anal. Chem.*, **26**, 1045 (1954).

OSMIUM

Ephedrine method.[1] If a drop of a saturated aqueous solution of ephedrine hydrochloride is added to a caustic solution of sodium osmate, an orange-colored species is formed that can be extracted by carbon tetrachloride to give an orange-yellow color, detectable if the initial osmium concentration was at least 10 μg/ml. Platinum and Rh produce no color reaction. Palladium and Au produce a faint yellow color, but the test is not very sensitive for these metals or for Ir, which produces a very faint green under the same conditions.

Tetroxide method.[2] Osmium tetroxide can be extracted from aqueous solution by carbon tetrachloride. Since OsO_4 possesses weakly acidic properties, it is extracted less easily from basic solutions. Osmium tetroxide can be stripped from carbon tetrachloride by means of a strong solution of NaOH.

Thiocarbanilide method.[3] Another extraction method for Os involves adding thiocarbanilide to the solution and shaking with ethyl ether. The ether takes on a deep-red color. Sensitivity of the test is 10 μg/ml Os.

REFERENCES: Osmium

1. S. O. Thompson, F. E. Beamish, and M. Scott, *Ind. Eng. Chem., Anal. Ed.*, **9**, 420 (1937).
2. E. B. Sandell, *Colorimetric Determination of Traces of Metals,* second edition, Interscience Publishers, Inc., New York, 1950, p. 480.
3. W. Singleton, *Ind. Chemist*, **3**, 121 (1927).

PALLADIUM

Diethyldithiocarbamate method.[1] Transfer a solution containing several hundred micrograms of Pd to a separatory funnel, add 10 ml 5% disodium ethylenediaminetetraacetate, and adjust the pH to 11.0. Add 1 ml 0.2% aqueous sodium diethyldithiocarbamate and 10 ml carbon tetrachloride; shake for 1 minute. The complex absorbs at 305 mμ. Copper, Ag, Hg, Bi, and Tl(III) are also extracted.

Dimethylglyoxime method.[2] To 50 ml of a solution containing Pd(II) in 1 M H_2SO_4, add 2 ml of a 1% aqueous solution of the sodium salt of dimethylglyoxime. Allow to stand for 10 minutes in a separatory funnel, shaking occasionally. Extract the Pd with two successive 4–5-ml portions of chloroform. In the presence of Au and Pt, addition of 1 ml concentrated HCl and 0.5 ml concentrated HNO_3 prevents these metals from interfering.

2-Nitroso-1-naphthol method.[3] To 5 ml of a solution in a small separatory funnel containing from 5–25 μg Pd, add 2 drops 3 N HCl and 1 ml of 3% disodium ethylenediaminetetraacetate. Dilute to about 10 ml with water, add 0.1 ml 1% ethanolic 2-nitroso-1-naphthol, mix and allow to stand for 10 minutes at room temperature. After the addition of 5.0 ml toluene and 1 ml (1:1) NH_4OH, shake vigorously and allow layers to separate. The complex absorbs both at 370 and 550 mμ (stronger at 370 mμ). Interference of Fe, Cu, Ni, Co, and Cr is eliminated by use of EDTA. The Pt metals do not interfere in this method.

REFERENCES: Palladium

1. H. Bode, *Z. anal Chem.,* **144,** 165 (1955).
2. R. S. Young, *Analyst,* **76,** 49 (1951).
3. K. L. Cheng, *Anal. Chem.,* **26,** 1894 (1954).

PHOSPHORUS

Anhydrous phosphate method.[1] Treat a phosphate-containing sample in the absence of water with 10 ml of concentrated H_2SO_4 and 160 ml of ethyl ether. Phosphoric acid is almost completely extracted. The following elements are partially or completely dissolved in the solvent mixture: As, Sb, V, Zr, Mo, and U. The following elements are practically insoluble under these conditions: Ag, Pb, Bi, Cu, Cd, Sn, Cr, Al, Ti, Th, Ca, Ba, Sr, Ni, Co, Mn, Zn, Mg, Na, K, and the rare earths. It should be noted that elements such as Mo, W, and V form heteropoly acids with phosphate in acidic solutions, and these complexes extract very well into a number of organic solvents.

Heteropoly acid method for P in steel.[2] Select a representative sample of a steel which will dissolve in 5 M HNO_3. If the P content is less than 0.1%, weigh a sample of approximately 50 mg. If the P content is higher, weigh a correspondingly smaller sample. Place the sample in a 50-ml conical flask and add a boiling chip. Add 5.0 ml of HNO_3 and let stand until all action ceases.

Boil the solution for 2 minutes, add 10 ml of ammonium peroxydisulfate (dissolve 2 g in 100 ml of water and prepare fresh daily), and boil

2 minutes more. Let cool to room temperature and add 10.0 ml of sodium molybdate solution (dissolve 1.5 g of sodium molybdate dihydrate in 100 ml of water and store in a polyethylene bottle). Transfer the solution to a separatory funnel and add 10 ml of extractant (100 ml of 1-butanol and 400 ml of chloroform), using the extractant to rinse the conical flask. Extract for 1 minute and let the layers separate. Drain the extractant (lower layer) into a 25-ml volumetric flask and repeat the extraction. Add the second portion of the extractant to the first and dilute to the mark with extractant. Measure the absorbance at 310 mμ. Steels containing up to 0.1% P can be successfully analyzed in the presence of as much as 1.4% Mn, 0.3% Si, 1.0% Cr, and 0.2% V.

REFERENCES: Phosphorus

1. F. H. Cripps, British Atomic Energy Research Establishment Report, CRL/AE-49.
2. C. Wadelin and M. G. Mellon, *Anal. Chem.*, **25**, 1668 (1953).

PLATINUM

Chloride method.[1] Transfer the desired volume of the sample solution to a 100-ml volumetric flask, add 10 ml of concentrated HCl, 25 ml of 20% NH$_4$Cl solution, and 20 ml of 1.0 M SnCl$_2$ solution. Dilute the mixture to volume. Extract a portion of this aqueous solution with an equal volume of amyl acetate. The transmittancy is measured at 398 mμ. Osmium and Ru do not interfere while Rh, Ir, Au, Te, and small amounts of Pd are extracted. The extraction procedure provides a method of concentrating Pt in cases where only a small amount is present or the volume of the solution is large.

Carrier-free radioactive Pt may be isolated from an Os target material by extracting a 3 M HCl solution after the addition of 1 ml of 10% SnCl$_2$ using ethyl ether previously saturated with 3 M HCl.[2] More than 95% of the carrier-free Pt is recovered in the organic phase.

REFERENCES: Platinum

1. G. H. Ayres and A. S. Meyer, *Anal. Chem.*, **23**, 299 (1951).
2. J. D. Gile, W. H. Harrison, and J. G. Hamilton, U.S. Atomic Energy Commission Report, UCRL-1418.

PLUTONIUM

A number of solvent extraction procedures for Pu have been developed [1,2] and are summarized in Table 13.1.

Table 13.1.   Extraction of Plutonium [1, 2]

Ion	Extraction Agent	pH Range of Extraction	Solvent
Pu(IV)	Acetylacetone	4.5	Chloroform
	Furoyltrifluoroacetone	0.5 N HNO₃	Benzene
	Thenoyltrifluoroacetone	0.5 N HNO₃	Benzene
	8-Quinolinol	−8	Amyl acetate
	5-p-Acetamidophenylazo- 8-quinolinol	4	Amyl acetate
	Anthranilic acid	3	Amyl acetate
	Cinnamic acid	2.5–4.5	Amyl acetate
	Cresotinic acid	2.5–4.5	Amyl acetate
	2,4-Dihydroxybenzoic acid	3	Methyl isobutyl ketone
	Disalicylideneethylenediimine	6.0	Chloroform
	2,4-Dinitrosalicylic acid	3	Amyl acetate
	3,5-Dinitrobenzoic acid	3	Amyl acetate
	Cupferron	1.5	Chloroform
	1-Nitroso-2-naphthol	2	Methyl isobutyl ketone
Pu(VI)	8-Quinolinol	4–8	Amyl acetate
	Sodium benzenesulfinate	2	Amyl acetate
	Sodium diethyldithiocarbamate	3	Amyl acetate or amyl alcohol
	Nitric acid, saturated ammonium nitrate		Ethyl ether

REFERENCES: Plutonium

1. D. C. Stewart, U.S. Atomic Energy Commission Report, CN-3905.
2. B. G. Harvey, H. G. Heal, A. G. Maddock, and E. L. Rowley, *J. Chem. Soc.* (*London*), **1947**, 1010.

POLONIUM

Chloride method for isolating carrier-free Po.[1]   Dissolve the Pb target in 6 M HNO₃ and evaporate the solution to concentrated HNO₃. Centrifuge off the precipitated Pb(NO₃)₂. Extract twice with equal volumes of amyl acetate to remove Tl, Hg, and Au. Add 1–2 mg Bi and Tl holdback carriers, and fume with HCl until HNO₃ is destroyed. Dilute the solution by adding 2 volumes of water. Add 1 mg of Te carrier and precipitate Te with a few drops of concentrated SnCl₂ solution and centrifuge the Te off, thereby removing Po and At. Dissolve the Te in 1 drop of concentrated HNO₃ and add 0.5 ml of concentrated HCl. Pass SO₂ into the solution in a hot-water bath. Tellurium precipitates carrying the At. The solution is now about 6 M in HCl and contains the Po. Centrifuge off the Te and extract the solution with an equal volume of 20% tributyl phosphate in dibutyl ether. Backwash the organic phase twice with 6 M HCl to remove Bi. Strip the Po from the organic phase with concentrated HNO_3.

Thenoyltrifluoroacetone (TTA) method.[2] Tracer levels of Po may be quantitatively extracted from HNO_3 solutions adjusted to a pH of 1.5–2.0 by shaking for 15 minutes with an equal volume of a 0.25 M TTA solution in benzene. Thorium will also extract under these conditions. If large quantities of Bi are present, it may be advisable to wash the benzene layer with dilute HNO_3 solution having a pH of 1.5 to remove the small quantity of Bi that extracts.

REFERENCES: Polonium

1. W. W. Meinke, U.S. Atomic Energy Commission Report, AECD-2738.
2. F. Hagemann, *J. Am. Chem. Soc.*, **72**, 768 (1950).

PROTACTINIUM

Chloride method.[1] Adjust the solution containing 0.02 mg/ml Pa to 7 M in HCl and 0.5 M in HF and extract with an equal volume of diisopropyl ketone. Repeat twice more with fresh solvent. Discard the organic phases. Complex the fluoride in the aqueous phase containing the Pa by saturating with $AlCl_3$. Extract with an equal volume of diisopropyl ketone. Separate the phases and wash the organic phase with 8 M HCl. Strip the Pa from the organic phase by shaking with a solution 0.5 M in HF and 8 M in HCl. A good separation from Th(IV), Al, Ti(IV), V(V), Mn, Ba, Mg, and Cr(III) is obtained. Tin(IV) is extracted.

Thenoyltrifluoroacetone (TTA) method.[2] Tracer level Pa in 4 N HNO_3 will be quantitatively extracted into an equal volume of 0.4 M TTA in benzene using a 5-minute shaking time. Zirconium and Nb are the only elements that interfere.

REFERENCES: Protactinium

1. J. Golden and A. G. Maddock, *J. Inorg. & Nuclear Chem.*, **2**, 46 (1956).
2. W. W. Meinke, U.S. Atomic Energy Commission Report, AECD-2750.

RARE EARTHS

Nitrate method.[1] Using tributyl phosphate and 12 M HNO_3, Peppard *et al.* obtained separation factors of approximately 1.6 between adjacent rare earth elements, and distribution ratios were satisfactory for operation of standard fractionation equipment. The investigation involved the use of tracers or low concentrations of rare earths, and multiple-batch and countercurrent distribution techniques were employed. Based on this method Weaver, Kappelman, and Topp [2] succeeded in isolating more than a kilogram of better than 95% Gd_2O_3 from a mixture of rare earths. The method has not been used for analytical purposes.

Thiocyanate method.[3] Appleton and Selwood studied the fractionation of the rare earths based on the selective extraction of their thiocyanates by butyl alcohol. The ratio of Nd to La in the organic layer to that in the aqueous layer is 1.06. Although the separation factor is quite small and will doubtless be considerably smaller between rare earths such as Nd and Pr, the process lends itself to fractionation methods and may lead to a comparatively rapid separation of these elements, possibly by a countercurrent technique.

Rare earths are extracted to a reasonable extent by 1-pentanol from aqueous solutions containing NH_4SCN.[4] Thorium is so much more extractable than any of the rare earths that a simple and effective means of separating Th from the rare earths is thereby afforded. Cerium, usually present in natural Th ores, must be reduced to Ce(III) prior to the addition of thiocyanate. The more basic rare earths are the most difficult to separate from Th using this process. Good separations may be obtained with Nd–Th mixtures by batch extractions.

Butylphosphoric acid method.[5] Dibutylphosphoric acid in butyl ether can be used to extract the Y group from the La group elements (see yttrium, page 244).

REFERENCES: Rare Earths

1. D. F. Peppard, J. P. Faris, P. R. Gray, and G. W. Mason, *J. Phys. Chem.*, **57**, 294 (1953).
2. B. Weaver, F. A. Kappelman, and A. C. Topp, *J. Am. Chem. Soc.*, **75**, 3943 (1953).
3. D. B. Appleton and P. W. Selwood, *J. Am. Chem. Soc.*, **63**, 2029 (1941).
4. G. F. Asselin, L. F. Audrieth, and E. W. Comings, *J. Phys. & Colloid Chem.*, **54**, 640 (1950).
5. E. M. Scadden and N. E. Ballou, *Anal. Chem.*, **25**, 1602 (1953).

RHENIUM

Benzildioxime method.[1] To a 0.5-ml aliquot of the sample in $6 M$ H_2SO_4 solution, 1–2 mg of benzildioxime and 0.5 ml benzyl alcohol are added. Four drops of a freshly prepared $SnCl_2$ solution (15 g $SnCl_2$ dissolved in 100 ml of 4.5 M H_2SO_4) are added and the mixture heated for 2–3 minutes just under boiling. One ml of water is added and the layers separated. Rhenium is quantitatively extracted into the alcohol layer. In the presence of Mo (up to 5 mg), careful reduction with $SnCl_2$ precedes the addition of the dioxime.

Pyridine method.[2] Pyridine is added to a solution containing 4–14 mg/ml of Re as perrhenate in a centrifuge bottle, and after shaking for a few seconds, 4 N NaOH is poured into the bottle. The mixture is shaken again for a few seconds and then centrifuged to separate the layers. Manganese(VII) and Tc(VII) also extract.

Tetraphenylarsonium chloride method.[3] Place 20 ml of a solution containing up to 10 μg Re in a separatory funnel with sufficient concentrated HCl to make the solution about 0.3 M in chloride ion and with sufficient concentrated H_2SO_4 to bring the sulfate concentration up to 1 M. The pH is then adjusted to between 8 and 9 with either $NaHCO_3$ or Na_2CO_3, as required. One ml of 0.05 M aqueous tetraphenylarsonium chloride is then added and the solution agitated. Next add 8 ml chloroform and shake the mixture for 2 minutes before allowing the phases to separate. The Re may be removed from the chloroform layer by shaking it with 6 N HCl. Molybdenum is not extracted with $(C_6H_5)_4AsCl$.

REFERENCES: Rhenium

1. S. Tribalat, *Compt. rend.*, **224**, 469 (1947).
2. W. Goishi and W. F. Libby, *J. Am. Chem. Soc.*, **74**, 6019 (1952).
3. S. Tribalat, *Anal. Chim. Acta*, **3**, 113 (1949).

RHODIUM

Pyridine method.[1] To 5 ml or less containing up to 30 mg Rh(III), add 5 ml water, 4 ml concentrated HCl, 1 ml 10% tartaric acid, and 8 ml pyridine. Boil gently for 1 minute. Carefully add 15 ml 12 M NaOH, stir, transfer to a separatory funnel, and separate the pyridine (upper) layer. Significant amounts of Ru and small amounts of Pd are also extracted. Tellurium, Ag, Cd, In, Sn, Sb, La, Ce, Nb, Zr, and U (kept in solution with Na_2CO_3) are not extracted.

Thenoyltrifluoroacetone (TTA) method.[2] To 2 ml of a solution containing up to 20 mg Rh(III), add 10 M NaOH drop by drop until a permanent precipitate just begins to form. Add 1 drop of concentrated $HClO_4$ to redissolve the precipitate. Add 10 ml of 0.5 M TTA in acetone and then 1–2 ml 1 M HAc–1 M NaAc buffer solution. Add acetone if the solution is not already as one phase. Heat in a boiling water bath for about 20 minutes to remove acetone. The solution will separate into two phases. Transfer to a separatory funnel with 30 ml of benzene and extract. The benzene layer containing Rh is washed successively with 15-ml portions of the following: 6 M HCl, two 15-ml portions each of 1 M NaOH, 8 M HNO$_3$, 6 M HCl, 2 M HF, and 6 M HCl.

REFERENCES: Rhodium

1. N. E. Ballou in C. D. Coryell and N. Sugarman, *Radiochemical Studies: The Fission Products*, McGraw-Hill Book Co., Inc., New York, 1951, p. 1563.
2. M. Lindner, U.S. Atomic Energy Commission Report, UCRL-4377.

RUBIDIUM

Sodium tetraphenylboride method.[1] Rubidium can be quantitatively extracted from NaB(C_6H_5)$_4$ solution into nitrobenzene. Cesium is also extracted.

REFERENCE: Rubidium

1. R. C. Fix and J. W. Irvine, Jr., *Mass. Inst. Technol., Lab. Nuclear Science, Ann. Progr. Rept.*, May 1956.

SCANDIUM

Benzoate method.[1] The sample solution of 5–15-ml volume containing from 0.2–5 μg Sc is brought to approximate neutrality with NaOH. Add 2.0 ml ammonium acetate solution (50 g/100 ml H_2O) and 1.0 ml sodium benzoate solution (25 g/100 ml H_2O), mix, and add 2–4 ml ethyl acetate. Phosphate and F^- hinder or prevent the extraction. Iron, Al, Ga, Be, and In are also extracted.

Chloride method.[2] Transfer an aliquot containing 10–120 μg of scandium oxide in concentrated HCl to a separatory funnel and adjust the volume to not less than 25 ml with concentrated HCl. Add 0.5 ml of 30% H_2O_2 and 25 ml of tributyl phosphate. Extract the Sc and discard the aqueous phase. Backwash the organic phase with three 25-ml portions of concentrated HCl. Discard all the washings. Add 70 ml of water to the separatory funnel and wash out the Sc by shaking the contents for 30 seconds. Transfer the aqueous solution to another separatory funnel, add 25 ml of ethyl ether, and extract the residual tributyl phosphate. Zirconium must be absent, for it prevents the complete removal of Sc from the organic phase. Scandium can be separated from Al, Be, Cr, and the rare earths. Hydrogen peroxide retains the Ce in the trivalent state and prevents its extraction as well as that of Ti. Uranium, Fe, and Th are extracted. Determination of Sc in a variety of minerals and ores can be done colorimetrically using Alizarin Red S if a cupferron extraction and iodate precipitation of Th is performed before the chloride extraction and is followed by multiple tartrate precipitations.

Quinalizarin method.[3] To a solution containing Sc, add enough (NH$_4$)$_2$CO$_3$ and NH$_4$OH to make the solution alkaline. Add a 1-ml portion of an isoamyl alcohol solution of quinalizarin; shake and separate. Repeat the extraction until the alcohol layer no longer changes from its original blue color. The Sc complex has an absorption maximum at 650 mμ.

8-Quinolinol method.[4] Adjust the pH of a solution containing Sc to 8.0–8.5. Add 10 ml of 1% 8-quinolinol in chloroform. Shake for 1 minute. The complex absorbs strongly at 373 mμ.

Thenoyltrifluoroacetone (TTA) method.[5] Scandium in milligram amounts can be quantitatively extracted from a solution of pH 1.5 by shaking with a 0.5 M TTA–benzene solution.

Thiocyanate method.[6] Evaporate an HCl solution of the sample to a moist mass, add 60 ml of 0.5 M HCl and 53 g of NH$_4$SCN. Adjust the volume of the solution to 100 ml and add 100 ml of ethyl ether. Extract for 5 minutes. Separate the phases and add 5 ml of 2 M HCl to the aqueous phase; extract again with 100 ml of ethyl ether. Evaporate the combined ether extracts after the addition of a few milliliters of HCl. Then add HNO$_3$ cautiously drop by drop at water bath temperature to destroy thiocyanate. Finally, boil the residue with a little concentrated HNO$_3$ until the orange-red decomposition products of thiocyanic acid are destroyed.

Sulfate and phosphate interfere with the extraction. A good separation is obtained from the rare earths, Th, Mn, Mg, and Ca. The extraction of Zr can be decreased by extracting at pH 4–5; however, more Sc remains in the aqueous phase in the almost neutral medium.[2] If the acid concentration is increased, the extraction of La, Ti, Zr, Th, and U increases. A good separation of Sc from Ti can be obtained by extracting at pH 3–4.[7] Elements that are extracted to a large extent with Sc are Be, Al, probably Ga, In, Fe(III), Co, and possibly a few others such as Mo and Re.

REFERENCES: Scandium

1. S. E. J. Johnson in E. B. Sandell, *Colorimetric Determination of Traces of Metals,* second edition, Interscience Publishers, Inc., New York, 1950, p. 537.
2. A. R. Eberle and M. W. Lerner, *Anal. Chem.,* **27,** 1551 (1955).
3. G. Beck, *Mikrochemie ver. Mikrochim. Acta,* **34,** 282 (1949).
4. L. Pokras and P. M. Bernays, *J. Am. Chem. Soc.,* **73,** 7 (1951); *Anal. Chem.,* **23,** 757 (1951).
5. A. Broido, U.S. Atomic Energy Commission Report, AECD-2616.
6. W. Fischer and R. Bock, *Z. anorg. u. allgem. Chem.,* **249,** 146 (1942).

7. E. B. Sandell, *Colorimetric Determination of Traces of Metals*, second edition, Interscience Publishers, Inc., New York, 1950, p. 534.

SELENIUM

3,3'-Diaminobenzidine method.[1] Add 2 ml 2.5 M formic acid to a sample containing up to 50 μg Se; dilute to 50 ml with water. Adjust the pH to a value between 2 and 3, add 2 ml 0.5% aqueous diaminobenzidine hydrochloride solution, and allow mixture to stand 30–50 minutes. Adjust the pH to between 6 and 7 with 7 M NH$_4$OH, add 10 ml toluene, and shake vigorously for 30 seconds to extract the Se compound (piazselenol) which absorbs strongly at 340 and 420 mμ. The reagent solution is stored in the refrigerator. Iron(III), Cu(II), V(V), and other oxidants interfere. Iron and copper interference can be eliminated by EDTA complexing at pH 2–3. Tellurium does not interfere.

Diethyldithiocarbamate method.[2] To a solution containing up to a hundred milligrams of Se(IV), add 10 ml of 5% EDTA, adjust the pH to a value between 5 and 6, and add 1 ml of 0.2% sodium diethyldithiocarbamate and 10 ml carbon tetrachloride. Shake the mixture for 1 minute. The complex absorbs in the ultraviolet region. A number of other elements including Te also extract.

REFERENCES: Selenium

1. K. L. Cheng, *Anal. Chem.*, **28**, 1738 (1956).
2. H. Bode, *Z. anal. Chem.*, **143**, 182 (1954).

SILVER

Diethyldithiocarbamate method.[1] Transfer a solution containing up to 300 μg Ag to a separatory funnel, add 10 ml of 5% EDTA, and adjust the pH to 11.0. Add 1 ml 0.2% aqueous sodium diethyldithiocarbamate, 10 ml carbon tetrachloride, and shake for at least 1 minute. The complex absorbs in the ultraviolet spectral region. Other metals extracted are Cu, Hg, Pd, Bi, and Tl(III).

Dithizone method.[2] Adjust the pH of the solution to about 2 in the absence of chloride. If Cl$^-$ is not over 1%, adjust to pH 3.5. At pH 5, Ag can be extracted even from 20% NH$_4$Cl. Extract with successive portions of 13 ppm dithizone in carbon tetrachloride (prepared by diluting a stock solution of 100 ppm) until a green-colored extract is obtained. Shake the combined carbon tetrachloride extracts with 3 ml of a mixture of equal volumes of 20% NaCl and 0.03 N HCl. The aqueous phase contains the Ag, and Cu and Hg remain in carbon tetrachloride. If more than 50 μg metal is present in the sample, use stronger dithizone solutions.

Silver in presence of large amounts of copper. Add 2 equivalents of EDTA [0.1 N solution (20 g/l of the disodium salt)] for each equivalent of Cu present in the solution. Extract the Ag by shaking with 5 portions of 13 ppm dithizone. Some Cu is also extracted. Back-extract the Ag as above with NaCl–HCl. The results tend to be low, and only 90% Ag was recovered from a mixture of 1 part Ag and 10,000 parts Cu.

Silver in the presence of large amounts of mercury. Up to several mg of Hg may be extracted with 100 ppm dithizone if the aqueous phase contains 10% NaCl and is 0.02 N HCl. The Ag may then be extracted from the aqueous phase as described above.

REFERENCES: Silver

1. H. Bode, *Z. anal. Chem.*, **144**, 165 (1955).
2. H. Friedeberg, *Anal. Chem.*, **27**, 305 (1955).

SODIUM

Chloroplatinate method for separating Na (and Li) from K.[1] Dissolve in 10 ml of water the chlorides of K and Na remaining after the removal of ammonium salts by ignition, and add a slight excess of a solution of chloroplatinic acid containing 10% of Pt; the amount required can be calculated by assuming that only NaCl is present. Evaporate on a steam bath until the solution is syrupy and solidifies on cooling, but do not evaporate to dryness, for this will dehydrate the sodium salt and make its solution in alcohol more difficult. Cool, then add 20–25 ml of 80% ethyl alcohol, and stir until everything except the yellow K_2PtCl_6 has dissolved. The alcohol must be colored by the excess of reagent. Wash with 80% alcohol three or four times by decantation, transfer to a filtering crucible, wash until the alcohol runs through colorless, dry at 135°C for 1 hour, repeating until constant weight is obtained, and weigh as K_2PtCl_6. Sodium or Li in the filtrate may be determined after removal of the Pt by reducing it to the metal with formaldehyde or hydrazine in slightly ammoniacal solution or by evaporating to dryness with a globule of Hg. The solubility of K_2PtCl_6 in 80% ethyl alcohol is about 8.5 mg per 100 ml; the free acid and the sodium and lithium salts are fairly soluble, although if a higher alcohol is used, these also become insoluble.

Perchlorate method for separating Na from Li, K, Rb, and Cs.[2] Dissolve the mixed chlorides in water, transfer to a Pyrex beaker, and treat with two or three times the equivalent quantity of pure perchloric acid (not less than 1 ml of 60–70% acid in any case). Evaporate to dryness on a hot plate (not over 350°C). Cool, dissolve the salts in 3–5 ml of water, and again evaporate to dryness. Cool, add 10–20 ml of a mixture of equal parts by volume of n-butyl alcohol and ethyl acetate, digest near the boiling point for 2–3 minutes, and cool to room temperature. Decant the supernatant liquid into a previously ignited and weighed Gooch crucible and wash three times by decantation with 5-ml portions of the alcohol-acetate mixture. Dissolve the residue in the crucible in a minimum of hot water, catch the solution in the original beaker, and again evaporate to dryness. Cool, add 10 ml of the solvent, digest and cool as before, and filter through the original crucible, which must first be dried. Transfer the residue to the crucible using the mixed solvent, and wash the crucible and contents ten to fifteen times with 0.1–1-ml portions of the solvent. Dry the crucible and precipitate at 110°C in an oven and finally for 15 minutes in a muffle furnace at 350°C. Cool, and weigh as $KClO_4$.

Evaporate the combined extracts and washings on a hot plate until the ethyl acetate is expelled, and continue the evaporation to 20-ml volume. Heat to 80 to 90°C, and add, drop by drop and with stirring, 2 ml of a 20% solution of HCl gas in butyl alcohol (prepared by passing dry HCl gas into butyl alcohol; 200 ml of a 20% solution (sp gr 0.905) can be prepared in 2–3 hours) and then 6 ml more. Cool to room temperature, collect the precipitate on a dry Gooch crucible, and wash eight to ten times with 1–2-ml portions of a 6–7% solution (sp gr 25°/4° 0.8425–0.8485) of hydrogen chloride in butyl alcohol (made by diluting 40 ml of the 20% solvent with 100 ml of butyl alcohol). Reserve the filtrate and washings for the determination of Li. Dry the crucible and contents for a few minutes at 110°C; then ignite for 5 minutes at 600°C in a muffle furnace. If the Na is to be determined gravimetrically, cool in a desiccator and weigh the crucible and impure NaCl. Dissolve the precipitate by means of a fine jet of water, thoroughly wash the crucible, and collect the filtrate and washings in a beaker. Dry the crucible and insoluble residue for 1 hour at 110°C; cool and weigh again. The loss in weight represents pure NaCl. (The filtrate and washings should not greatly exceed 50 ml.)

REFERENCES: Sodium

1. H. H. Willard and H. Diehl, *Advanced Quantitative Analysis*, D. Van Nostrand Co., Inc., Princeton, N. J., 1943, p. 259.
2. W. F. Hillebrand, G. E. F. Lundell, H. A. Bright, and J. I. Hoffman, *Applied Inorganic Analysis*, second edition, John Wiley & Sons, Inc., New York, 1953, p. 652.

STRONTIUM

8-Quinolinol method.[1] An aqueous solution containing somewhat less than 0.1 mg Sr is brought to a pH of 11.3 with 0.1 M NaOH and brought to 15-ml volume. This is shaken with 15 ml of 1 M 8-quinolinol in chloroform. Slightly more than 96% of the Sr will be extracted.

REFERENCE: Strontium

1. D. Dyrssen, *Svensk Kem. Tidskr.*, **67**, 311 (1955).

TANTALUM

Butylphosphoric acid method.[1] About 85% extraction will be obtained for traces of Ta from a solution which has been made 1 M in HNO_3 by extracting for 5 minutes with an equal volume of 0.6 M dibutylphosphoric acid (containing some monobutylphosphoric acid) in n-butyl ether. Under these conditions, trace levels of Zr, Nb, Y, In, and Sn(IV) are quantitatively extracted while Mo is 23% extracted.

For milligram quantities of Ta, about 35% extraction may be achieved by using the conditions described elsewhere (see niobium, page 221).

Fluoride method for separating Ta from U- and Zr-base alloys.[2] To the sample solution containing up to 100 mg of Ta, add 20 ml of concentrated H_2SO_4, 10 ml of concentrated HF, and 4 g of NH_4F, and dilute to 100-ml volume. Extract the aqueous phase twice in a polyethylene bottle with 50-ml portions of pre-equilibrated ethyl methyl ketone. Niobium is also extracted. Alternatively, Ta and Nb can be separated from U- and Zr-base alloys by extraction of an aqueous phase which is 10 M in HF, 6 M in H_2SO_4, and 2.2 M in NH_4F using methyl isobutyl ketone. The organic phase is stripped of Ta and Nb by shaking several times with 5% H_2O_2 solution.

Fluoride method for separating Ta from Nb.[3] Five ml of a mixture of 10 mg each of Ta and Nb adjusted to 3 M in HCl and 0.4 M in HF are extracted for 1 minute with an equal volume of diisopropyl ketone which has been pre-equilibrated with pure aqueous phase. Separate the phases and extract the aqueous phase again. Backwash the combined organic phases with 5 ml of a solution of 3 M HCl and 0.4 M HF. Discard the washing. Strip the organic phase with two small portions of water. Fluoride can be complexed by the addition of boric acid.

REFERENCES: Tantalum

1. E. M. Scadden and N. E. Ballou, *Anal. Chem.*, **25**, 1602 (1953).
2. G. W. C. Milner, G. A. Barnett, and A. A. Smales, *Analyst*, **80**, 380 (1955).
3. P. C. Stevenson and H. C. Hicks, *Anal. Chem.*, **25**, 1517 (1953).

TECHNETIUM

Pyridine method.[1] Technetium can be extracted as pertechnetate from 4 M NaOH solution with pyridine. The distribution ratio is 778 when extracting carrier-free Tc^{99} as NH_4TcO_4. Rhenium(VII) and Mn(VII) are also extracted.

Tetraphenylarsonium chloride method.[2] Dissolve the sample [e.g., MoO_3 in NaOH, U_3O_8 in H_2SO_4 followed by $(NH_4)_2CO_3$], heating with 0.1 g $Na_2S_2O_8$ to ensure oxidation to Te(VII). Adjust the pH to 10–11, make the solution $5 \times 10^{-5} M$ in $(C_6H_5)_4AsCl$ using a 0.001 M aqueous reagent solution, and shake for 5 minutes with an equal volume of chloroform. The Tc, quantitatively extracted into the chloroform phase, will not be contaminated by either Mo or fission products.

REFERENCES: Technetium

1. W. Goishi and W. F. Libby, *J. Am. Chem. Soc.*, **74**, 6109 (1952).
2. S. Tribalat and J. Beydon, *Anal. Chim. Acta*, **6**, 96 (1952); **8**, 22 (1953).

TELLURIUM

Diethyldithiocarbamate method.[1] To a solution containing up to several hundred micrograms of Te(IV), add 10 ml of 5% disodium ethylenediaminetetraacetate, adjust the pH to 8.5, add 5 ml of 10% NaCN, and readjust the pH to 8.5–8.8. Add 1 ml 0.2% sodium diethyldithiocarbamate and 10 ml carbon tetrachloride. Shake the mixture for 1 minute. The complex absorbs at 428 mμ. Selenium is not extracted but Sb(III) is.

REFERENCE: Tellurium

1. H. Bode, *Z. anal. Chem.*, **144**, 90, 165 (1955).

THALLIUM

Chloride method.[1] The sample solution should be 6 M in HCl and should have a volume as small as feasible (not over 50 ml). Add 5 ml, or more if necessary, of freshly prepared chlorine water to oxidize Tl to the trivalent state. Shake for 1 minute in a separatory funnel with an equal volume of ethyl ether previously shaken with 6 M HCl. Extract with two more portions of ether and combine the ether extracts. The latter may be backwashed with a little 6 M HCl to remove elements which are slightly extracted. Remove ether by evaporating the organic extract over a few milliliters of water to retain the Tl. Antimony (V), As(III), Ge, Au(III), Fe(III), and Mo(VI) are extracted.

Carrier-free Tl can be isolated from the cyclotron target material (Hg) by extraction of the Tl(III) from a 3 M HCl solution of the material using an equal volume of ethyl ether previously shaken with 3 M HCl.[2] More than 95% of the radiothallium is extracted.

Diethyldithiocarbamate method.[3] Transfer a solution containing up to 300 μg Tl(III) to a separatory funnel and add 10 ml of a solution that is 2 M with respect to NH$_4$OH and 5% each with respect to NaCN and EDTA. Adjust pH to 11, add 1 ml 0.2% aqueous sodium diethyldithiocarbamate and 10 ml carbon tetrachloride, and shake for 1 minute. The complex absorbs strongly at 426 mμ. Only Bi is also extracted.

8-Quinolinol method.[4] Adjust the pH of a solution containing 200 μg Tl(III) in about 50 ml to a value between 6.5–7.0 using powdered sodium acetate and 5 N NaOH. Extract with 10 ml of 1% 8-quinolinol in chloroform. The complex absorbs strongly at 400 mμ. In the original paper an incomplete extraction (89%) was reported when a 0.01% reagent solution was used.

Thenoyltrifluoroacetone (TTA) method.[5] Traces of Tl(III) can be extracted from a solution whose pH has been adjusted to 3.8 or higher with an equal volume of 0.25 M TTA in benzene using a 15-minute shaking period. In the presence of Bi, strip the benzene layer with a 0.01 M HNO$_3$ solution (pH 2). This will leave most of the Bi in the organic layer. The aqueous layer is then readjusted to pH 3.8 and extracted as before. In the presence of Pb, although careful pH adjustment might provide a basis for separation, it might be more expedient to reduce the Tl(III) to Tl(I) as the extraction of Tl(I) occurs in a much higher pH range. Following the reduction, adjust the pH to 5.0 and extract the Pb with 0.25 M TTA. The Tl(I) remains quantitatively in the aqueous layer and can be extracted at a pH of 7–8.

REFERENCES: Thallium

1. E. B. Sandell, *Colorimetric Determination of Traces of Metals*, second edition, Interscience Publishers, Inc., New York, 1950, p. 560.
2. J. D. Gile, W. M. Garrison, and J. G. Hamilton, U.S. Atomic Energy Commission Report, UCRL-1420.
3. H. Bode, *Z. anal. Chem.*, **144**, 165 (1955)

4. T. Moeller, *Anal. Chem.*, **22**, 686 (1950).

5. F. Hagemann, *J. Am. Chem. Soc.*, **72**, 768 (1950).

THORIUM

Cupferron method.[1] Add 1.2 g cupferron to 20 ml of a solution containing as much as 100 mg Th which is 0.5 N in H_2SO_4. Add 25 ml butyl acetate and shake for 3–5 minutes. Ninety-eight per cent of Th will be extracted. A proportional decrease of cupferron can accompany lower quantities of Th.

Nitrate method.[2] Adjust a sample solution containing 50–100 mg of Th to a volume of 20 ml which is 1 M in HNO_3. Add 16 g of $LiNO_3$, warm the mixture to effect solution, and cool to room temperature. Add 25 ml of mesityl oxide and extract for 30 seconds. Separate the phases and wash the organic extract three times with 20-ml portions of 1 M HNO_3 solution saturated with $LiNO_3$. Strip the Th from the organic phase by extracting three times with 20-ml portions of water and combine these aqueous extracts for the determination of Th. Phosphate and other anions which form stable complexes or insoluble compounds with Th interfere with extraction. Uranium(VI) is completely extracted with Th, but Zr and Fe(III) extract 25% and 10%, respectively.

Uranium can be separated from Th by extraction of an aqueous solution saturated with $Al(NO_3)_3$ and buffered with sodium acetate and acetic acid using ethyl ether as solvent.[3] Uranium is preferentially extracted into the solvent, Th remaining in the aqueous phase.

8-Quinolinol method.[4] Adjust the pH of a solution containing Th to 4.9 or higher and extract with 10-ml portions of 1% 8-quinolinol in chloroform. The complex absorbs at 375 mμ but apparently does not obey Beer's law.

Thenoyltrifluoroacetone (TTA) method.[5] Tracer quantities of Th are extracted from HNO_3 solutions of pH 1 or higher by an equal volume of 0.25 M TTA solution in benzene using a 15-minute shaking period. At this pH, only Po is appreciably extracted along with the Th. For separation from U, carefully adjust pH to 1.0 and back-extract the benzene phase with pH 1.0 acid to remove U.[6]

REFERENCES: Thorium

1. Z. Hagiwara, *Technol. Repts. Tôhoku Univ.*, **16**, 22 (1953).
2. C. V. Banks and R. E. Edwards, *Anal. Chem.*, **27**, 947 (1955).
3. D. F. Peppard *et al.*, *J. Am. Chem. Soc.*, **75**, 4576 (1953).
4. T. Moeller and M. V. Ramaniah, *J. Am. Chem. Soc.*, **75**, 3946 (1955).

5. F. Hagemann, *J. Am. Chem. Soc.,* **72,** 768 (1950).
6. W. W. Meinke, U.S. Atomic Energy Commission Report, AECD-2750.

TIN

Butylphosphoric acid method.[1] Over 95% $Sn(IV)$ can be removed from an aqueous solution, which contains 3 $\mu g/ml$ $Sn(IV)$ and which has been made 1 M in HNO_3 and 3% in H_2O_2, by extracting for 5 minutes with an equal volume of 0.6 M dibutylphosphoric acid (containing some monobutylphosphoric acid) in n-butyl ether. Zirconium, Nb, Y, and In will also be quantitatively extracted, and substantial amounts of Ta (85%), Nb (60%), and Mo (23%) will also accompany the $Sn(IV)$. Less than 5% of Sb, As, and other elements tested are extracted.

Fluoride method.[2] Extract 5 ml of a sample solution containing approximately 10 mg of either $Sn(II)$ or $Sn(IV)$ and 4.6 M in HF with 20 ml of ethyl ether. Pyrex separatory funnels can be used since the extraction is performed rapidly. Platinum ware should be used after the extraction step. Arsenic(III), Sb, Se, and Mo are partially extracted, whereas Ni, Cr, Co, Mn, K, Ti, Zr, Ga, Ag, U, Bi, Te, Cd, and Os are not extracted.

Iodide method.[3] Extract 5 ml of sample solution 6.9 M in HI with 20 ml of ethyl ether, shaking for 5 minutes. Antimony(III), Hg(II), Cd, and Au are also completely extracted, and Bi, Zn, Mo(VI), Te(IV), and In are extracted to a lesser extent.

Alternatively, extraction of an aqueous phase 1.5 M in KI and 1.5 N in H_2SO_4 using ethyl ether will completely remove $Sn(II)$.[4] Cadmium and In are also completely extracted. Antimony, Zn, Hg, Bi, and Cu are extracted to some extent, but Mo(VI), W(VI), and Al are only slightly extracted.

8-Quinolinol method.[5] Adjust the pH of a solution containing up to 200 μg $Sn(IV)$—H_2O_2 may be used to oxidize $Sn(II)$ to $Sn(IV)$—to a value between 2.5 and 6.0. Transfer to a separatory funnel, add 10 ml 1% 8-quinolinol in chloroform, and shake for 1 minute. The Sn complex absorbs at 385 mμ. Tartrate seriously interferes with the extraction of Sn, but in the presence of 0.4 g $(NH_4)_2C_2O_4$, 95% of 200 μg Sn present could be extracted at pH 5–6.

REFERENCES: Tin

1. E. M. Scadden and N. E. Ballou, *Anal. Chem.,* **25,** 1602 (1953).
2. S. Kitahara, *Bull. Inst. Phys. Chem. Research (Tokyo),* **25,** 165 (1949).
3. S. Kitahara, *Bull. Inst. Phys. Chem. Research (Tokyo),* **24,** 454 (1948).

4. H. M. Irving and F. J. C. Rossotti, *Analyst*, **77**, 801 (1952).
5. C. H. R. Gentry and L. G. Sherrington, *Analyst*, **75**, 17 (1950).

TITANIUM

8-Quinolinol method.[1] Add 5 ml of 0.02 M EDTA to a solution containing up to 200 μg Ti, adjust the pH to 8–9, and dilute to 100 ml. Add two successive 10-ml portions of 1% 8-quinolinol in chloroform and extract by shaking for 2 minutes. Copper and U are the only interfering metals. Probably Cu extraction can be eliminated by the use of KCN. The Ti complex absorbs at 400 mμ.

REFERENCE: Titanium

1. R. P. Taylor, Ph.D. Thesis, Princeton University, 1954.

TUNGSTEN

Heteropoly acid method.[1] Add to the sample solution containing 0.1 g of W excess Na_3PO_4 (one and a half times the amount of W present) and enough H_2SO_4 to result in a 15-ml aqueous phase which is 6 N in H_2SO_4. Extract for 3 minutes with an equal volume of 1-pentanol. More than 99% of the W is removed. Other elements that extract include As, 36%; Fe, 20%; Cr, 30%; and Cu, 1%. The extraction of W decreases with decreasing concentration.

8-Quinolinol method.[2] Add 5 ml of 0.02 M EDTA to a solution containing up to 1.5 mg W(VI), adjust to pH 2.4, and dilute to 100 ml. Extract with two successive 10-ml portions of 1% 8-quinolinol in chloroform. The complex absorbs at 400 mμ.

Thiocyanate method.[3] In strong HCl medium, thiocyanate in the presence of $SnCl_2$ produces a yellow-colored complex with W(VI) which can be extracted by various immiscible organic solvents including ethyl ether, isopropyl ether, and a 1:1 mixture of isoamyl alcohol and chloroform. The extraction can be used in the colorimetric determination of this element and has been applied to the determination of small amounts of W in silicate rocks. The ether extraction of the complex is preceded by the separation of Fe, Ti, etc., by double NaOH precipitation, and by the separation of Mo by H_2S precipitation with Sb_2S_5 as collector.

Toluenedithiol method.[4] This method is applicable to the determination of W in steel and involves prior extraction of Mo (see molybdenum, page 219).

To a fumed aliquot representing 15 mg of sample, add 5 ml HCl (sp gr 1.06), warm gently until salts are completely dissolved, and cool to room temperature. Add 5 drops of a 10% hydroxylamine sulfate solution and 10 ml of a 1% toluene-3,4-dithiol solution in amyl acetate (freshly prepared). Allow to stand in a bath at 20°–25°C for 15 minutes with periodic shaking. Transfer the contents quantitatively to a separatory funnel using small portions of amyl acetate for washing. Shake and allow the layers to separate. Draw off the lower acid layer containing the W and reserve. Wash the amyl acetate layer with two consecutive 5-ml portions of HCl (sp gr 1.06), combining the acid washes with the original acid layer. Discard the molybdenum-containing amyl acetate layer. Evaporate the acid W solution carefully, adding a few drops of concentrated HNO_3, and finally fume. Add a few additional drops of HNO_3 during fuming to clear up any charring organic matter. Add 5 ml of a 10% $SnCl_2$ solution (in concentrated HCl) to the fumed liquid and heat on a steam bath for 4 minutes. Add 10 ml of 1% toluenedithiol solution and continue to heat for 10 minutes longer, shaking the flask periodically. Transfer to a separatory funnel, rinsing three times with 2-ml portions of amyl acetate. Shake, separate, and draw off the lower layer and discard it. Add 5 ml of concentrated HCl to the organic layer, repeat the extraction, and again discard the lower layer. (For samples containing appreciable amounts of Co, follow this with two further washes with HCl (sp gr 1.06) and a final wash with concentrated HCl.) The amyl acetate layer contains the red tungsten complex. Small amounts of Fe will also extract to impart a pale-yellow color to the amyl acetate layer.

REFERENCES: Tungsten

1. G. H. Morrison and J. F. Cosgrove, unpublished work.
2. R. P. Taylor, Ph.D. Thesis, Princeton University, 1954.
3. E. B. Sandell, *Ind. Eng. Chem., Anal. Ed.*, **18**, 163 (1946).
4. B. Bagshawe and R. J. Truman, *Analyst*, **72**, 189 (1947).

URANIUM

Cupferron method.[1] A sample of approximately 30-ml volume containing from 0.5–5.0 mg U(VI) and 2.5 ml H_2SO_4 is transferred to a separatory funnel using sufficient 1:200 H_2SO_4 as wash solution to bring the volume to 50 ml. Three ml of a liquid Zn amalgam (2.4% Zn) are added and the mixture vigorously agitated for 5 minutes. The reduced solution is now extracted with five successive portions of 1.5 ml ether and 1.5 ml ethereal cupferron, shaking for 1 minute each time. The liquid Zn amalgam is prepared by heating 50 g of 20-mesh granular Zn which has been thoroughly washed with dilute H_2SO_4 (1:50), and 2 kg of Hg overnight under 100 ml 1 N H_2SO_4 on a low-temperature sand bath. After cooling, the aqueous layer is discarded and the amalgam is stored under 1 N H_2SO_4 until needed.

Ethereal cupferron is prepared by extracting a solution of 2 g cupferron in 25 ml H_2O to which 5 ml 6 N H_2SO_4 has been added with 25 ml ether.

Dibenzoylmethane method.[2] Extract a 20-ml sample containing 50–500 μg U(VI) with 10 ml of 0.5% dibenzoylmethane in ethyl acetate by shaking for 5 minutes. Repeat the extraction with an additional 15 ml of reagent and shake for 10 minutes. If other cations are present (Cu, Fe, Al, etc.), treat the slightly acid solution with a 5% EDTA solution and bind the excess by adding 1% $Ca(NO_3)_2$. Adjust to pH 7 with NH_4OH and extract with three 10-ml portions of reagent for 10 minutes each. Beryllium will also extract. Anions that complex U such as oxalate, tartrate, citrate, carbonate, and phosphate should be absent.

Nitrate method.[3] Place an appropriate aliquot (usually 5 ml) containing 50 mg U_3O_8 in 5% HNO_3 in a separatory funnel. Add 6.5 ml of aluminum nitrate solution * per 5 ml of sample solution. The aluminum nitrate salting solution should be added while hot (above 110°C). Cool the solution to room temperature and add 20 ml of ethyl acetate. Shake the mixture for 1 minute. Occasionally crystallization will take place in the separatory funnel near the stopcock. Should this happen, place the lower part of the funnel in a beaker of hot water until the solidified portion dissolves.

After the layers have separated, drain off the aqueous layer. Occasionally a cloudiness will appear at the interface. This cloudy portion should not be drained off. Add 10 ml of aluminum nitrate wash solution (add 100 ml of aluminum nitrate salting solution to 73 ml of

---

* *Aluminum nitrate salting solution:* Place approximately 450 g of reagent grade $Al(NO_3)_3 \cdot 9H_2O$ in a 600-ml beaker and add 25–50 ml of distilled water. Cover the beaker and heat the mixture on a hot plate. If a clear solution does not result after 5–10 minutes of boiling, add 20 ml of water and continue the boiling for 5 more minutes. Repeat this step until a clear solution is obtained after boiling. Remove the cover glass and concentrate the solution by boiling until a boiling point of 130°C is reached. Cover the beaker with a watch glass and either transfer the solution to a constant-temperature apparatus or keep the solution warm, finally heating to just under boiling before use. If the solution is allowed to cool to approximately 60°, recrystallization of aluminum nitrate will take place. It is necessary, therefore, to dilute the salting agent solution by about one-third in order to prevent recrystallization if the solution cools to room temperature.

water and 4 ml of concentrated nitric acid) to the funnel and again shake the mixture for 1 minute. Drain off the aqueous layer, once again being careful to retain the cloudy portion in the funnel. Strip the U from the ethyl acetate with one 15-ml and four 5-ml portions of water. Combine these aqueous fractions. The U may be conveniently measured by the $NaOH-H_2O_2$ colorimetric method at 370 mμ. A second extraction should be used for larger amounts of U. Vanadium, Fe, Mo, Cu, As, P, Co, Ca, Mg, and Mn do not extract. Small amounts of Al from the salting agent and Th extract. In the colorimetric procedure, Th precipitates and is removed by centrifugation before the absorbance is read.

8-Quinolinol method.[4] Add 5 ml of 0.02 M EDTA to a solution containing up to 900 μg U(VI), adjust the pH to 8.8, and dilute to 100 ml. Extract with two successive 10-ml portions of 1% 8-quinolinol in chloroform. The complex absorbs at 400 mμ. Titanium, which will also extract under these conditions, can probably be removed by washing the chloroform extracts twice with aqueous pH 6.0 buffer solution ($HOAc-NH_4OAc$).

Tridecylphosphine oxide method.[5] Uranium can be quantitatively extracted out of a solution that has as much as 0.5 M sulfate ions provided the nitrate ion concentration is at least 0.3 M and the pH about 1, by shaking the solution with an equal volume of 0.1 M tridecylphosphine oxide in kerosene. Under these conditions, Th is not extracted in significant amounts. The U may be stripped from the organic phase with HF, H_3PO_4, sulfates at pH 2, or Na_2CO_3.

Trioctylamine method.[6] Uranium(VI) can be quantitatively extracted out of a sulfate solution whose pH is adjusted to a value of 0.85 by shaking the solution for 1 minute with half its volume of a 0.1 M trioctylamine solution in kerosene containing 2% capryl alcohol. In the presence of sufficient Al, fluoride does not interfere. Molybdenum(VI) will also extract. Vanadium(V) will extract if Mo(VI) is present. Nitrates, and to a lesser extent chlorides, interfere with U extraction. The U may be stripped from the organic phase with 1 M Na_2CO_3, 1 M NaCl, or 0.2 M HNO_3.

REFERENCES: Uranium

1. N. H. Furman, W. B. Mason, and J. S. Pekola, *Anal. Chem.,* **21,** 1325 (1949); also as quoted by C. J. Rodden, *Analytical Chemistry of the Manhattan Project,* McGraw-Hill Book Co., Inc., New York, 1950, p. 38.
2. R. Přibíl and M. Jelinek, *Chem. Listy,* **47,** 1326 (1953).
3. R. J. Guest and J. B. Zimmerman, *Anal. Chem.,* **27,** 931 (1955).
4. R. P. Taylor, Ph.D. Thesis, Princeton University, 1954.

5. C. A. Blake, K. B. Brown, and C. F. Coleman, U.S. Atomic Energy Commission Report, ORNL-1964.
6. D. J. Crouse and K. B. Brown, U.S. Atomic Energy Commission Report, ORNL-1959.

VANADIUM

Acetylacetone method.[1] Vanadium (III) may be extracted by a 1:1 mixture of acetylacetone and chloroform to the extent of 93% from a solution whose pH is 2.0.

8-Quinolinol method.[2] Add 5 ml of masking solution * to a solution containing up to 300 μg V(V), adjust to pH 5.0, and dilute to 100 ml. Extract with two successive 10-ml portions of 1% 8-quinolinol in chloroform. The complex absorbs at 400 and 550 mμ. Although Mo also extracts at this pH, the Mo complex does not absorb at 550 mμ. This method was successfully applied to the analysis of V in a vanadium steel (NBS 61).

Tridecylphosphine oxide method.[3] Vanadium(V) may be quantitatively extracted out of a solution that is 0.5 M in sulfate and 1 M in nitrate by shaking with an equal volume of 0.4 M tridecylphosphine oxide in kerosene. The pH of the aqueous phase should range between 1 and 2. Vanadium will not extract if present as V(IV). Uranium extracts to a much greater extent than V. The V may be stripped from the organic phase by using 0.5 M Na$_2$CO$_3$ or 0.25 M oxalic acid.

REFERENCES: Vanadium

1. J. P. McKaveney, Ph.D. Thesis, University of Pittsburgh, 1957.
2. R. P. Taylor, Ph.D. Thesis, Princeton University, 1954
3. C. A. Blake, K. B. Brown, and C. F. Coleman, U.S. Atomic Energy Commission Report, ORNL-1964.

YTTRIUM

Butylphosphoric acid method.[1] Yttrium is quantitatively removed from a solution containing 1 mg/ml Y that has been made 1 M in H$_2$SO$_4$, 2.5 M in (NH$_4$)$_2$SO$_4$, 0.004 M in oxalic acid, and 6% in H$_2$O$_2$ by extracting for 5 minutes with an equal volume of 0.6 M dibutylphosphoric acid (containing some monobutylphosphoric acid) in n-butyl ether. By this means, the Y group of rare earths can be

---

* *Masking solution:* Dissolve 2.00 millimoles disodium ethylenediaminetetraacetate and 3.00 millimoles calcium acetate in sufficient 0.4 M ammonium acetate to make 100 ml of solution.

separated from the La group, for under these conditions less than 2% of La and Ce extract.

REFERENCE: Yttrium

1. E. M. Scadden and N. E. Ballou, *Anal. Chem.*, **25**, 1602 (1953).

ZINC

Diethyldithiocarbamate method.[1] Adjust the pH of a solution containing up to 300 μg Zn to 11 with ammonia. Add 1 ml 0.2% aqueous sodium diethyldithiocarbamate and 10 ml carbon tetrachloride. Shake for 1 minute. The Zn complex absorbs in the ultraviolet spectral region. The following metals will also extract if not masked: Ag, Cu, Cd, Hg, Pb, Pd, Co, Ni, Bi, and Tl. It is quite likely that the masking agents described under the dithizone method would be effective here.

Dithizone method.[2,3] To 10–25 ml of a solution which contains at least 5 μg Zn and which is at approximately pH 1, add sufficient 0.5 M sodium acetate to bring the pH to 5–5.5. Then add sufficient sodium thiosulfate to mask the interfering elements; for each milligram of foreign metal add the indicated number of milligrams of $Na_2S_2O_3 \cdot 5H_2O$: Hg, 650–750; Cu, 500–600; Bi, 300–350; Ag, 50–60; Pb, 32–40. Next, shake the solution vigorously with 3 ml of dithizone solution (5 mg/100 ml carbon tetrachloride) for 1 minute, transfer the extract to a second funnel, and wash the first with 1 ml carbon tetrachloride. Repeat the extraction until the last portion of dithizone remains unchanged in color after a 3-minute shaking period. The combined carbon tetrachloride extracts are washed several times with 5-ml portions of a wash solution (prepared by mixing 225 ml 0.5 M sodium acetate, 10 ml sodium thiosulfate solution containing 50 g $Na_2S_2O_3 \cdot 5H_2O$ per 100 ml H_2O, 40 ml 10% HNO_3, and sufficient water to make 500 ml). Then wash once with water and several times with 5-ml portions of 0.04% Na_2S until the last portion remains colorless. The Zn complex absorbs strongly at 535 mμ.

Interference from Ni and Co may be eliminated by first neutralizing the solution with NH_4OH and then adding 5% KCN to dissolve the precipitate first formed. Dilute HCl is then added drop by drop to bring the pH to 3–4 followed by sufficient 0.5 M sodium acetate to obtain pH 5–5.5. Extract the solution with dithizone as described above. Fourteen ml of 5% KCN are sufficient to mask 100 mg of either Ni or Co.

Large amounts of Cd will react with dithizone despite the use of thiosulfate. Up to 70 μg Cd may be present, however, if the combined extract is washed five to six times with Na_2S solution to remove Cd.

Aluminum hinders the extraction of Zn from slightly acid solution, and if it is present in amounts greater than 100 mg, it becomes necessary to extract Zn from a faintly ammoniacal solution containing citrate. Under these conditions other heavy metals are also extracted and, unless these are present in large amounts (for then too much dithizone would be used), this extract containing Zn as well as the other reacting metals is shaken with 0.1 N HCl to return Zn to the aqueous phase. The Zn may now be determined by the procedure above.

Methyldioctylamine method.[4] Adjust an aqueous solution containing 20 mg of Zn to a volume of 5 ml which is 2 M in HCl. Add 10 ml of 8% methyldioctylamine in trichloroethylene and extract for 5 minutes. Separate the phases and wash the organic phase with fresh aqueous phase of the same volume and acidity as used initially. Strip the Zn from the organic phase by shaking with 0.05 M HCl. Zinc can be quantitatively separated from Mn, Co, and Ni. Copper interference can be removed by any conventional method, since there is considerable difference in the chemical properties of Zn and Cu. Iron interference can be eliminated by a preliminary extraction of Fe(III) from 8 M HCl with isopropyl ether. Three such chloride extractions completely remove Fe with only a 0.03% loss of Zn.

REFERENCES: Zinc

1. H. Bode, *Z. anal. Chem.*, **144**, 165 (1955).
2. H. Fischer and G. Leopoldi, *Z. anal. Chem.*, **107**, 241 (1937).
3. H. Fischer and G. Leopoldi, *Aluminum*, **25**, 356 (1943).
4. H. A. Mahlman, G. W. Leddicotte, and F. L. Moore, *Anal. Chem.*, **26**, 1939 (1954).

ZIRCONIUM

Acetylacetone method.[1] Adjust the pH of the solution to a value of 2.5 or over and extract with pure acetylacetone to get 70% extraction in one stage. Probably the use of 50% acetylacetone in chloroform would improve the extraction. A number of other metals are also extracted at this pH.

Butylphosphoric acid method.[2] Zirconium will be almost quantitatively removed (98%) from a solution containing 1 mg Zr/ml which has been made 1 M in H_2SO_4, 2.5 M in $(NH_4)_2SO_4$, 0.004 M in oxalic acid, and 6% in H_2O_2 by extracting for 15 minutes with an equal volume of 0.06 M dibutylphosphoric acid (containing some monobutylphosphoric acid) in butyl ether. Under these conditions, 15% Sn(IV) and 85% In will also be extracted, although less than 5% of other elements tested will accompany the Zr. The butylphosphoric acid mixture is obtained by washing the ether solution of commercial butylphosphoric acid four times with water.[3] The Zr is most satisfactorily removed from the organic phase by extracting this with 4 M HF.

Thenoyltrifluoroacetone (TTA) method.[4] Make the sample solution, containing milligram quantities of Zr, 6 M in HCl and extract with an equal volume 0.5 M TTA in xylene for a 10-minute period. In this way Zr can be separated from Al, Fe, rare earths, Th, and U.

Tracer levels of Zr may be quantitatively extracted with two successive 10-minute extractions from a 2 M HNO$_3$ solution using equal volume portions of 0.5 M TTA in xylene. Oxalate, fluoride, sulfate, and phosphate ions should be removed prior to extraction.

REFERENCES: Zirconium

1. J. F. Steinbach, Ph.D. Thesis, University of Pittsburgh, 1953.
   A. Krishen, Ph.D. Thesis, University of Pittsburgh, 1957.
2. E. M. Scadden and N. E. Ballou, *Anal. Chem.,* **25,** 1602 (1953).
3. D. C. Stewart and H. W. Crandall, *J. Am. Chem. Soc.,* **73,** 1377 (1951).
4. F. L. Moore, *Anal. Chem.,* **28,** 997 (1956).

Solvents

Those properties of the solvents have been selected that will be of value in identification and as criteria of purity, together with those that are pertinent to the consideration of solvent selection. The user of this book is referred to the text by Weissberger *et al.*[1] for a comprehensive treatment of solvents and their purification. However, it might be useful to note that purity requirements of extraction solvents are such that it is seldom necessary to employ elaborate purification procedures. To be sure, ethers and other oxygenated solvents must be free of peroxides, especially if oxidation-sensitive materials are employed. It is advisable to test ethers for peroxide formation. As mentioned earlier in the book, some chelating extraction agents such as dithizone are easily oxidized, so solvents employed in connection with these should be free of oxidants.

In general, washing with water or sodium hydroxide solutions will serve to remove oxidants from solvents. The washed solvent need not be redistilled.

REFERENCE: Appendix

1. A. Weissberger, E. S. Proskauer, J. A. Riddick, and E. E. Toops, Jr., in *Technique of Organic Chemistry,* edited by A. Weissberger, Vol. VII, Interscience Publishers, Inc., New York, 1955.

Table 1. Physical Constants of Organic Solvents

	Formula	Density	Boiling Point, °C	n_D	Dielectric Constant	Solubility Parameter	Solubility in Water
HYDROCARBONS							
Cyclohexane	C_6H_{12}	$0.7831_{15°}$	80.738	$1.42623_{20}•$	2.0	8.2	0.01 g/100 g at 20°
Hexane	$CH_3(CH_2)_4CH_3$	$0.6603_{20°}$	69.0	$1.37486_{20°}$	1.9	7.3	0.138 g/l at 15.5°
Heptane	$CH_3(CH_2)_5CH_3$	$0.6842_{0°}$	98.52	$1.3867_{23°}$	1.9	7.4	0.052 g/l at 15.5°
Benzene	C_6H_6	$0.8944_{0°}$	80.103	$1.50110_{20°}$	2.3	9.2	0.180 g/100 g at 25°
Toluene	$C_6H_5CH_3$	$0.866_{20}•$	110.8	$1.49782_{16·4°}$	2.4	8.9	0.47 g/l at 16°
Xylene, ortho	$C_6H_4(CH_3)_2$	$0.8745_{20°}$	144	$1.50543_{20°}$	2.6	9.0	
meta	$C_6H_4(CH_3)_2$	$0.8684_{15°}$	138.8	$1.49721_{20}•$	2.4	8.8	0.196 g/l at 25°
para	$C_6H_4(CH_3)_2$	$0.8611_{20°}$	138.5	$1.49581_{20°}$	2.3	8.8	0.19 g/l at 25°
1,3,5-Trimethylbenzene (mesitylene)	$(CH_3)_3C_6H_3$	$0.8634_{20°}$	164.6	$1.4967_{20°}$	2.3		Insoluble
SUBSTITUTED HYDROCARBONS							
Carbon disulfide	CS_2	$1.2626_{20}•$	46.3	$1.62950_{18°}$	2.6	10.0	2.2 g/l at 22°
Carbon tetrachloride	CCl_4	$1.595_{20°}$	76–77	$1.46305_{15°}$	2.2	8.6	0.8 g/l at 20°
Chloroform	$CHCl_3$	$1.49845_{15°}$	61.26	$1.44643_{18°}$	4.8	9.3	10 g/l at 15°
Dichloromethane (methylene chloride)	CH_2Cl_2	$1.336_{20°}$	40.1	$1.42456_{20}•$	9.1	9.7	20 g/l at 20°
Nitromethane	CH_3NO_2	$1.14476_{15°}$	101.25	$1.38189_{20°}$	35.9	12.7	9.5 ml/100 ml
1,2-Dichloroethane (ethylene chloride, ethylene dichloride)	$ClCH_2CH_2Cl$	$1.257_{20°}$	83.5–83.7	$1.44759_{15°}$	10.4	9.8	9 g/l at 0°
Nitroethane	$CH_3CH_2NO_2$	$1.5028_{20°}$	114	$1.3920_{20°}$	28.1	11.1	4.5 ml/100 ml at 20°
Tetrachloroethylene	C_2Cl_4	$1.6311_{15°}$	121.20	$1.50566_{20°}$	2.3	9.4	0.015 g/100 g
1,1,2,2-Tetrachloroethane (acetylene tetrachloride)	$C_2H_2Cl_4$	$1.600_{20°}$	146.3	$1.49678_{15°}$	8.2		0.288 g/100 g at 25°
1,1,1-Trichloroethane (methyl chloroform)	CH_3CCl_3	$1.3249_{26}•$	74.1	$1.43765_{21°}$	7.5	8.5	0.132 g/100 g at 20°
1,1,2-Trichloroethane	$ClCH_2CHCl_2$	$1.443_{20°}$	113.5	$1.4711_{20°}$			0.436 g/100 g at 20°
Trichloroethylene	C_2HCl_3	$1.4556_{25°}$	87	$1.4767_{21·7°}$	3.4	9.3	1 g/l
o-Dichlorobenzene	$C_6H_4Cl_2$	$1.30033_{25°}$	180.48	$1.54911_{25°}$	9.9	10.0	Almost insoluble
m-Dichlorobenzene	$C_6H_4Cl_2$	$1.28280_{25°}$	173.00	$1.54337_{25°}$	5.0	9.8	0.0123 g/100 ml at 25°
p-Dichlorobenzene	$C_6H_4Cl_2$	$1.4581_{20·5°}$	174.12	$1.52849_{60°}$	2.4		0.077 g/1000 g at 30°
1,2,3-Trichlorobenzene	$C_6H_3Cl_3$		219				Insoluble
1,2,4-Trichlorobenzene	$C_6H_3Cl_3$	$1.574_{10°}$	213	1.5671			Insoluble
1,3,5-Trichlorobenzene	$C_6H_3Cl_3$		208.5				Insoluble

HYDROXY COMPOUNDS

Monohydric Alcohols

Methanol	CH_3OH	$0.7960_{15}°$	64.7	$1.33118_{14.5}°$	32.6	14.5	Completely soluble
Ethanol	C_2H_5OH	$0.7893_{20}°$	78.325	$1.36242_{18.4}°$	24.3	12.7	Completely soluble
1-Propanol	$CH_3(CH_2)_2OH$	$0.8074_{15}°$	97.2	$1.3855_{20}°$	20.1	11.9	Completely soluble
2-Propanol (isopropyl alcohol)	$(CH_3)_2CHOH$	$0.7891_{15}°$	82.3	$1.3747_{25}°$	18.3	11.5	79 g/l at 20°
1-Butanol	$CH_3(CH_2)_3OH$	$0.81337_{15}°$	117.71	$1.39922_{20}°$	17.1	11.4	95 g/l
2-Methyl-1-propanol (isobutyl alcohol)	$(CH_3)_2CHCH_2OH$	$0.8169_{20}°$	107–108	$1.39768_{15}°$	17.7	10.8	2.19% by weight at 25°
1-Pentanol (n-amyl alcohol)	$CH_3(CH_2)_3CH_2OH$	$0.8144_{20}°$	138.06	$1.40999_{20}°$	13.9	10.9	2.67% by weight
3-Methyl-1-butanol (isoamyl alcohol)	$(CH_3)_2CHCH_2CH_2OH$	$0.81289_{15}°$	130.5	$1.40853_{15}°$	14.7		0.706% by weight
1-Hexanol	$CH_3(CH_2)_4CH_2OH$	$0.82239_{15}°$	155–158	$1.41816_{20}°$	13.3	10.7	18 g/l
4-Methyl-2-pentanol (methyl isobutyl carbinol)	$(CH_3)_2CHCH_2CHOHCH_3$	$0.80747_{25}°$	131.4	$1.4089_{25}°$		10.0	Slightly soluble
2,4-Dimethyl-3-pentanol (diisopropyl carbinol)	$[(CH_3)_2CH]_2CHOH$	0.959	140	1.42259			Insoluble
2,6-Dimethyl-4-heptanol (diisobutyl carbinol)	$[(CH_3)_2CHCH_2]_2CHOH$	$0.8237_{0}°$	172–174	$1.4232_{1}°$		9.5	0.14% at 25°
2-Ethyl-1-hexanol	$CH_3(CH_2)_3CH_2C_2H_5CH_2OH$	0.8344	184.6	1.4300	10.3	10.3	0.0638% by weight
2-Octanol (capryl alcohol)	$CH_3(CH_2)_5CHOHCH_3$	$0.8193_{20}°$	178.5	$1.4260_{20}°$	8.2	8.5	Insoluble
Cyclohexanol	$C_6H_{11}OH$	$0.9684_{25}°$	161.5	$1.4656_{22.6}°$	15.0	11.4	0.567% at 15°
Benzyl alcohol	$C_6H_5CH_2OH$	$1.05_{15}°$	205.2	$1.54033_{20}°$	13.1	11.1	4% at 17°

Polyhydric Alcohols

1,2-Ethanediol (ethylene glycol)	$HOCH_2CH_2OH$	$1.11710_{15}°$	197.2	$1.43312_{15}°$	37.7	14.2	Completely soluble
1,2-Propanediol (propylene glycol)	$CH_3CHOHCH_2OH$	$1.0364_{20}°$	189	$1.4331_{20}°$	32.0	12.6	Completely soluble
1,2,3-Propanetriol (glycerol)	$CH_2OHCHOHCH_2OH$	$1.26134_{20}°$	290	$1.47352_{25}°$	42.5	16.5	Completely soluble

Alcohol Ethers

Furfuryl alcohol	$C_4H_3OCH_2OH$	$1.1238_{30}°$	170	$1.4873_{20}°$		11.2	Completely soluble
Tetrahydrofurfuryl alcohol	$C_4H_7OCH_2OH$	$1.1326_{25}°$	177–178	$1.4505_{25}°$		10.8	Very soluble
2-Methoxyethanol (ethylene glycol monomethyl ether, methyl cellosolve)	$CH_3OCH_2CH_2OH$	$0.96648_{15}°$	124.3	$1.4017_{20}°$	16.0		Completely soluble
2-Ethoxyethanol (cellosolve, ethylene glycol monoethyl ether)	$C_2H_5OCH_2CH_2OH$	$0.9297_{20}°$	135.1	$1.40751_{20}°$		9.9	Completely soluble
2-Butoxyethanol (butyl cellosolve, ethylene glycol mono-n-butyl ether)	$C_4H_9OCH_2CH_2OH$	$0.9027_{20}°$	170.6	$1.4190_{25}°$		8.9	Mixes with an equal volume of water
Diethylene glycol (2,2'-dihydroxyethyl ether)	$HO(CH_2)_2O(CH_2)_2OH$	1.177	244.5	$1.4475_{20}°$		9.1	Soluble
2-(2-Methoxyethoxy) ethanol (methyl carbitol, diethylene glycol monomethyl ether)	$CH_3O(CH_2)_2O(CH_2)_2OH$	$1.0354_{20}°$	193.2	$1.4264_{27}°$			Completely soluble
2-(2-Ethoxyethoxy) ethanol (carbitol, diethylene glycol monoethyl ether)	$C_2H_5O(CH_2)_2O(CH_2)_2OH$	$0.9855_{25}°$	201.9	$1.4254_{25}°$		9.6	Very soluble
2-(2-Butoxyethoxy) ethanol (butyl carbitol, diethylene glycol mono-n-butyl ether)	$C_4H_9O(CH_2)_2O(CH_2)_2OH$	$0.9553_{20}°$	231.2	$1.4290_{27}°$		8.9	Completely soluble

Table 1. Physical Constants of Organic Solvents (continued)

	Formula	Density	Boiling Point, °C	n_D	Dielectric Constant	Solubility Parameter	Solubility in Water
Triethylene glycol (2,2'-ethylenedioxydiethanol)	$HO(CH_2)_2O(CH_2)_2O(CH_2)_2OH$	$1.1274_{15°}$	280–290	$1.4578_{15°}$		10.8	Completely soluble
Keto Alcohol							
4-Hydroxy-4-methyl-2-pentanone	$CH_3COCH_2C(CH_3)_2OH$	$0.9385_{20°}$	169.1	$1.42416_{20°}$	18.2	9.2	Completely soluble
ETHERS							
Ethyl ether	$C_2H_5OC_2H_5$	$0.71925_{15°}$	34.5	$1.35424_{17.1°}$	4.3	7.4	7.42% by weight at 20°
n-Propyl ether	$CH_3(CH_2)_2O(CH_2)_2CH_3$	$0.75178_{15°}$	91	$1.3803_{20°}$	3.4		0.25% by weight
Isopropyl ether	$(CH_3)_2CHOCH(CH_3)_2$	$0.72813_{20°}$	67.5	$1.36882_{20°}$	3.9	7.0	0.65% by volume at 25°
n-Butyl ether	$CH_3(CH_2)_3O(CH_2)_3CH_3$	$0.769_{20°}$	142	$1.39925_{20°}$	3.1	7.6	Practically insoluble
β,β'-Dichlorodiethyl ether	$Cl(CH_2)_2O(CH_2)_2Cl$	$1.2192_{20°}$	178.5	$1.45750_{20°}$	21.2	9.8	1.02%
p-Dioxane	$C_4H_8O_2$	$1.03375_{20°}$	101.32	$1.42241_{20°}$	2.2	9.9	Soluble
Diethyl cellosolve	$C_2H_5O(CH_2)_2OC_2H_5$	$0.8417_{20°}$	121.4				
Dibutyl carbitol	$C_4H_9O(C_2H_4O)_2C_4H_9$	$0.8853_{20°}$	254.6				
ALDEHYDES							
Butyraldehyde	$CH_3CH_2CH_2CHO$	$0.8016_{20°}$	74.78	$1.37912_{20°}$	13.4		7.1% at 25°
KETONES							
Acetone	CH_3COCH_3	$0.79079_{20°}$	56.5	$1.35886_{19.4°}$	20.7	10.0	Completely soluble
2,4-Pentanedione (acetylacetone)	$CH_3COCH_2COCH_3$	0.9753	140.5	$1.45178_{18.5°}$	25.7		Soluble in water acidified with HCl
2-Butanone (methyl ethyl ketone, MEK)	$CH_3COCH_2CH_3$	$0.8052_{20°}$	79.6	$1.38071_{15.9°}$	18.5	9.3	35.3% at 10°
2-Pentanone	$CH_3CO(CH_2)_2CH_3$	$0.812_{15°}$	101.7	$1.38946_{20.2°}$	15.4		Very slightly soluble
3-Pentanone	$(C_2H_5)_2CO$	$0.80953_{25°}$	101.70	$1.39240_{20°}$	17.0	8.8	4.7 g/100 ml at 20°
3-Methyl-2-butanone	$CH_3COCH(CH_2)_2$	$0.815_{15°}$	93	$1.38788_{16°}$			Very slightly soluble
4-Methyl-2-pentanone (hexanone, methyl isobutyl ketone, MIBK)	$(CH_3)_2CHCH_2COCH_3$	$0.8006_{20°}$	115.8	$1.3959_{20°}$	13.1	8.4	2 parts/100 parts at 20°
2-Heptanone	$CH_3CO(CH_2)_4CH_3$	$0.822_{15°}$	150		11.9		Very slightly soluble
2,6-Dimethyl-4-heptanone (diisobutyl ketone)	$(CH_3)_2CHCH_2COCH_2CH(CH_3)_2$	0.938	164–166	$1.4300_{9°}$		7.8	Soluble
2,4-Dimethyl-3-pentanone (diisopropyl ketone)	$[(CH_3)_2CH]_2CO$	$0.8062_{20°}$	123.7			8.0	Insoluble
Cyclohexanone	$(CH_2)_5CO$	$0.95099_{15°}$	156.7	$1.45203_{15°}$	18.3	9.9	5 g/100 ml at 30°
Mesityl oxide	$(CH_3)_2C=CHCOCH_3$	$0.8539_{20°}$	128.7	$1.446_{16°}$	15.6		3 g/100 ml
Isophorone	$CH_2\begin{smallmatrix}\\ CO\\ C(CH_3)_2\cdot CH\\ C(CH_3){:}CH\end{smallmatrix}$	$0.9229_{20°}$	215.2			9.1	Slightly soluble

ESTERS

Methyl acetate	CH_3COOCH_3	$0.9274_{25°}$	57.1	$1.3619_{20°}$	6.7	9.6	31.9% at 20°
Ethyl acetate	$CH_3COOC_2H_5$	$0.9012_{0°}$	77.15	$1.37216_{18-9°}$	6.0	9.1	8.6% at 20°
n-Propyl acetate	$CH_3COOC_3H_7$	$0.8867_{20°}$	101.6	$1.38442_{20°}$	5.7	8.8	1.89% at 20°
Isopropyl acetate	$CH_3COOCH(CH_3)_2$	$0.869_{25°}$	89	$1.37730_{20°}$		8.4	3.09% at 20°
n-Butyl acetate	$CH_3COOC_4H_9$	$0.8813_{20°}$	126.5	$1.39406_{20°}$	5.0	8.5	0.5% at 25°
2-Butyl acetate	$CH_3COOCHCH_3C_2H_5$	$0.8648_{25°}$	112–113	$1.3866_{25°}$		8.2	3%
Isobutyl acetate	$CH_3COOCH_2CH(CH_3)_2$	$0.871_{20°}$	116.5	$1.39018_{20°}$	5.3	8.3	0.63% at 25°
n-Amyl acetate	$CH_3COOC_5H_{11}$	$0.8753_{20°}$	149.2	$1.40228_{20°}$	4.8	8.5	0.2 ml/100 ml at 20°
Benzyl acetate	$CH_3COOC_6H_5$	$1.057_{16°}$	215.0	$1.5200_{20°}$	5.1		Slightly soluble
Ethyl propionate	$C_2H_5COOC_2H_5$	$0.8846_{25°}$	99.10	$1.38394_{20°}$	5.7	8.4	2% at 20°
Butyl propionate	$C_2H_5COOC_4H_9$	$0.8828_{15°}$	145.4			8.8	Insoluble
Amyl propionate	$C_2H_5COOC_5H_{11}$	0.870–0.873	140–170				0.1 ml/100 ml at 20°
Butyl butyrate	$C_3H_7COOC_4H_9$	0.870–0.880	160–165	$1.4049_{20°}$		8.1	Insoluble
Methyl benzoate	$C_6H_5COOCH_3$	$1.09334_{15°}$	199.6	$1.51810_{16°}$	6.6		Insoluble
Ethyl benzoate	$C_6H_5COOC_2H_5$	$1.05112_{15°}$	212.6	$1.50748_{15°}$	6.0	9.4	0.08 g/100 g at 20°
Diethyl malonate	$CH_2(COOC_2H_5)_2$	$1.05496_{20°}$	199.30	$1.41363_{20°}$	7.9		2.08 g/100 ml at 20°
Diethyl oxalate	$(COOC_2H_5)_2$	$1.0785_{20°}$	185.4	$1.41239_{15°}$	8.1		Slightly soluble
n-Butyl phosphate (tributyl phosphate)	$(C_4H_9)_3PO_4$	$0.9727_{27°}$	177–178 at 25 mm (decomposes at 289°)	$1.4226_{20°}$	8.0	8.8	0.6 parts/100 parts

NITROGENOUS COMPOUNDS

Ethyl acetoacetate	$CH_3COCH_2COOC_2H_5$	$1.0250_{20°}$	180–181		15.7		Slightly soluble
Diethylamine	$(C_2H_5)_2NH$	$0.7108_{18°}$	55.5	$1.38730_{18°}$	3.6	7.7	Soluble
Dipropylamine	$(C_3H_7)_2NH$	$0.7340_{20°}$	110.7	$1.40455_{19-5°}$	2.9	8.1	Soluble
Dibutylamine	$(C_4H_9)_2NH$	$0.7601_{20°}$	159–161	$1.41766_{20°}$			Soluble
Diamylamine	$(C_5H_{11})_2NH$	$0.77-0.78_{20°}$	202–203 at 745 mm	$1.430_{20°}$			Slightly soluble
Diethanolamine	$(HOCH_2CH_2)_2NH$	$1.0966_{20°}$	269.1	$1.4776_{20°}$	3.6		Soluble
Dibenzylamine	$(C_6H_5CH_2)_2NH$	$1.026_{22°}$	300.0	$1.57432_{22°}$			Insoluble
Pyridine	C_6H_5N	$0.98783_{15°}$	115.3	$1.50919_{21°}$	12.3		Soluble
Quinoline	C_9H_7N	$1.095_{20°}$	237.7	$1.62450_{24-9°}$	9.0	10.7	6 g/100 ml

Index of Extraction of Elements

For convenience of reference, the many reagents used in extraction are here listed in alphabetical order under the elements for which they are employed. The page numbers on which procedures are given appear in bold face type.

Actinium, thenoyltrifluoroacetone (TTA), 160, **190**
Aluminum, acetylacetone, 158, **190**
   benzoic acid, 145, **190**
   butyric acid, 145
   cupferron, 170
   morin, 162
   perfluorobutyric acid, 146
   quinalizarin, 162
   8-quinolinol, 164, **190**
   thenoyltrifluoroacetone (TTA), 160
   thiocyanate, 136, 137
   thiosalicylideneethylenediimine, 184
Americium, cupferron, 170
   nitrate, 138, 140, **191**
   thenoyltrifluoroacetone (TTA), 160, **191**
Antimony, antipyrine, 180
   azobenzene dyes, 154
   bromide, 131, 132
   chloride, 128, 129, **191**
   cupferron, 170, **191**
   diethyldithiocarbamate, 181, **192**
   fluoride, 125, 126, 127
   iodide, 133, 134, **192**
   malachite green, 154

Antimony, methyl violet, 154
   morin, 162
   rhodamine B, 154, **192**
   thiosalicylideneethylenediimine, 184
   trioctylphosphine oxide, 149
   xanthate, 182
Arsenic, bromide, 131, 132
   chloride, 128, 129, **193**
   diethyldithiocarbamate, 181, **193**
   fluoride, 125, 126, 127
   heteropoly acid, 143, 144, **194**
   iodide, 133, 134
   nitrate, 138, 140
   xanthate, 182

Berkelium, thenoyltrifluoroacetone (TTA), 160, **194**
Beryllium, acetylacetone, 158, **195**
   benzoic acid, 145
   butyric acid, 145, **195**
   morin, 162
   perfluorobutyric acid, 146
   thenoyltrifluoroacetone (TTA), 160
   thiocyanate, 135, 136
Bismuth, antipyrine, 186
   cupferron, 170

255

Bismuth, diethyldithiocarbamate, 180, 181, **195**
  dithizone, 175, 176, 178, **195**
  iodide, 133, 134
  nitrate, 138, 140
  1-(2-pyridylazo)-2-naphthol, 173
  8-quinolinol, 164, **196**
  thenoyltrifluoroacetone (TTA), 160
  thiocyanate, 135
  thiosalicylideneethylenediimine, 184
Boron, borate, **196**
  nitrate, 140
  tetraphenylarsonium chloride, 153, **196**

Cadmium, cupferron, 170
  diethyldithiocarbamate, 181, **196**
  dithizone, 175, 176, 177, 178, **197**
  iodide, 133, 134
  isonitrosoacetophenone, 169
  2-mercaptobenzothiazole, 183
  1-(2-pyridylazo)-2-naphthol, 173
  8-quinolinol, 164
  thiocyanate, 135, **197**
  thiosalicylideneethylenediimine, 184
Calcium, nitrate, 139, 140, **198**
  perfluorooctanoic acid, 146
  8-quinolinol, 164, **199**
  stearic acid, 146
  thenoyltrifluoroacetone (TTA), 160
Cerium, acetylacetone, 158
  cupferron, 170, **199**
  morin, 162
  nitrate, 138, 140, **199**
  1-(2-pyridylazo)-2-naphthol, 173
  8-quinolinol, 164, **200**
Cesium, hexafluorophosphate, **201**
  iodide, 134
  tetraphenylboride, **200**
Chromium, acetylacetone, 158, 159, **201**
  diethyldithiocarbamate, 181
  diphenylcarbazide, **201**
  methyldioctylamine, 150
  nitrate, 138, 140
  peracid, **201**
  perfluorobutyric acid, 146
  trioctylphosphine oxide, 149
Cobalt, acetylacetone, 158, 159, **202**
  chloride, 128, 129, 130
  cupferron, 170
  diethyldithiocarbamate, 181

Cobalt, dithizone, 175, 176, 177, 178, **202**
  isonitrosoacetophenone, 169
  methyldioctylamine, 150
  1-nitroso-2-naphthol, 168, **202**
  1-(2-pyridylazo)-2-naphthol, 173
  8-quinolinol, 164, **203**
  2,2′,2″-terpyridyl, 155
  tetraphenylarsonium chloride, **203**
  thiocyanate, 135, 136, **203**
  thiosalicylideneethylenediimine, 184
  triphenylmethylarsonium chloride, 153
  xanthate, 182
Copper, acetylacetone, 158, 159
  butyric acid, 145, **204**
  n-capric acid, 145, **204**
  cupferron, 170, **205**
  diethyldithiocarbamate, 180, 181, **205**
  4,7-diphenyl-1,10-phenanthroline, 155
  dithizone, 175, 176, 177, 178, **205**
  3-hydroxyl-1,3-diphenyltriazine, 172
  iodide, 133, 134
  isonitrosoacetophenone, 169
  2-mercaptobenzothiazole, 183
  methyldioctylamine, 150
  neocuproine, 155, **205**
  o-nitrosophenol, 169
  phenylthiourea, 185
  1-(2-pyridylazo)-2-naphthol, 173
  8-quinolinol, 164, 165, **206**
  salicylaldoxime, 168
  thenoyltrifluoroacetone (TTA), 160
  thiocyanate, 135
  thiosalicylideneethylenediimine, 184
  triphenylmethylarsonium chloride, 153
  xanthate, 182
Curium, cupferron, 170
  thenoyltrifluoroacetone (TTA), 160, **206**

Fluorine, tetraphenylstibonium sulfate, 153, **207**

Gallium, acetylacetone, 158, **207**
  benzoic acid, 145, **207**
  bromide, 131, 132
  chloride, 128, 129, 130, **208**
  diethyldithiocarbamate, 181
  Erio OS, 173

Gallium, fluoride, 127
  morin, 162
  8-quinolinol, 164, **208**
  rhodamine B, 154
  thiocyanate, 135, 136
  thiosalicylideneethylenediimine, 184
  trioctylphosphine oxide, 149
Germanium, chloride, 128, 129, **209**
  fluoride, 125, 126
Gold, bromide, 131, 132, **209**
  chloride, 128, 129, 130
  p-dimethylaminobenzalrhodanine,
    210
  dithizone, 178
  iodide, 133, 134
  nitrate, 138, 140
  rhodamine B, 154
  thiosalicylideneethylenediimine, 184
  trioctylphosphine oxide, 149

Hafnium, thenoyltrifluoroacetone
    (TTA), 160, **210**
  thiocyanate, 135, **210**
  trifluoroacetylacetone, 160
  trioctylphosphine oxide, 149

Indium, acetylacetone, 158, **211**
  benzoic acid, 145, **211**
  bromide, 131, 132, **211**
  butylphosphoric acid, 147, **211**
  cupferron, 170
  diethyldithiocarbamate, 181, **211**
  dithizone, 178, **211**
  Erio OS, 173
  iodide, 133, 134, **211**
  morin, 162
  1-(2-pyridylazo)-2-naphthol, 173
  8-quinolinol, 164
  thiocyanate, 135, 136
  thiosalicylideneethylenediimine, 184
Iron, acetylacetone, 158, 159, **212**
  benzoic acid, 145, **212**
  bromide, 131, 132
  butyric acid, 145
  chloride, 127, 128, 129, **212**
  cupferron, 170, **212**
  diethyldithiocarbamate, 181
  dimethylglyoxime, 167
  4,7-diphenyl-1,10-phenanthroline, 155,
    213
  dithizone, 175, 178

Iron, fluoride, 127
  iodide, 133
  isonitrosoacetophenone, 169
  methyldioctylamine, 150
  nitrate, 138, 140
  1-nitroso-2-naphthol, 168
  o-nitrosophenol, 169
  perfluorobutyric acid, 146
  perfluorooctanoic acid, 146
  1,10-phenanthroline, 155
  1-(2-pyridylazo)-2-naphthol, 173
  2-(2-pyridyl)-benzimidazole, 155
  quinalizarin, 162
  8-quinolinol, 164, **213**
  thenoyltrifluoroacetone (TTA), 160
  thiocyanate, 135, 136, 137, **213**
  thiosalicylideneethylenediimine, 184
  trioctylphosphine oxide, 149
  triphenylmethylarsonium chloride,
    153
  xanthate, 182

Lanthanum, N-benzoylphenylhydroxyl-
    amine, 172
  cinnamic acid, 145, **214**
  5,7-dihalo-8-quinolinols, 165
  3,5-dinitrobenzoic acid, 145
  methoxybenzoic acid, 145
  1-(2-pyridylazo)-2-naphthol, 173
  salicylic acid, 145
  thenoyltrifluoroacetone (TTA), 160
Lead, diethyldithiocarbamate, 181, **214**
  dithizone, 175, 176, 178, **214**
  iodide, 133, 134, **215**
  isonitrosoacetophenone, 169
  perfluorooctanoic acid, 146
  1-(2-pyridylazo)-2-naphthol, 173
  8-quinolinol, 164
  thenoyltrifluoroacetone (TTA), 160
  thiosalicylideneethylenediimine, 184
Lithium, chloride, 129, 130, **215, 216**
  dipivaloylmethane, **216**
  iodide, 134

Magnesium, cupferron, 170
  perfluorooctanoic acid, 146
  8-quinolinol, 163, 164, **216**
  sulfate, 156, **216**
Manganese, acetylacetone, 158
  butyric acid, 145
  diethyldithiocarbamate, 181

Manganese, dithizone, 175, 178
isonitrosoacetophenone, 169
methyldioctylamine, 150
pyridine, **217**
8-quinolinol, 165, **217**
tetraphenylarsonium chloride, 153, **217**
thiosalicylideneethylenediimine, 184
xanthate, 182
Mercury, bromide, 131, 132
chloride, 128, 129
cupferron, 170
diethyldithiocarbamate, 181, **218**
dithizone, 175, 176, 177, 178, **218**
iodide, 133, 134, **218**
isonitrosoacetophenone, 169
o-nitrosophenol, 169
1-(2-pyridylazo)-2-naphthol, 173
rhodamine B, 154
thiosalicylideneethylenediimine, 184
Molybdenum, acetylacetone, 158, 159, **218**
α-benzoinoxime, 168
bromide, 131, 132
butylphosphoric acid, 147
chloride, 128, 129
cupferron, 170
diethyldithiocarbamate, 181
fluoride, 125, 126, 127
heteropoly acid, 143, 144
iodide, 133, 134
8-quinolinol, 164, **219**
thiocyanate, 135, 136, **219**
toluene-3,4-dithiol, 180, **219**
trioctylamine, 151, **219**
trioctylphosphine oxide, 149
triphenylmethylarsonium chloride, 153
xanthate, 182

Neptunium, nitrate, 138, 140, 141, **220**
1-phenyl-4,4,5,5,6,6,6-heptafluoro-1,3-hexanedione, 161
thenoyltrifluoroacetone (TTA), 160, **220**
Nickel, α-benzoinoxime, 167
cupferron, 170
cyclohexanedionedioxime, 167
diethyldithiocarbamate, 181
dimethylglyoxime, 166, **220**
dithizone, 175, 176, 177, 178

Nickel, α-furildioxime, 167
3-hydroxyl-1,3-diphenyltriazine, 172
isonitrosoacetophenone, 169
o-nitrosophenol, 169
1-(2-pyridylazo)-2-naphthol, 173
8-quinolinol, 164, **221**
salicylaldoxime, 168
thiocyanate, 135
thiosalicylideneethylenediimine, 184
xanthate, 182
Niobium, butylphosphoric acid, 146, 147, 148, **221**
chloride, 128, 129
cupferron, 170
diethyldithiocarbamate, 181
fluoride, 125, 126, 127, **221**
methyldioctylamine, 150
8-quinolinol, 164, **221**
thiocyanate, 135, **222**
tribenzylamine, 150, **222**

Osmium, diethyldithiocarbamate, 181
ephedrine, 185, **223**
tetroxide, **223**
thiocarbanilide, 183, **223**

Palladium, diethyldithiocarbamate, **223**
dimethylglyoxime, 166, **223**
dithizone, 175, 177, 178
3-hydroxyl-1,3-diphenyltriazine, 172
iodide, 133
5-methyl-8-quinolinol, 165
2-nitroso-1-naphthol, 169, **224**
phenylthiourea, 185
1-(2-pyridylazo)-2-naphthol, 173
8-quinolinol, 164
thiosalicylideneethylenediimine, 184
Phosphorus, fluoride, 125, 126
heteropoly acid, 143, 144, **224**
nitrate, 138, 140
phosphate, **224**
Platinum, bromide, 131
chloride, 128, 129, 130, **225**
dithizone, 175, 178
phenylthiourea, 185
1-(2-pyridylazo)-2-naphthol, 173
thiosalicylideneethylenediimine, 184
thiosemicarbazide, 183
Plutonium, acetylacetone, 158, **226**
anthranilic acid, **226**

Plutonium, cinnamic acid, 145, **226**
cupferron, **226**
dibenzoylmethane, 159
diethyldithiocarbamate, **226**
3,5-dinitrobenzoic acid, 145
furoyltrifluoroacetone, **226**
nitrate, 138, 140, 141, **226**
1-nitroso-2-naphthol, **226**
8-quinolinol, 164, **226**
salicylic acid, 145
thenoyltrifluoroacetone (TTA), 160, **226**
Polonium, chloride, 128, 129, 130, **226**
thenoyltrifluoroacetone (TTA), 160, **227**
Potassium, iodide, 134
Protactinium, chloride, 128, 129, **227**
cupferron, 170
fluoride, 126
nitrate, 138, 140
8-quinolinol, 164
thenoyltrifluoroacetone (TTA), 160, **227**

Rare earths, butylphosphoric acid, 147, **210, 228**
5,7-dichloro-8-quinolinol, 165, **207, 220**
neocupferron, 170
nitrate, 138, 139, 140, **227**
1-(2-pyridylazo)-2-naphthol, 173
8-quinolinol, 164
thenoyltrifluoroacetone (TTA), 160
thiocyanate, 135, **228**
Rhenium, α-benzildioxime, 167, **228**
bromide, 131
diethyldithiocarbamate, 181
dimethylglyoxime, 166
fluoride, 125, 126
pyridine, **229**
tetraphenylarsonium chloride, 153, **229**
tetraphenylphosphonium chloride, 153
thiocyanate, 135
toluene-3,4-dithiol, 180
triphenylbenzylphosphonium chloride, 153
Rhodium, iodide, 133, 134
pyridine, **229**
thenoyltrifluoroacetone (TTA), **229**

Rubidium, iodide, 134
tetraphenylboride, **230**
Ruthenium, butyric acid, 145
iodide, 134
8-quinolinol, 164
thiocarbanilide, 183
thiocyanate, 135

Scandium, benzoic acid, 145, **230**
chloride, 128, 129, **230**
morin, 162
nitrate, 138, 140
1-(2-pyridylazo)-2-naphthol, 173
quinalizarin, 162, **231**
8-quinolinol, 164, **231**
thenoyltrifluoroacetone (TTA), 160, **231**
thiocyanate, 135, 136, **231**
Selenium, bromide, 131, 132
3,3'-diaminobenzidine, **232**
diethyldithiocarbamate, 181, **232**
fluoride, 125, 126, 127
Silicon, heteropoly acid, 143, 144
Silver, diethyldithiocarbamate, 181, **232**
dithio-β-isoindigo, 185
dithizone, 175, 176, 177, 178, **232, 233**
rhodamine B, 154
thiosalicylideneethylenediimine, 184
Sodium, chloroplatinate, **233**
iodide, 134
perchlorate, 143, **233**
Strontium, 8-quinolinol, 163, 164, **235**
thenoyltrifluoroacetone (TTA), 160

Tantalum, butylphosphoric acid, 147, **235**
fluoride, 125, 126, 127, **235**
Technetium, pyridine, **236**
tetraphenylarsonium chloride, 153, **236**
Tellurium, chloride, 128, 129
diethyldithiocarbamate, 181, **236**
fluoride, 125, 126, 127
iodide, 133, 134
thiosalicylideneethylenediimine, 184
xanthate, 182
Thallium, bromide, 131, 132
chloride, 128, 129, **236**
diethyldithiocarbamate, 181, **237**
dithizone, 175, 178
iodide, 133, 134

Thallium, nitrate, 138, 140
  8-quinolinol, 164, **237**
  rhodamine B, 154
  thenoyltrifluoroacetone (TTA), 160, **237**
  thiosalicylideneethylenediimine, 184
Thorium, acetylacetone, 158
  N-benzoylphenylhydroxylamine, 172
  cinnamic acid, 145
  cupferron, 170, **238**
  5,7-dihalo-8-quinolinols, 165
  3,5-dinitrobenzoic acid, 145
  1-phenyl-4,4,5,5,6,6,6-heptafluoro-1,3-
    hexanedione, 161
  methoxybenzoic acid, 145
  morin, 162
  nitrate, 138, 139, 140, 141, **238**
  1-(2-pyridylazo)-2-naphthol, 173
  quinalizarin, 162
  8-quinolinol, 164, **238**
  salicylic acid, 145
  thenoyltrifluoroacetone (TTA), 160, **238**
  thiocyanate, 135
Tin, bromide, 131, 132
  butylphosphoric acid, 147, **239**
  chloride, 128, 129
  cupferron, 170
  diethyldithiocarbamate, 181
  dithizone, 175, 176, 177, 178
  fluoride, 125, 126, **239**
  iodide, 133, 134, **239**
  morin, 162
  1-(2-pyridylazo)-2-naphthol, 173
  8-quinolinol, 164, **239**
  thiocyanate, 135, 136
  thiosalicylideneethylenediimine, 184
  trioctylphosphine oxide, 149
Titanium, acetylacetone, 158
  cupferron, 170
  morin, 162
  quinalizarin, 162
  8-quinolinol, 164, 165, **240**
  thiocyanate, 135, 136, 137
  trioctylphosphine oxide, 149
Tungsten, α-benzoinoxime, 168
  cupferron, 170
  diethyldithiocarbamate, 181
  fluoride, 125, 126, 127
  heteropoly acid, 143, **240**
  8-quinolinol, 164, **240**

Tungsten, thiocyanate, 135, **240**
  toluene-3,4-dithiol, 180, **240**

Uranium, acetylacetone, 158
  N-benzoylphenylhydroxylamine, 172
  cinnamic acid, 145
  cupferron, 170, **241**
  dibenzoylmethane, 159, **242**
  diethyldithiocarbamate, 181
  5,7-dihalo-8-quinolinols, 165
  3,5-dinitrobenzoic acid, 145
  methoxybenzoic acid, 145
  nitrate, 138, 140, 141, **242**
  perchlorate, 143
  perfluorobutyric acid, 146
  1-(2-pyridylazo)-2-naphthol, 173
  8-quinolinol, 164, **243**
  salicylic acid, 145
  thenoyltrifluoroacetone (TTA), 160
  thiocyanate, 135, 136
  tridecylphosphine oxide, **243**
  trioctylamine, 151, **243**
  trioctylphosphine oxide, 149
  xanthate, 182

Vanadium, acetylacetone, 158, **244**
  benzohydroxamic acid, 172
  N-benzoylphenylhydroxylamine, 171
  chloride, 129
  cupferron, 170
  diethyldithiocarbamate, 181
  fluoride, 125, 126
  heteropoly acid, 143, 144
  8-quinolinol, 164, 165, **244**
  thiocyanate, 136
  tridecylphosphine oxide, **244**
  trioctylphosphine oxide, 149
  xanthate, 182

Yttrium, butylphosphoric acid, 147, 148, **244**
  thenoyltrifluoroacetone (TTA), 160

Zinc, acetylacetone, 158
  cupferron, 170
  diethyldithiocarbamate, 181, **245**
  dinaphthylthiocarbazone, 179
  dithizone, 175, 176, 177, 178, **245**
  iodide, 133, 134
  isonitrosoacetophenone, 169

Zinc, methyldioctylamine, 150, **246**
  perfluorooctanoic acid, 146
  1-(2-pyridylazo)-2-naphthol, 173
  8-quinolinol, 164
  thiocyanate, 135, 136
  thiosalicylideneethylenediimine, 184
  tribenzylamine, 150
Zirconium, acetylacetone, 158, **246**
  butylphosphoric acid, 146, 147, 148, **246**

Zirconium, cupferron, 170
  morin, 162
  nitrate, 140
  quinalizarin, 162
  8-quinolinol, 164
  thenoyltrifluoroacetone (TTA), 160, **247**
  thiocyanate, 135, 137
  trifluoroacetylacetone, 160
  trioctylphosphine oxide, 149

Subject Index

5-*p*-Acetamidophenylazo-8-quinolinol, 226

Acetic acid extraction, 155

Acetone (solvent), in chloride extractions, 130
in nitrate extractions, 140

Acetylacetone extractions, 157–159, 190, 195, 201, 202, 207, 211, 212, 218, 226, 244, 246

Acid-base character, 16
Brönsted theory of, 19
extraction and, 53
Lewis theory of, 16
of chelating agents, 22
of ligands, 20, 22
solubility and, 37

Activity coefficients, effect on distribution coefficient, 9, 35
in mixed electrolytes, 67–68
of uranyl nitrate solutions, 69–70

Agitation, and extraction kinetics, 73

Alkylphosphoric acid systems, 146–148

Ammonium acetate, as masking agent for Th, 164

Amyl acetate (solvent), in chloride extractions, 129

Amyl alcohol, *see* Pentanol

Anthranilic acid, 226

Antipyrine, 185

Azo dyes, 154

Backwashing, 108

Basicity, of chelates, 21
of solvents, 41

Batch, *see* Extraction *and* Extractors

Bathophenanthroline, *see* Diphenylphenanthroline

Benzene (solvent), in carboxylic acid extractions, 145
in chloride extractions, 129
in iodide extractions, 134
in rhodamine B extractions, 154

α-Benzildioxime, 167, 228

Benzohydroxamic acid, 172

Benzoic acid, 145, 190, 207, 211, 212, 230

α-Benzoinoxime, 168

N-Benzoylphenylhydroxylamine, 171

Benzyl alcohol (solvent), in dimethylglyoxime extractions, 167

Beta particle counting, 119

Bond type, polarizability and, 17

Bromide systems, 131–132, 209, 211

Buffer components, extraction of, 49

Butanol (solvent), in carboxylic acid extractions, 145
in heteropoly acid extractions, 144
in perchlorate extractions, 143
in thiocyanate extractions, 135

n-Butyl acetate (solvent), in chloride extractions, 129
in heteropoly acid extractions, 144

263

n-Butyl acetate (solvent), in thiocyanate extractions, 137

Butyl cellosolve (solvent), in chelate extractions, 40

in nitrate extractions, 140

Butylphosphoric acid, see Dibutylphosphoric acid

Butyraldehyde (solvent), in iodide extractions, 134

Butyric acid, 145, 195, 204

n-Capric acid, 145, 204

Capryl alcohol, to control emulsions, 151

Carbon tetrachloride (solvent), in chloride extractions, 129

in trialkylphosphine oxide extractions, 148

Carboxylic acid systems, 145

Chelate systems, 157–186

Chelates, extraction of, masking agents in, 57–58

metal hydrolysis in, 53

pH and, 53, 55, 57

reagent concentration in, 52

separation factors in, 57, 59

separation schemes for, 57

stability of, 26–30

electronegativity and, 27

entropy effect and, 28

extraction and, 53

metals, acid nature of, 28

sequence in, 29

number of rings and, 27

reagent basicity and, 26

resonance effect and, 29

size of ring and, 27

stereochemical factors and, 30

see also Coordination complexes

Chelating agents, basic groups in, 22

classification of, 22–26

Chloride systems, 127–30, 191, 193, 208, 209, 212, 215–216, 225, 226, 230, 236

Chloroform (solvent), in carboxylic acid extractions, 145

in high molecular weight amine extractions, 150

in tetraphenylarsonium chloride extractions, 153

Chloroplatinic acid, 233

Cinnamic acid, 145, 214, 226

Colorimetry, 120–121

Coordination complexes, bond type in, 17

classification, 20

Lewis theory and, 16

stability of, 18–20

Born equation and, 17, 28

electronegativity and, 19, 27

ionic potential and, 18

oxidation state and, 19

stereochemical factors in, 20

see also Chelates

Coordination number, 16

Countercurrent distribution, see Extraction

Counting techniques, see Radiochemistry

Cresotinic acid, 226

Cupferron, 169–170, 191, 199, 205, 212, 226, 238, 241

fluorenyl homolog, 171

naphthyl homolog, 170

Cyanide, as masking agent, 164, 176

Cyclohexane (solvent), in trialkylphosphine oxide extractions, 149

Cyclohexanedionedioxime, 167

3,3'-Diaminobenzidine, 232

Dibenzoylmethane, 159, 242

Dibutoxytetraethylene glycol (solvent), in nitrate extractions, 140

Dibutyl carbitol (solvent), in nitrate extractions, 140

Dibutyl cellosolve (solvent), in nitrate extractions, 140

Dibutyl ether, as diluent in dibutylphosphoric acid extractions, 146

as diluent for tributyl phosphate, 130, 140

Dibutyl phosphate, see Dibutylphosphoric acid

Dibutylphosphoric acid, 146–148, 210, 211, 221, 228, 235, 239, 244, 246

o-Dichlorobenzene (solvent), in tetraphenylarsonium chloride extractions, 153

β,β'-Dichloroethyl ether (solvent), in chloride extractions, 129

Dichloromethane (solvent), in high molecular weight amine extractions, 150
Dichlorophenylheptafluoro-1,3-hexanedione, 161
5,7-Dichloro-8-quinolinol, 165, 207, 220
Dielectric constant, ion-pair formation and, 31
of solvents, tables, 250–253
of water, effect of salts on, 31, 45
Diethyldithiocarbamate, sodium salt, 180–181, 192, 193, 195, 196, 214, 218, 223, 226, 232, 236, 237, 245
as masking agent, 177
Diethyl ketone (solvent), in nitrate extractions, 139
2,4-Dihydroxybenzoic acid, 226
Diisopropyl carbinol (solvent), in chloride extractions, 129
in nitrate extractions, 140
Diisopropyl ketone (solvent), in chloride extractions, 129
in fluoride extractions, 126
in nitrate extractions, 140
Diluent solvents, in oxonium extractions, 43, 107
p-Dimethylaminobenzalrhodanine, 210
Dimethylglyoxime, 166, 220, 223
2,9-Dimethyl-1,10-phenanthroline, 155, 205
Di-β-naphthylthiocarbazone, 179
3,5-Dinitrobenzoic acid, 145, 226
2,4-Dinitrosalicylic acid, 226
Diphenylcarbazide, 201
4,7-Diphenylphenanthroline, 155, 213
Diphenylthiocarbazone, see Dithizone
Dipivaloylmethane, 216
Distribution coefficient, definition of, 8
solubility, relation to, 35
variation of, with activity coefficients, 9, 35–36
with mutual solubility, 9
Distribution equilibria, see Extraction equilibria
Distribution factor and distribution ratio, 87
Distribution law, 7
thermodynamic derivation, 8
Distribution ratio, definition of, 10
methods of increasing, 112
per cent extraction and, 12

Dithio-β-isoindigo, 185
Dithizone, 173–178, 195, 197, 202, 205, 211, 214, 218, 232–233, 245
o-Ditolylthiocarbazone, 179

EDTA, see Ethylenediaminetetraacetic acid
Emulsions, treatment of, 108–109, 151
Ephedrine, 185, 223
Erio OS, 173
Ethanol (solvent), in nitrate extractions, 139
in perchlorate extractions, 143
Ethyl acetate (solvent), in carboxylic acid extractions, 145
in chloride extractions, 129
in heteropoly acid extractions, 144
in iodide extractions, 134
in perchlorate extractions, 143
in rhodamine B extractions, 154
Ethyl acetoacetate (solvent), in heteropoly acid extractions, 144
Ethylenediaminetetraacetic acid, as masking agent, 58, 111–112
Ca salt as masking agent, 165
Ca complex, structure of, 26
ionization equilibria, 58
metal complex formation constants, 112
Ethyl ether (solvent), in bromide extractions, 132
in carboxylic acid extractions, 145
in chloride extractions, 127–129
in fluoride extractions, 125–126
in heteropoly acid extractions, 143
in iodide extractions, 133–134
in nitrate extractions, 137–140
in perchlorate extractions, 143
in thiocyanate extractions, 136
2-Ethylhexanol (solvent), in chloride extractions, 129
Extract, organic, drying agents for, 85
removal of entrained water from, 85
Extractable species, 13
formation, role of solvent in, 5
organic phase reactions of, 14
polymerization of, 14
Extraction, batch, 80–86
colorimetry and, 120–121
continuous, 86–98
countercurrent distribution, 101–105

Extraction, kinetic factors in, 72–75
  masking agents in, 110–112
  non-equilibrium, 74–75
  of solids, 98–101
  oxidation state in, 110
  radioisotopes and, 117–120
  salting agents in, 112–114
Extraction equilibria, of chelates, 51–59
  chelate stability and, 53
  general expression for, 52
  masking agents in, 57–58
  pH role, 53, 55
  reagent concentration, 52
  of ion association systems, general, 14
  of iron(III) chloride, 62–65
  of osmium tetroxide, 12
  of 8-quinolinol, 11
  of tetraphenylarsonium perrhenate,
    60–62
  of uranyl nitrate, 65–71
Extraction systems, 123–186
  classification of, 5
  general comparison of, 123
Extraction time and selectivity, 74–75
Extractors, batch, 80–86
  for chelates, 85
  for microextraction, 82, 83, 84
  continuous, 86–98
  countercurrent, 95–98
  evaluating efficiency of, 86
  for chelates, 91
  for use at superatmospheric pres-
    sures, 90
  micro, 93–94, 95
  with high-density solvents, 93–95
  with low-density solvents, 87–93
  with non-volatile solvents, 94
  countercurrent distribution, 103–105
  infusion, 99–101
  comparison of, 100
  continuous, 99–100
  discontinuous, 99–100
  Soxhlet type, 99–100
  micro, 82–84, 93–94, 95
  remote control, 118

Fission products, 117
  nitrate extractions of, 141
Fluoride systems, 125–127, 221, 227, 235,
  239·

α-Furildioxime, 167
Furoyltrifluoroacetone, 226

Gamma ray counting, 119
  scintillation spectrometry in, 119
Geiger counters, 119

Hafnium chloride, non-aqueous extraction of, 15
Half-extraction volume, 86
  extractor for measuring, 92
Heterocyclic polyamine extractions, 155
Heteropoly acids, extractions, 143–144,
  194, 224, 240
  structure, 20
Hexone, see Methyl isobutyl ketone
High molecular weight amines, extractions, 150–152
  micelle formation with, 151
  structure and selectivity of, 151
Hildebrand theory of regular solutions,
  38
Hydrolysis of metals and chelate extractions, 53
3-Hydroxyl-1,3-diphenyltriazine, 172
8-Hydroxyquinoline, see 8-Quinolinol

Iodide extractions, 133–134, 192, 211,
  215, 218, 239
Ion association, extraction equilibria,
  activity corrections and, 59
  general, 14
  extraction systems, 123–156
Ion association complexes, micelle formation in, 33, 48
  polymerization of, 48
  stability of, 31–33
  concentration and, 33
  dielectric constant and, 31
  ionic size and, 32
Ion exchange analogy in solvent extraction, 33
Ion-pair formation, Bjerrum theory of,
  31
  equilibrium constants of, 30–31
Iron(III) chloride extraction, compound
  extracted in, 62
  equilibria, 62–65
  nature of complex extracted, 62–63
  dissociation and, 63
  polymerization and, 63–64

Iron(III) chloride extraction, nature of
 complex extracted, solvation and,
 62–63
Isonitrosoacetophenone, 169
Isopropyl ether (solvent), in bromide
 extractions, 132
 in chloride extractions, 129
 in rhodamine B extractions, 154

Kerosene (solvent), in high molecular
 weight amine extractions, 150
 in trialkylphosphine oxide extractions, 148, 149
Kinetic factors in extraction, 72–75
 agitation and, 73
 complex formation and, 73–75
 diffusion processes and, 72–73
 in dithizone extractions, 74
 in EDTA complexes, 73–74
 in TTA extractions, 71
 mass transfer and, 72–73
 reagent concentration and, 74
 selectivity derived from, 74–75

Ligands, basicity of, 20, 22
 complexing tendencies of, 19–20

Malachite green, 154
Masking agents, 26
 in chelate extraction equilibria, 57–58
 use of, 110–112, 164, 176, 177
Metal salts, as salting-out agents, 113
 solubility of, 4, 35
Methoxybenzoic acid, 145
Methyl amyl ketone (solvent), in chloride extractions, 129
 in iodide extractions, 134
3-Methyl-1-butanol (solvent), in heteropoly acid extractions, 144
Methyldioctylamine, 150, 246
Methyl ethyl ketone (solvent), in bromide extractions, 132
Methyl isobutyl ketone (MIBK—solvent), in bromide extractions, 132
 in carboxylic acid extractions, 145
 in chloride extractions, 135
 in fluoride extractions, 126
 in nitrate extractions, 138, 139, 140
 in thiocyanate extractions, 137
Methyl isopropyl ketone (solvent), in
 iodide extractions, 134

Methyl n-propyl ketone (solvent), in
 heteropoly acid extractions, 144
 in iodide extractions, 134
Methyl violet, 154
Micelle formation, 6, 33
Monobutyl ether of ethylene glycol, see
 Butyl cellosolve
Monobutylphosphoric acid, 146

Neocupferron, 170
Neocuproine, see 2,9-Dimethyl-1,10-
 phenanthroline
Nioxime, see Cyclohexanedionedioxime
Nitrate extractions, 137–142, 191, 198,
 199, 220, 226, 227, 238, 242
Nitrobenzene (solvent), in phenanthroline extractions, 155
 in terpyridyl extractions, 155
Nitromethane (solvent), in polyiodide
 extractions, 134
1-Nitroso-2-naphthol, 168, 202, 226
2-Nitroso-1-naphthol, 169, 224
N-Nitrosonaphthylhydroxylamine, ammonium salt, see Neocupferron
o-Nitrosophenol, 169
N-Nitrosophenylhydroxylamine, ammonium salt, see Cupferron

1-Octanol (solvent), in heteropoly acid
 extractions, 144
2-Octanol (solvent), in chloride extractions, 129
Octylphosphoric acids, 148
Organic compounds, extraction of, 14
Osmium tetroxide, 223
 distribution equilibria, 12
Oxidation state, and complex stability,
 18, 19
 and extraction, 110
Oxine, see 8-Quinolinol
Oxonium extraction systems, 5
Oxonium solvents, and chelates, 40
 diluents for, 43

Pentaether (solvent), in nitrate extractions, 140, 142
Pentanol (solvent), in bathophenanthroline extractions, 155
 in carboxylic acid extractions, 145
 in chloride extractions, 129
 in iodide extractions, 134

Pentanol (solvent), in neocuproine extractions, 155
in thiocyanate extractions, 135
Pentanone (solvent), in nitrate extractions, 140
Per cent extraction, distribution ratio and, 12
solvent volume ratio and, 81
Perchlorate extractions, 143, 233
Perchromic acid, 201
Perfluorobutyric acid, 146
Perfluorooctanoic acid, 146
$pH_{1/2}$ value, 55
Phase rule, 7
1,10-Phenanthroline, 155
as masking agent for Fe, 164
sterically hindered derivatives, 30
Phenazone, 186
Phenylthiourea, 184–185
Phosphoric acid, 224
effect of Fe on extraction of, 156
pK_a and basicity, 22
Polyiodides, extraction of alkali metals, 134
Polymerization, of extractable species, 14
of ion association complexes, 48
of iron(III) chloride complex, 63–64
of tetraphenylarsonium perrhenate, 62
Potassium hexafluorophosphate, 201
Pyridine, 217, 229, 236
in dimethylglyoxime extractions, 167
in thiocyanate extractions, 135, 197
1-(2-Pyridylazo)-2-naphthol, 172
2-(2-Pyridyl)-benzimidazole, 155

Quinalizarin, 161–162, 231
8-Quinolinol, 162–165, 190, 196, 199, 200, 203, 206, 208, 213, 216, 217, 219, 221, 226, 231, 235, 237, 238, 239, 240, 242, 244
butyl cellosolve with, 163, 216
distribution equilibria, 11
sterically hindered derivatives of, 30

Radiochemistry, use of extraction in, 115–117
Radioisotopes, counting techniques for, 119–120
use of, 54, 117–120

Rate effects, *see* Kinetic factors
Regular solutions, Hildebrand theory of, 38
Remote control extractor, 118
Rhodamine B, 154, 192

Salicylaldoxime, 168
Salicylic acid, 145
Salicylideneethylenediimine, 226
Salting-out agents, 43
effect on dielectric constant, 31, 45
in extraction, use of, 112–114
in iron(III) chloride extraction, 45, 66
in nitrate extractions, 138
in thorium nitrate extraction, 45
in uranyl nitrate extraction, 44, 67
Separation factor, 79
in chelate extractions, 57
masking, effect of, 59
Separation scheme, in chelate extractions, 57
Separation techniques, comparison of, 4, 33
for low-separation factors, 80
phase distribution in, 7
Sequestering agents, *see* Masking agents
Sodium benzenesulfinate, 226
Sodium bis(2-hydroxyethyl)-dithiocarbamate, as masking agent, 177
Sodium diethyldithiocarbamate, *see* Diethyldithiocarbamate, sodium salt
Solubility, acid-base character and, 37, 41
distribution and, 35
intermolecular forces and, 36–38
of chelates, 38, 39
of metal salts, 4
of oxonium complexes, 41
organic solvents role, 41
Solubility parameters, 38
table of, 250–253
Solvation, role in solubility, 36
Solvents, basicity of, 41
choice of, 106–107
drying agents for, 85
for chelates, 5, 26
mutual solubility of, 9
properties tabulated, 250–253
purification of, 249
role in complex formation, 5

Spectrophotometry, 120
   flame, 120
Stearic acid, 146
Stripping, 107–108
Sulfate extraction, 216
4-Sulfobenzenearsonic acid, masking
   agent for Th, 164
2-Sulfoethanearsonic acid, masking
   agent for Zr, 164

Temperature, effect in high molecular
   weight amine extractions, 152
   effect in thiocyanate extractions, 137
2,2′,2″-Terpyridyl, 155
Tetraphenylarsonium chloride, 62, 152–
   153, 196, 203, 217, 229, 236
Tetraphenylarsonium perrhenate, extraction equilibria, 60–62
   effect of chloride on, 62
   dimerization and, 62
Tetraphenylboride, sodium, 200, 230
Tetraphenylphosphonium chloride, 152–
   153
Tetraphenylstibonium chloride, 153, 207
Thenoyltrifluoroacetone (TTA), 159–
   160, 190, 191, 194, 206, 210, 220,
   226, 227, 229, 231, 237, 238, 247
Thiocarbanilide, 183, 223
Thiocyanate, as masking agent, 176
Thiocyanate systems, 135–137, 203, 210,
   213, 219, 222, 228, 231, 240
Thiosalicylideneethylenediimine, 184
Thiosemicarbazide, 183
Thiosulfate, as masking agent, 176
Toluene-3,4-dithiol, 180, 219, 240

Trialkylphosphine oxide systems, 43,
   148
Tribenzylamine, 150, 222
Tributyl phosphate (solvent), in acetic
   acid extractions, 155
   in chloride extractions, 129
   in nitrate extractions, 138, 140
   in thiocyanate extractions, 137
Trichloroacetic acid (solvent), in chloride extractions, 129
Trichlorobenzene (solvent), in carboxylic acid extractions, 146
Trichloroethylene (solvent), in high
   molecular weight amine extractions, 150
Tri-n-decylphosphine oxide, 148, 243,
   244
Tri-n-dodecylphosphine oxide, 148
Trifluoroacetylacetone, 160
3,5,5-Trimethylhexylphosphine oxide,
   148
Trioctylamine, 243
Tri-n-octylphosphine oxide, 148, 219
Triphenylbenzylphosphonium chloride,
   153

Uranyl nitrate, extraction equilibria, 65–
   71
   heats of solution of, 42

Xanthate, potassium, 182
Xylene (solvent), in high molecular
   weight amine extractions, 150

Zirconium chloride, non-aqueous extraction of, 15